MODERN ANALYTICAL DESIGN OF INSTRUMENT SERVOMECHANISMS

MODERN ANALYTICAL DESIGN OF INSTRUMENT SERVOMECHANISMS

BRUCE A. CHUBB, *Manager*
Analytical Design Technology Group
Instrument Division, Lear Siegler, Incorporated
Grand Rapids, Michigan

ADDISON-WESLEY PUBLISHING COMPANY
READING, MASSACHUSETTS · PALO ALTO · LONDON · DON MILLS, ONTARIO

To Janet

PREFACE

The purpose of this book is to provide engineering personnel with the latest analytical techniques developed for instrument servomechanism design. This book should not be confused with a general text on control theory, many of which are already in existence. Our goal is to develop an extensive ability to design optimized instrument servomechanisms with an assuredness that they will perform as predicted. Close attention is paid to bridging the gap between theory and practice. All component tolerance effects are considered, specification techniques are discussed, and emphasis is placed on obtaining design data from component specifications.

The design and analysis techniques presented lend themselves directly to programming on the digital computer. Computer print-out sheets obtained during the design cycle are included for illustration throughout the text. The input data format sheet is introduced as an aid for the practicing design engineer to better communicate with the computer program. This computerized approach leads directly to computer-aided design concepts and finally to completely automated design—the only practical method of obtaining complete optimization. For this reason, a section is presented on optimization theory using the principle of steepest descent, and its application to the servomechanism design problem is illustrated.

This book presents a first concerted effort to combine, using a digital computer, statistical tolerance techniques and servo design. It provides a simple, straightforward, and realistic method of considering all tolerance effects. From this the designer can optimize the often overlooked trade-offs between the numerous component tolerances and the total system requirements such as accuracy, cost, reliability, and response.

An application of the modern state-variable concept is made to determine, using a digital computer, the transient behavior of the linear and nonlinear system. The parallel between this approach, that of the analog computer, and that of the phase plane is presented, thereby giving a clear picture of the effects of amplifier saturation, coulomb friction, gear train stiffness, and backlash.

Actual instrument servomechanism manufacture has been considered a combination art and science. This book has been written with a desire to definitize that portion currently based upon experience factors so that the instrument servo designer might benefit more from an analytical approach. For example, previous texts mention only briefly, if at all, gear stiffness and its effect on system stability. In this book, gear stiffness is introduced as a design parameter. Equations are developed for its calculation, test procedures are described, and stability requirements are

vii

derived. The same detailed coverage is presented regarding backlash and its effects. Equations are presented not only to calculate the amount of backlash that exists in a gear design, but also to determine the amount of allowable backlash. The concept of a backlash-friction diagram is introduced as a new design method of ensuring that a limit cycle will not exist.

The instrument servo to be discussed consists of an ac servomotor, gear train, followup, and amplifier. The use of a feedback generator, inertial damper, or a velocity-damped motor is optional, and each is thoroughly presented. Although this book covers positional-type instrument servomechanisms with this particular configuration of components, many of the techniques and discussions presented may be carried over into the general area of control systems.

The book has evolved from a course in servomechanism design and analysis which is taught by the author at the Instrument Division of Lear Siegler, Inc. Also, the material presented has been thoroughly "field tested" in that the techniques it describes have been automated and repeatedly applied to instrument servo design and hardware production with increasingly successful results over the last few years.

The author would like to express his appreciation to the management of the Instrument Division of Lear Siegler, Inc., whose full cooperation and permission to use the computation facilities made it possible for this book to be written. Personal thanks are extended to the many individuals who have aided either directly or indirectly in the preparation of this manuscript. Stephen Higgins, Jr., of the Honeywell Corporation, deserves many thanks as he reviewed the original manuscript and offered many constructive comments. Special thanks are due to my associates at Lear Siegler, Inc., especially Gerald Garvelink for his research and encouragement, which made Chapters 2 and 6 possible, and Robert Riddle, whose many suggestions and thorough reading of the complete manuscript are gratefully appreciated. Thanks are also due Mrs. Maryann Smith for her patience in typing the complete manuscript. Finally, my wife, Janet, deserves much credit as well as appreciation; her continuous encouragement was most important to the successful completion of this book.

Grand Rapids, Michigan   B.A.C.
November 1966

CONTENTS

CHAPTER 1

INTRODUCTION

The purpose of this chapter is to outline the material to follow and also to provide a common understanding and foundation on which to base the theory and design of instrument servomechanisms. Chapter 2 provides an analytical description of the servomotor and Chapter 3 presents a detailed description of the gear train and its associated characteristics. The remainder of the components that comprise the instrument system are described in Chapter 4.

Chapter 5 develops the system concept and associated mathematical models by combining the elements of the preceding chapters. The similarity between the instrument servomechanism and the conventional second-order system is explained, and the destabilizing effect of finite gear train stiffness is illustrated with the use of the fourth-order system model. The response of the system is obtained by using the modern state model concept and the digital and analog computers as well as by using more conventional methods. The last two sections of Chapter 5 illustrate how the design procedure is varied when a viscous or inertial damper is included in a system.

No design is complete without a study of the effect of all the component tolerances on the total system. Because of the involved multivariable nature of the instrument system, this can be satisfactorily achieved only by using statistical techniques. For this reason, Chapter 6 is devoted to the application of Taylor series, approximate slope, and Monte Carlo tolerance techniques to the design of instrument servomechanisms.

Any judicious design must also include the effects of nonlinearities. These are presented in Chapter 7 by extending the state model, by using describing function and phase plane techniques, and by using the analog and digital computers. Special emphasis is placed on the effects of quadrature, amplifier saturation, and the interrelated nonlinearities of load friction and gear train backlash.

The accuracy of the instrument system is of utmost concern. It is a measure of how well the output response follows the input command. Chapter 8 provides an analysis of both the static and dynamic errors that can exist and develops analytical expressions for the accuracy of the system. As system requirements become more stringent, the designer must become increasingly concerned with designing optimized systems. Automated techniques for engineering such a system become essential because of stricter system performance requirements and the multitude of candidate components available. For this reason, Chapter 8 concludes the text by demonstrating how automated design and optimization techniques can be applied to the design of the complete servosystem.

1.1. OPEN-LOOP INSTRUMENT SYSTEM

Before we progress with the theory and design of instrument servomechanisms, which are by definition closed-loop systems, it is worthwhile first to confirm the concept of an open-loop instrument system. An example of such a system is the conventional instrument meter movement which is schematically illustrated in Fig. 1.1.

A voltage applied across the input terminals creates a current through the moving coil, which in turn generates a magnetic field. This field, acting with that of the permanent magnet, creates a torque which acts on the moving coil assembly. The moving coil, with the attached pointer, is displaced until a countertorque due to the coil spring balances the system.

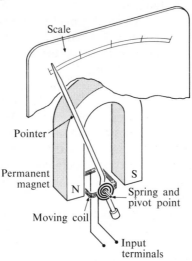

Fig. 1.1. Conventional instrument meter movement.

Ideally, the meter indication is proportional to the source voltage. Therefore, the instrument can be calibrated to read fuel level, revolutions per minute (rpm), etc., by connecting it to an appropriate transducer, as illustrated in block diagram form in Fig. 1.2.

Although satisfactory for many applications, the simple instrument meter movement has two distinct limitations. First, the accuracy of the indication is a direct function of the accuracy of each component. For example, any variations of spring constant, magnet strength, or coil impedance directly affect the instrument reading. Although the error initially may be calibrated out at one position, the accuracy will be degraded at other positions due to the accumulated linearity errors of each component. Additional errors are introduced with changes in temperature, etc. The second limitation of the simple meter movement is its inability to overcome disturbances such as friction and unbalance. This limits its use to applications where the object to be controlled presents a negligible load.

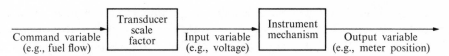

Fig. 1.2. Open-loop instrument system block diagram.

In summary, this type of instrument requires continuous attention to ensure continued correct performance. It must be calibrated and maintained in calibration against wear and changes in environment. There are many factors which alter its performance and therefore limit its usefulness as a precision control device.

1.2. CLOSED-LOOP INSTRUMENT SYSTEM

The preceding discussion illustrated what is defined as open-loop control. Careful manufacture and calibration of a servomechanism establish a direct relationship between the command and output variables. However, this ideal relationship is seldom approached in reality. Consequently, for precision control of a given variable, it often is not sufficient to use open-loop control and merely set the input at a certain value. It is necessary, as in everyday life, to check the way in which a command is carried out and, if there is a discrepancy, to make the required corrections. This leads to the concept of control with feedback, namely servomechanisms.

In feedback control systems, the control of the output is not only a function of the input but is also a function of the output itself. The output is compared with the input and any difference is amplified and applied to control the output in such a way as to reduce the difference (error variable) to zero. A block diagram of this type of system is illustrated in Fig. 1.3.

The general type of instrument servomechanism to be discussed in this text consists of the following:

1. *Followup* (*error detector*). The primary followup to be considered consists of a pair of synchros, namely a control transmitter (CX) driving a control transformer (CT). The command variable is connected to the CX shaft and the output variable to the CT shaft. By exciting the CX with a fixed ac reference voltage, we obtain an

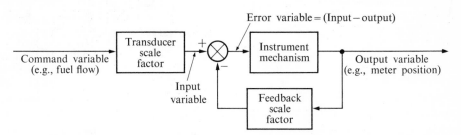

Fig. 1.3. Closed-loop instrument system block diagram.

error voltage from the CT which is essentially proportional to the angular difference between the CX and CT. The purpose of the synchro pair, of course, is to measure the difference between the input and output and produce a voltage proportional to this difference.

2. *Amplifier.* The amplifier used is the electronic type which produces an ac output voltage essentially proportional to the input but of a greater magnitude. Its purpose is to amplify the low-level error signal from the followup to a level that can be used to actuate the prime mover.

3. *Motor-generator.* A typical two-phase ac servomotor is used as the prime mover. One phase is energized by a fixed reference voltage and the other is coupled to the amplifier output. The amplified error signal acts through the motor to produce torque and drive the output toward zero error. The generator, if used, provides damping to the system, as will be explained later. The specific function of the generator is to produce a voltage that is proportional to the velocity of the output. The generator is almost always connected to the motor and contained with it in an integral housing.

4. *Gear train.* The gear train is used to couple the motor to the output or load. Its primary function is to amplify the torque output of the motor so that the torque becomes large compared to load friction and disturbance torques.

A schematic diagram of the preceding components combined to form an instrument servomechanism is shown in Fig. 1.4. The error voltage e_ϵ is summed in series with the generator voltage e_g and applied to the amplifier input terminals. The generator voltage is zero only when the position of the CT is equal to that of the

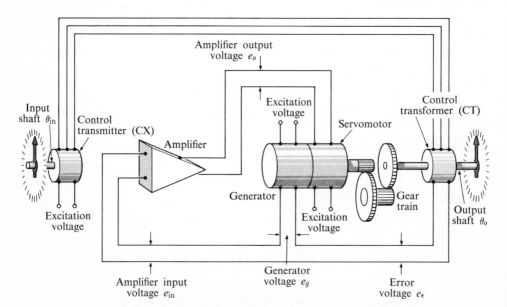

Fig. 1.4. Schematic diagram of motor-generator instrument servomechanism.

CX. The polarity of the error is represented by the relative phase of the followup signal. Therefore the motor drives until a null is reached at the amplifier input and the position of the output equals that of the input.

As shown in Fig. 1.4, the servomechanism continuously positions the pointer on the output shaft equal to that of the input shaft. However, the output could just as well position an automatic speed-control throttle or any other type of mechanism. Many additional operations are often geared to the output, e.g., switches, resolvers, potentiometers, cams, etc., for controlling all types of equipment. A common advantage is that the input CX can be remotely located from the rest of the mechanism.

1.3. THE STABILITY PROBLEM

Stability is a problem facing the designer of any closed-loop or feedback system. This can be illustrated for the instrument servo shown in Fig. 1.4 as follows. Consider for simplicity that the CT is connected directly to the amplifier so that the generator is not in the system and there is no other form of damping in the system. Let the CX shaft be given an instantaneous step displacement at time t_1 as shown in Fig. 1.5.

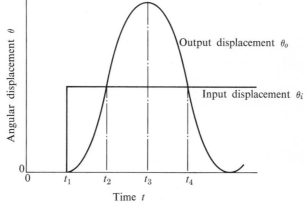

Fig. 1.5. Plot of a response to a step input displacement without damping.

The step displacement on the CX results in a step voltage applied to the motor. This causes the output to be accelerated as shown in Fig. 1.5. The system continues to accelerate until the output equals the input at t_2. At this point the control voltage applied to the motor is zero, but momentum causes the output to coast beyond the desired displacement. The error voltage then reverses phase, and the output is decelerated until it stops at t_3. At this point an error exists, and the motor again accelerates the output and the process is repeated.

If successive oscillations are reduced in amplitude so that they eventually dampen out, the system is said to be *convergent* or *stable*. Conditions can exist in a feedback system, however, such that each successive oscillation is of a greater amplitude, and such a system is said to be *divergent* or *unstable*.

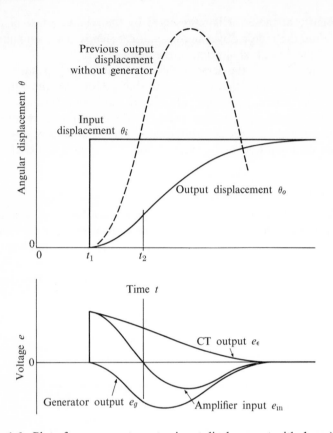

Fig. 1.6. Plot of a response to a step input displacement with damping.

The oscillatory response illustrated in Fig. 1.5 is not satisfactory; therefore, damping is required in the system. Actually, there is some inherent damping in the servomotor and load. This often is not sufficient, however, and a generator is added, as was shown in Fig. 1.4. Adding the generator causes the motor to begin decelerating the output before it is in correspondence with the input and thereby reduces the overshooting. This effect is demonstrated by the response curves shown in Fig. 1.6. The amplifier input voltage is no longer obtained as a mirror image of the output response. It also is shown in Fig. 1.6 along with its two components—generator and CT. At time t_1 the step displacement is applied again. Now as the output is accelerated, the generator feeds back a voltage proportional to the velocity attained. This voltage subtracts from the error voltage, resulting in a reduced acceleration; consequently, the output response lies below the previous response, which is shown as a dashed line. At time t_2, when the magnitude of the generator voltage equals that of the CT, the voltage applied to the motor reverses phase and the output is decelerated until it eventually comes to rest at the value equal to the step size. By controlling the amount of generator feedback, we can obtain various degrees of damping.

1.4. UNITS AND USE OF CONVERSION FACTORS

The mathematical model most often used in servo design is the differential equation describing the balance of forces acting on a mass M. That is,

$$\sum F = M \frac{d^2 X}{dt^2}.$$ (1.1)

Usually this relationship is expressed in rotational notation as a sum of torques acting on an inertia J:

$$\sum T = J \frac{d^2 \theta}{dt^2}.$$ (1.2)

A simple glance through an appropriate component manufacturer's catalog will illustrate the variety of units of measurement conventionally used in instrument servo design. For example, consider the following:

Torque — oz-in,

Inertia — gm-cm^2,

Acceleration — rad/sec^2,

Velocity — rpm or deg/sec,

Displacement — deg or min of arc.

These units have received nearly universal acceptance in the instrument servo field, even though they do not provide a consistent set. An engineer can use directly such a configuration only by extensive use of conversion factors.

With the use of the digital computer for most engineering calculations, conversion of units presents no particular problem. All inputs and outputs are specified in the units most common to the user. The conversion factors necessary to obtain a consistent set are made part of the computer program. However, the method of including conversion factors becomes very awkward in writing equations. As a result, most of the equations shown in this book do not include conversion factors. The reader, therefore, must make unit conversions before using many of the equations. The ounce-inch-second system is recommended for actual calculations. Therefore, for illustration we will discuss the value of inertia in gm-cm^2; this value must be multiplied by the conversion factor of 1.42×10^{-5} oz-in-sec^2/gm-cm^2 before it is used in an equation such as (1.2).

Once the reader becomes familiar with this procedure, it proves to be most convenient.

1.5. SUMMARY

In this chapter we have seen that the open-loop instrument system has two basic faults. First, the accuracy of the open-loop system is a direct function of the linearity error of each component, and second, it has a basic inability to overcome disturbances such as friction and load torques.

The closed-loop system, or servomechanism, overcomes these limitations by using a feedback signal that indicates the true position of the instrument system output. This signal is then compared to the input, and the difference, which is called the error signal, is used to drive the output to the commanded position.

The general type of instrument servomechanism to be considered consists of a synchro followup, electronic amplifier, motor-generator, and gear train. The generator is normally required to minimize overshoot and maintain stability of the closed-loop system. The servomechanism engineer not only has the problem of obtaining a design that has the necessary stability, he must at the same time meet other requirements such as response time, resolution, and accuracy.

CHAPTER 2

THE AC SERVOMOTOR

The two-phase ac servomotor is the heart of most servomechanism systems currently used in instrument design and production. One phase, typically called the *reference phase*, is connected to a voltage which is fixed except for a relatively small tolerance due to line variations. The other phase, called the *control phase*, is connected to the amplifier output and therefore is variable in nature.

There are literally hundreds of different motor designs available today from numerous manufacturers. The instrument servo designer must be able to select an optimum motor for each application and determine the performance expected for each situation. To develop this capability, let us first consider the ideal motor.

2.1. THE IDEAL MOTOR

The ideal motor is assumed to have no internal torque losses. Therefore, all the developed torque is usable. Also, for the ideal motor, the assumption is made that the speed vs. torque characteristic is linear for any given set of applied voltages, as shown in Fig. 2.1. For a fixed reference voltage, the motor develops a torque at stall which is proportional to the voltage applied to the control phase winding. Once the motor begins to run, with any value of applied voltage the torque available for acceleration decreases. This decrease in torque may be thought of as providing

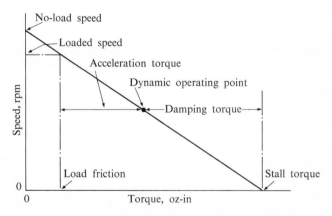

Fig. 2.1. Idealized speed-torque relationship in a servomotor.

9

motor damping since it is a function of motor velocity and it subtracts from the otherwise available stall torque. If a motor is operated for a long enough period of time under constant excitation, the damping torque becomes essentially equal to the stall torque minus the load friction. The motor then runs at a steady-state speed, which is the loaded speed shown in Fig. 2.1.

The amount of stall torque developed in an ac servomotor may be expressed in terms of the two applied voltages as

$$T_s = KE_cE_r \sin \alpha, \tag{2.1}$$

where

K = a constant determined by the fixed motor parameters,

E_r = root mean square (rms) voltage applied to the reference winding,

E_c = rms voltage applied to the control windings,

α = phase angle between E_r and E_c.

The value of K used in Eq. (2.1) may be computed on the basis of the rated data available from the motor manufacturer. Substituting the rated values of stall torque T_s(rated), reference voltage E_r(rated), and control voltage E_c(rated) into Eq. (2.1) and solving for K, we obtain

$$K = \frac{T_s(\text{rated})}{E_c(\text{rated})E_r(\text{rated})}. \tag{2.2}$$

Substituting this value of K into Eq. (2.1), we see that the general equation for the motor stall torque becomes

$$T_s = \frac{T_s(\text{rated})}{E_c(\text{rated})E_r(\text{rated})} E_cE_r \sin \alpha. \tag{2.3}$$

Equation (2.3) demonstrates that, neglecting any saturation effects, the higher the applied excitations, the greater the stall torque. The same relationship does not hold true for no-load speed. For example, a situation can exist in which an increase in control voltage causes a decrease in motor speed. In fact, the two-phase servomotor runs at maximum speed when the power being supplied to the control phase equals that being supplied to the reference phase. This situation is called *balanced operation*.

Let c be defined as the ratio of control voltage to reference voltage required for balanced operation. In equation form:

$$c \equiv \left[\frac{E_c}{E_r}\right]_{\text{balanced}}. \tag{2.4}$$

The power being supplied to a resistive-inductive type of load may be computed by using the equation

$$P = E^2\left[\frac{R}{R^2 + X^2}\right], \tag{2.5}$$

where P = power being supplied (watts),

                                         E = rms voltage being applied (volts),

                                         R = resistive component of the load (ohms),

                                         X = reactive component of the load (ohms).

By writing Eq. (2.5) once for the control winding and once for the reference winding and setting the two powers equal, we may write the ratio c of control voltage to reference voltage required for balanced operation in terms of the impedance values as

$$c = \sqrt{R_r(R_c^2 + X_c^2)/R_c(R_r^2 + X_r^2)}, \qquad (2.6)$$

where the subscripts r and c indicate reference and control windings, respectively.

For the case where the two winding impedances are identical, balanced operation exists for $E_r = E_c$. In this case c has a value of unity. This is the case for many of the servomotors being used in instrument design and production. However, the reference and control winding impedances are not always identical. When they are not, balanced conditions exist only for E_c as some multiple of E_r, namely, c.

Since the torque losses are assumed to be zero for the ideal motor, the no-load speed will be the synchronous speed of the motor so long as balanced operation is maintained. The synchronous speed of a motor of this type is given by the equation

$$\dot{\theta}_s = \frac{120f}{p}, \qquad (2.7)$$

where

                                    $\dot{\theta}_s$ = synchronous speed (rpm),

                                    f = frequency of excitation voltage (cps),

                                    p = number of poles in the motor.

Because of the nature of servomotor applications, we must be able to describe operation under unbalanced conditions. The equations describing motor performance under unbalanced conditions will now be developed by the use of symmetrical component theory and superposition. The control and reference voltages will be resolved

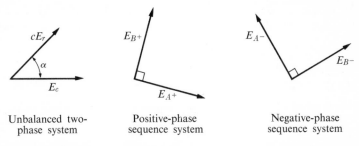

| Unbalanced two-phase system | Positive-phase sequence system | Negative-phase sequence system |

Fig. 2.2. Schematic representation of an unbalanced two-phase servomotor.

into two balanced systems rotating in opposite directions. The positive sequence produces only positive torque and the negative sequence produces only negative torque. Figure 2.2 shows by vector diagrams how unbalanced phase voltages can be resolved into two counterrotating sets of balanced voltages.

By definition, from Fig. 2.2, we can establish the following vector equations:

$$\overline{E_{B+}} + \overline{E_{B-}} = cE_r\angle\alpha, \qquad \overline{E_{A+}} + \overline{E_{A-}} = E_c\angle 0°,$$

$$E_{B+} = jE_{A+}, \qquad E_{B-} = -jE_{A-}. \tag{2.8}$$

Then

$$E_{A+} = \frac{E_c - j(cE_r\cos\alpha + jcE_r\sin\alpha)}{2},$$

$$E_{A-} = \frac{E_c + j(cE_r\cos\alpha + jcE_r\sin\alpha)}{2}. \tag{2.9}$$

Each of these two balanced phase sequence systems will produce a rotating field proportional to the value of the voltage component, one system rotating in one direction and the other system in the opposite direction. The subject of interest, therefore, is the magnitude of these two fields. The magnitude of the forward rotating field E_F is

$$E_F = \sqrt{\frac{(E_c + cE_r\sin\alpha)^2 + (cE_r\cos\alpha)^2}{4}}, \tag{2.10}$$

and the magnitude of the reverse rotating field E_R is

$$E_R = \sqrt{\frac{(E_c - cE_r\sin\alpha)^2 + (cE_r\cos\alpha)^2}{4}}. \tag{2.11}$$

Since the torque is proportional to the square of these fields,

$$T = \frac{T_s(\text{rated})}{E_c(\text{rated})E_r(\text{rated})}\frac{E_F^2 - E_R^2}{c}. \tag{2.12}$$

As the motor speed increases in the direction of rotation of the flux field set up by E_F, the torque produced by E_F will decrease. Also, as the rotor speed increases, the torque produced by E_R will increase.

Since the torque produced is directly proportional to the difference in speed between the rotor and the flux fields, Eq. (2.12) may be written in the following form:

$$T = \frac{T_s(\text{rated})}{E_c(\text{rated})E_r(\text{rated})}[SE_F^2 - (2 - S)E_R^2], \tag{2.13}$$

where S is the slip. This is defined by the equation

$$S = \frac{\dot{\theta}_s - \dot{\theta}_m}{\dot{\theta}_s}, \tag{2.14}$$

where

$$\dot{\theta}_s = \text{synchronous speed},$$
$$\dot{\theta}_m = \text{actual speed}.$$

The torque produced may be written in terms of the control and reference voltages directly by substituting for E_F and E_R using Eqs. 2.10 and 2.11:

$$T = \frac{T_s(\text{rated})}{E_c(\text{rated})E_r(\text{rated})}\left[(c^2E_r^2 + E_c^2)\left(\frac{S-1}{2}\right) + cE_rE_c \sin \alpha\right]. \qquad (2.15)$$

The no-load speed under unbalanced conditions may now be derived by using Eq. (2.15). Since this is a lossless motor, T may be set equal to zero; then solving for S gives the no-load slip as

$$S(NL) = 1 - \frac{2cE_rE_c \sin \alpha}{c^2E_r^2 + E_c^2}. \qquad (2.16)$$

From Eq. (2.14) we can define the no-load speed in terms of the synchronous speed and the slip as

$$\dot{\theta}_m(NL) = \dot{\theta}_s[1 - S(NL)]. \qquad (2.17)$$

Substituting for $\dot{\theta}_s$ using Eq. (2.7) and for $S(NL)$ using Eq. (2.16), we may write the general equation for the no-load speed of an ideal motor as

$$\dot{\theta}_m(NL) = \frac{120f}{p} \frac{2cE_rE_c \sin \alpha}{c^2E_r^2 + E_c^2}. \qquad (2.18)$$

Dividing the numerator and denominator of Eq. (2.16) by the quantity $(cE_r)^2$ and dividing both sides by the synchronous speed yields the equation

$$\frac{\dot{\theta}_m(NL)}{\dot{\theta}_s} = \frac{2(E_c/cE_r)}{1 + (E_c/cE_r)^2}. \qquad (2.19)$$

Equation (2.19) deserves special notice. Figure 2.3 shows a plot of the velocity ratio $\dot{\theta}_m/\dot{\theta}_s$ as a function of the voltage ratio E_c/cE_r. This shows that *maximum* speed exists for *balanced* operating conditions. Therefore *raising* or *lowering* either the reference or control voltage from the balanced values *decreases* the no-load speed. Also, Fig. 2.3 shows that the level of these voltages does not affect the speed so long as the ratio of the two voltages is maintained at the same value. This is true,

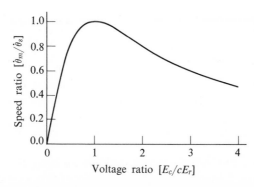

Fig. 2.3. Speed ratio vs. voltage ratio for an ideal ac servomotor.

of course, only in the case of a lossless motor. As these voltages approach zero for a motor having losses, the no-load speed will drop. However, for voltages above 50% of the rated voltage, this drop is negligible. Therefore, it may be seen that the effect of line voltage amplitude variations on no-load speed is insignificant for normal voltage levels, but frequency variations affect no-load speed in a directly proportional manner.

The preceding equations may now be used to derive equations for the motor damping coefficient and motor torque gain.

The motor damping coefficient, B_m, is defined as the inverse slope of the speed torque curve. Therefore an equation for the damping coefficient is

$$B_m = \frac{T_s}{\dot{\theta}_m(NL)}. \tag{2.20}$$

Substituting for T_s and $\dot{\theta}_m(NL)$ from Eqs. (2.3) and (2.18), (2.20) gives

$$B_m = \frac{T_s(\text{rated})}{E_c(\text{rated})E_r(\text{rated})} \frac{p}{120f} \frac{c^2 E_r^2 + E_c^2}{2c}. \tag{2.21}$$

Equation (2.21) demonstrates that even when it is assumed that the speed-torque curve is a straight line for a given set of excitations, B_m varies with E_c. Each single line may be straight, but members of a family of lines are not parallel. The damping decreases with decreasing amplifier output voltage. Therefore, when the stability near null is of major interest, Eq. (2.22) should be used:

$$B_m = \frac{T_s(\text{rated})}{E_c(\text{rated})E_r(\text{rated})} \frac{p}{120f} \frac{cE_r}{2}. \tag{2.22}$$

Motor torque gain is by definition given by

$$K_m \equiv \frac{T_s}{E_c}. \tag{2.23}$$

Substitution for T_s from Eq. (2.3) gives

$$K_m = \frac{T_s(\text{rated})}{E_c(\text{rated})E_r(\text{rated})} E_r \sin \alpha. \tag{2.24}$$

2.2. MOTOR LOSSES AND THEIR EFFECTS

The previous section discussed the performance of an ideal motor, that is, one in which there are no losses. However, such a motor does not exist. Therefore, we shall discuss below the losses which do exist in a typical servomotor.

Windage is the resistance to rotation due to the friction of the air in the air gap between the rotor and stator.

Bearing friction is the resistance to rotation caused by the bearings supporting the motor rotor.

Magnetic slot lock is the resistance to rotation caused by the magnetic attraction which exists from nonuniformity of the magnetic field near the air gap.

We can illustrate the effects and magnitudes of these three losses by considering a typical size 8 servomotor.

The first parameter to be investigated is windage. The effect of windage may be measured by running the motor in a vacuum chamber. The motor no-load speed using rated operating voltage is measured while the motor is running in a vacuum (e.g., 2.5 in. of mercury). This vacuum is then released while the motor speed is monitored. Any resulting difference in speed is directly related to windage. However, due to its small rotor diameter and smooth gap surfaces, the instrument servomotor typically exhibits no appreciable change in speed under these conditions. The windage losses, therefore, are usually assumed to be negligible, and we will not consider them further.

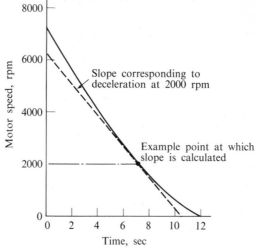

Fig. 2.4. Motor speed vs. time after removal of all excitation voltage for a typical size 8 servomotor.

The next parameter to be studied is bearing friction. This may be measured by using a sensitive nonabsorption dynamometer coupled to the motor being tested with all excitation voltages removed. Another method is to run the motor at no-load speed, remove all excitation voltages, and monitor speed vs. time as the motor runs down to a standstill. The slope of this curve is a function of the deceleration torque and the rotor inertia. Neglecting windage effects, we see that this torque is made up of bearing friction only. A typical run-down curve for a size 8 motor is shown in Fig. 2.4. Given the rotor moment of inertia by measurement or specification, we may compute the bearing friction torque T_{bf} by using the equation

$$T_{bf} = J_m \frac{d\dot{\theta}_m}{dt}, \qquad (2.25)$$

where

$$T_{bf} = \text{bearing friction torque},$$
$$J_m = \text{rotor moment of inertia},$$
$$d\dot{\theta}_m/dt = \text{motor deceleration}.$$

Using this equation and the data presented in Fig. 2.4, we may calculate the bearing friction as a function of speed. For example, $d\theta_m/dt$ at 2000 rpm is 6240/10.5 or 594 rpm/second. The inertia of the rotor is 0.9 gm-cm^2. Therefore, using the proper unit conversion factors, we obtain

$$T_{bf} = [(0.9)(1.42 \times 10^{-5})][(594)(2\pi/60)]$$
$$= 0.000794 \text{ oz-in.}$$

This process can be repeated for various velocities. Figure 2.5 represents a plot of the resulting friction values as a function of velocity. This plot illustrates that bearing friction is not a constant but varies with rotor velocity.

Approximating this curve by the best straight line over the full velocity range yields values representing the viscous friction coefficient and the coulomb friction, as shown in Fig. 2.5.

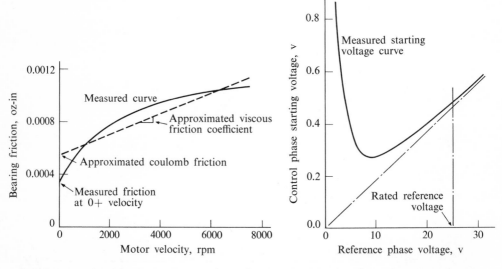

Fig. 2.5. Bearing friction vs. rotor velocity for a typical size 8 servomotor.

Fig. 2.6. Starting voltage vs. reference voltage for a typical size 8 servomotor.

The remaining parameter to be discussed is magnetic slot lock. The sum of the torque losses at start (that is friction plus slot lock) may be computed on the basis of the applied voltage necessary for starting. A plot of starting voltage (applied to the control winding) vs. reference voltage is shown in Fig. 2.6.

Using these voltages along with Eq. (2.3), we can construct a plot of total starting torque vs. reference voltage as shown in Fig. 2.7. As the reference voltage approaches zero, the magnetic slot-lock effect becomes less noticeable. Therefore, the limit of the total loss curve shown in Fig. 2.7 as the reference voltage approaches zero must equal the friction level at zero speed determined from the run-down characteristics, Fig. 2.6. A comparison of these two values shows a high degree of correlation.

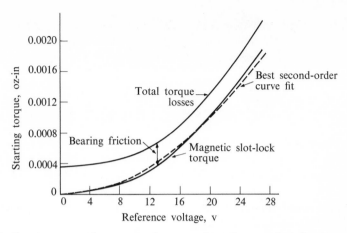

Fig. 2.7. Starting-torque losses vs. reference voltage for a typical size 8 servomotor.

The effect of magnetic slot lock alone may be determined by subtracting the bearing friction torque at stall from the total starting torque, as illustrated in Fig. 2.7. Also plotted in Fig. 2.7 is the second-order curve which best fits the hardware data. The correlation substantiates our premise that the magnetic slot-lock torque is proportional to the square of the applied voltage. This is true for both the reference and the control phase voltages. However, for starting conditions, E_c is small enough so that the slot-lock torque due to it may be ignored.

Starting voltage may be expressed by the following equation:

$$E_c(\text{start}) = \frac{E_r(\text{rated})E_c(\text{rated})\left[T_{\text{bf}} + T_{mr}(\text{rated})\left[\dfrac{E_r}{E_r(\text{rated})}\right]^2\right]}{E_r[T_s(\text{rated}) + T_{\text{bf}} + T_{mr}(\text{rated})]\sin\alpha}, \qquad (2.26)$$

where

$$T_{\text{bf}} = \text{bearing friction at zero rpm,}$$

$$T_{mr}(\text{rated}) = \text{magnetic slot-lock torque for rated reference voltage.}$$

It should be noted at this point that the motor starting voltage can increase as well as decrease with increased reference voltage. For high reference voltages, the friction is negligible, the slot-lock torque increases by the square of E_r, and the torque gain increases by the first power. Hence, the starting voltage is directly proportional to the reference voltage. For low reference voltages, the slot lock is negligible and because of the constant friction the starting voltage varies inversely with the reference voltage.

Taking the derivative of the starting voltage with respect to the reference voltage and setting this equal to zero, we obtain the reference voltage value at which the starting voltage is minimum:

$$E_r(\text{min start}) = E_r(\text{rated})\sqrt{T_{\text{bf}}/T_{mr}(\text{rated})}. \qquad (2.27)$$

The effect of the above-described losses on no-load speed and torque output will now be discussed. No-load speed may be computed by setting the output torque of Eq. (2.15) equal to the losses due to bearing friction and magnetic slot lock and solving for the slip S:

$$S = 1 - \frac{2cE_rE_c \sin \alpha}{c^2E_r^2 + E_c^2} + \frac{2E_c(\text{rated})E_r(\text{rated})}{c^2E_r^2 + E_c^2} \cdot \frac{T_L}{T_s(\text{rated})}, \qquad (2.28)$$

where T_L is the torque due to bearing friction and slot lock. Thus,

$$T_L = T_{\text{bf}} + T_{mr}(\text{rated})\left(\frac{E_r}{E_r(\text{rated})}\right)^2 + T_{mc}(\text{rated})\left(\frac{E_c}{E_c(\text{rated})}\right)^2. \qquad (2.29)$$

The no-load speed previously given by Eq. (2.18), if we now consider the losses of bearing friction and slot lock, becomes

$$\dot{\theta}_m(NL) = \frac{120f}{p} \frac{2cE_rE_c \sin \alpha - 2E_c(\text{rated})[T_L/T_s(\text{rated})]}{c^2E_r^2 + E_c^2}. \qquad (2.30)$$

The torque output of a motor, with losses considered, is given by subtracting the bearing friction and magnetic slot-lock torque from the torque equations for an ideal motor as given in Eqs. (2.3) and (2.15).

2.3. PERFORMANCE CALCULATIONS FROM MANUFACTURER'S DATA

The previous two sections presented the basic theory of the ideal motor and the extensions required to include the losses associated with the nonideal motor. However, they do not answer directly all the needs of the instrument designer. A servo designer must be able to predict the performance of a motor for any specific application directly from the manufacturer's data. The manufacturer specifies the performance of a motor at one particular set of excitation conditions that are constant, e.g., 26 v, 26 v, 400 cps. These are called the *rated conditions*. In general, the servo designer is interested in the application of a particular motor to a different set of excitations that are peculiar to his design. Furthermore, the latter are usually not constants because of the tolerances associated with the amplifier, line voltage, and frequency, e.g., 18 ± 5 v, 26 ± 3 v, 400 ± 20 cps. These latter conditions are called the *actual conditions*.

The problem continually facing the instrument servo designer is how to calculate the performance parameters to be expected under the actual excitation conditions directly from the manufacturer's specified characteristics at rated excitation. This problem is illustrated in Fig. 2.8. The performance outputs required to model the servomotor in a system are stall torque, no-load speed, torque gain, damping coefficient, starting voltage, and inertia.

One difficulty remains in that the motor losses of bearing friction and slot lock are not normally specified. Therefore, the equations developed in the previous sections cannot be used directly to calculate actual speed, starting voltage, etc.

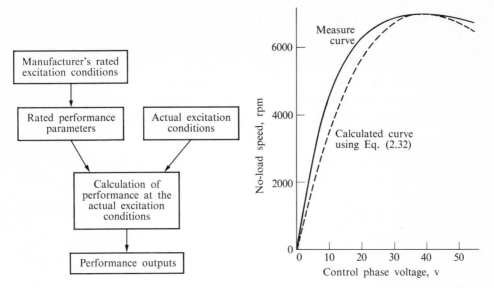

Fig. 2.8. Outline of required motor performance calculations.

Fig. 2.9. Measured and calculated no-load speed vs. control phase voltage.

There are, however, reasonable approximations that can be made so that these quantities are not required. Let us consider the following:

1. *Stall torque.* The reference voltage is normally operated reasonably close to the rated value. The total loss torque is then small compared to the stall torque; therefore the stall torque may be computed by using the equation

$$T_s = \frac{T_s(\text{rated})}{E_c(\text{rated})E_r(\text{rated})} \, E_c E_r \sin \alpha. \tag{2.31}$$

2. *No-load speed.* Because of the usual lack of rated data on the slot-lock torques T_{mr} and T_{mc} and the bearing friction T_{bf}, complicated by the fact that the latter varies with speed, it is normally impractical to calculate the torque losses by using Eq. (2.29). Hence, Eq. (2.30) cannot be used to calculate the actual speed. The losses cannot be neglected since they appreciably affect the speed. By modifying Eq. (2.18), to force the answer to concur with the rated conditions, we can generate the following approximation. In place of the synchronous speed portion, the quantity $(120f/p)$, of the equation, the actual balanced no-load speed is substituted. This gives

$$\dot{\theta}_m = \dot{\theta}_m(\text{bal}) \frac{2cE_rE_c \sin \alpha}{c^2 E_r^2 + E_c^2} \frac{f}{f(\text{rated})}. \tag{2.32}$$

A comparison of the no-load speed computed by using Eq. (2.32) with hardware data is shown in Fig. 2.9. The speeds agree near the balanced operating point, but they differ considerably in the unbalanced region. This is primarily due to the assumption that the rated speed-torque curve is a straight line, which is the basis for the derivation of Eqs. (2.18) and (2.32). However, since the speed obtained from Eq. (2.32) is always slightly slower than the actual speed at which the hardware operates, the equation assures safe design and is usually considered adequate.

3. *Torque gain.* As with the stall torque, losses can usually be neglected and the torque gain can be represented by the equation

$$K_m = \frac{T_s(\text{rated})}{E_c(\text{rated})E_r(\text{rated})}\, E_r \sin \alpha. \tag{2.33}$$

4. *Damping coefficient.* Following the same assumption made for stall torque and no-load speed, we can calculate the damping coefficient as

$$B_m = \frac{T_s(\text{rated})}{E_c(\text{rated})E_r(\text{rated})}\, \frac{1}{\dot\theta_m(\text{rated bal})}\, \frac{c^2E_r^2 + E_c^2}{2c}\, \frac{f(\text{rated})}{f}. \tag{2.34}$$

5. *Starting voltage.* The motor starting voltage could be computed directly from Eq. (2.26) except that the bearing friction and the rated reference phase slot-lock torque are usually unknown. Because of the usual lack of information about these quantities, we must dispense with them by making approximations.

Assuming the reference voltage to be approximately equal to the rated value, we are able to make the following approximation:

$$T_{mr}(\text{rated})\left(\frac{E_r}{E_r(\text{rated})}\right)^2 \gg T_{\text{bf}}. \tag{2.35}$$

Therefore, the starting voltage may be assumed to be independent of the bearing friction. This property was illustrated previously by Fig. 2.6. Also, since the rated stall torque is large compared to the magnetic slot lock, the starting voltage equation may then be rewritten as

$$E_c(\text{start}) = \frac{E_c(\text{rated})[T_{mr}(\text{rated})][E_r/E_r(\text{rated})]}{T_s(\text{rated})}. \tag{2.36}$$

However, when the reference voltage is approximately equal to the rated reference voltage, the equation

$$\frac{E_c\left(\dfrac{\text{rated}}{\text{start}}\right)}{E_c(\text{rated})} = \frac{T_{mr}(\text{rated})}{T_s(\text{rated})} \tag{2.37}$$

also holds. Substituting this relationship for the former gives the following equation for motor starting voltage:

$$E_c(\text{start}) = E_c\left(\frac{\text{rated}}{\text{start}}\right)\left(\frac{E_r}{E_r(\text{rated})}\right). \tag{2.38}$$

Equations (2.31) through (2.34) and (2.38) provide a practical method of converting manufacturer's rated data to those required by the designer. Reasonable assumptions were introduced so that the equations are compatible with conventionally specified input parameters. Figure 2.10 illustrates a logic flow diagram that

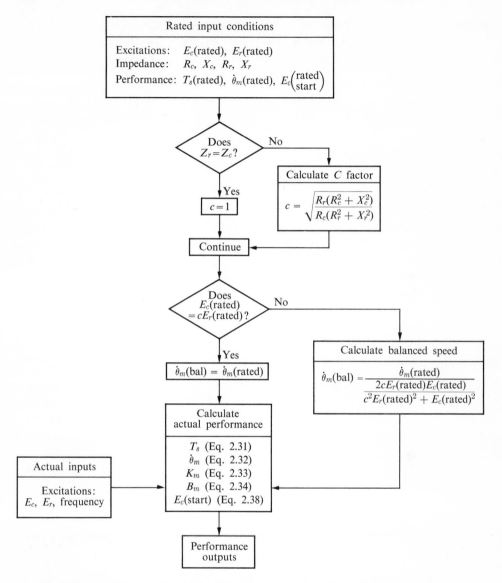

Fig. 2.10. Logic flow diagram for calculating ac servomotor performance parameters.

summarizes the performance calculations required to convert from rated to actual excitations.

The manufacturer's rated conditions often coincide with the balanced conditions since the latter provide maximum motor speed. However, sometimes other criteria such as high torque per control phase watt override the desirability of maximum speed, and consequently the motor is rated at some unbalanced condition. Under

Table 2.1*

EXAMPLE OF A COMPUTER OUTPUT SHEET
USED FOR SERVOMOTOR PERFORMANCE CALCULATIONS

```
                                                        LEAR SIEGLER INC.
                                                        INSTRUMENT DIVISION
                                                        PROGRAM SD004D


                        SERVO MOTOR PERFORMANCE CALCULATIONS


                            RATED EXCITATION CONDITIONS

      E-R(RATED)  E-C(RATED)     R-R          X-R          R-C          X-C
       (VOLTS)     (VOLTS)      (OHMS)       (OHMS)       (OHMS)       (OHMS)
      2.600E+01   1.800E+01   2.150E+02    1.360E+02    3.600E+02    3.000E+02

                            RATED INPUT PARAMETERS

                          T-S      THETA DOT-M      E-C          J-M
                        (OZ IN)      (RPM)        (VOLTS)    (GM-CM-CM)
            MAXIMUM   1.200E-01    6.200E+03    7.000E-01    7.700E-01
               MEAN   1.075E-01    6.000E+03    5.250E-01    7.000E-01
            MINIMUM   9.500E-02    5.800E+03    3.500E-01    6.300E-01


                        ACTUAL EXCITATION CONDITIONS

                            E-C(SAT)       E-R       FREQUENCY
                            (VOLTS)      (VOLTS)      (CPS)
               MAXIMUM    2.200E+01    2.860E+01    4.200E+02
                  MEAN    2.000E+01    2.600E+01    4.000E+02
               MINIMUM    1.800E+01    2.340E+01    3.800E+02

        CALCULATED PARAMETERS AT ACTUAL EXCITATION CONDITIONS

          T-S      THETA DOT-M    K-M          B-M        E-C(START)     J-M
        (OZ-IN)      (RPM)    (OZ-IN/VOLT)  (OZ-IN-SEC)   (VOLTS)   (GM-CM-CM)
MAXIMUM  1.413E-01   7.005E+03   6.888E-03   2.159E-04    7.077E-01   7.700E-01
   MEAN  1.194E-01   6.380E+03   5.972E-03   1.787E-04    5.250E-01   7.000E-01
MINIMUM  9.757E-02   5.754E+03   5.056E-03   1.416E-04    3.422E-01   6.300E-01

        E SIGNIFIES CONVENTIONAL POWER-OF-TEN NOTATION
```

* Reprinted by courtesy of Lear Siegler, Inc., Instrument Division, Grand Rapids, Michigan.

these conditions, the corresponding balanced no-load speed is calculated. Once this is accomplished, all the performance parameters can be computed for any desired set of actual excitation conditions. When the manufacturer's rated conditions are balanced, one can proceed directly with the latter computations.

The procedure outlined in Fig. 2.10 can be easily implemented to a digital computer. Table 2.1 illustrates the output sheet from such a computer program. This automated approach enables the servo designer to quickly obtain actual torque, speed, gain, damping, and starting voltage parameters for any set of excitation conditions. The first line of data on the computer output sheet represents the winding rated conditions. The second group, labeled "Rated input parameters," is the specified performance for rated excitation. Maximum and minimum values are shown as well as the mean to account for the motor tolerances. The third group, labeled "Actual excitation conditions," represents the conditions at which the performance of the servomotor is to be calculated. The above inputs are used in accord with the procedure outlined by Fig. 2.10 to determine the performance outputs summarized at the bottom of the computer output sheet. Statistical techniques are used to determine the output tolerances and will be discussed in Chapter 6. We will see in Chapter 8 that the rated conditions for a large group of "standard motors" can be stored in the digital computer as a data set to the motor performance program. This permits the engineer to try a multitude of candidate components merely by referring to part numbers or some set of desired characteristics.

2.4. THE CENTER-TAPPED SERVOMOTOR

Many of the instrument servomotors now in use have a center-tapped control phase winding, which allows them to be driven by a push-pull type amplifier and eliminates the need for a coupling transformer. This configuration can be represented by an equivalent diagram (Fig. 2.11). Let us now consider the impedance, voltage, and current relationships which exist in such a motor between the half-windings and full-winding.

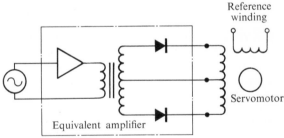

Fig. 2.11. Equivalent schematic representing a push-pull amplifier driving a center-tapped motor.

Operation of the center-tapped motor is equivalent to alternately driving one-half of the winding and then the other with a rectified sine wave. This may be equated to driving one-half with a full sine wave with the remaining lead open. Figure 2.12 shows such an equivalent diagram, where Z_L represents the losses and Z represents the self-impedance of one-half of the control phase winding. The two Z's are inductively coupled because of the transformer effect which exists in the motor.

Ordinarily it is impossible to separate the losses and self-impedance since they cannot be individually measured at the motor terminals. Similarly, only the terminal impedance is furnished by the manufacturer and includes the losses. For these reasons, it is desirable to establish relationships between quantities which are normally specified and directly measurable. Referring again to Fig. 2.12, we see

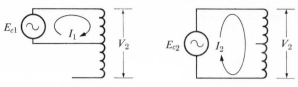

Fig. 2.13. Alternative connections for specifying center-tapped control winding excitation.

Therefore, the coupling factor k' is given in terms of the control winding impedance by

$$k' = Z_T/2Z_{1/2} - 1. \tag{2.42}$$

The equivalent end-to-end voltage V_2 corresponding to E is given by

$$V_2 = V_1 + E, \qquad V_2 = k'E + E, \qquad V_2 = (1 + k')E. \tag{2.43}$$

We shall now compare the amount of flux produced in a motor due to the voltage applied to the control phase for two methods of voltage application. The first method consists in applying a voltage to half of the winding leaving the other half open, and the second consists in applying a voltage to the entire winding. In both cases the applied voltage is adjusted to give the same measured voltage V_2 across the entire winding, as shown in Fig. 2.13. The current I_1 will be

$$I_1 = E_{c1}/Z_{1/2}, \tag{2.44}$$

and I_2 will be

$$I_2 = E_{c2}/Z_T. \tag{2.45}$$

Since E_{c2} is adjusted so that it equals the voltage measured across the entire winding when half the winding is excited by E_{c1}, the following relationship holds from Eq. (2.43):

$$E_{c2} = E_{c1}(1 + k'). \tag{2.46}$$

Also, from Eq. (2.40),

$$Z_T = 2(1 + k')Z_{1/2}. \tag{2.47}$$

Therefore, the ratio of I_1 to I_2 becomes

$$\frac{I_1}{I_2} = \frac{E_{c1}/Z_{1/2}}{E_{c1}(1 + k')/2Z_{1/2}(1 + k')} = 2. \tag{2.48}$$

Since the motor output is directly proportional to the ampere-turns, and since the ampere-turns are equal for both of the above excitations, the motor output will be the same in each case. Therefore, a center-tapped servomotor produces a given torque for a given voltage measured across the total control phase winding. The torque is not a function of how the voltage is applied, whether directly or to only half the winding.

Substantiation of the above theory may be made by testing a motor having a center-tapped control winding. Stall torque and no-load speed are measured as a function of the voltage across the entire control winding, with rated voltage applied

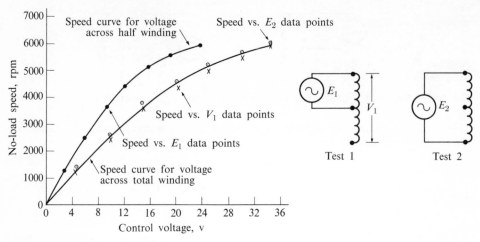

Fig. 2.14. No-load speed vs. voltage curves for voltage applied to half and total control phase winding.

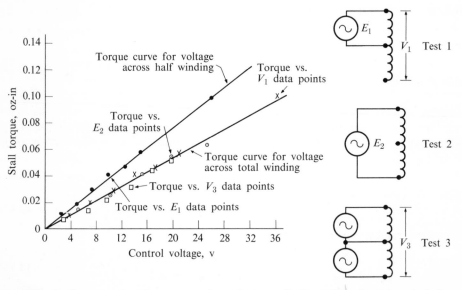

Fig. 2.15. Stall torque vs. voltage curves for voltage applied to half and total control phase winding.

to the fixed phase winding. This is repeated for different methods of excitation. Figures 2.14 and 2.15 illustrate results of a typical test. It can be seen, as in the derivation, that the total voltage across the control winding can be used to specify motor performance under all conditions. Therefore the motor stall torque and speed may be specified and measured in the same manner for a center-tapped motor as for a motor which is not center tapped.

2.5. MOTOR REPRESENTATION

To design the typical motor-generator servo, we need a mathematical description which defines each component or block. One such mathematical model is the transfer function. The transfer function of a component is the ratio of output to input, usually expressed by using the Laplace operator.*

$$\frac{\text{Output } (s)}{\text{Input } (s)} = \text{transfer function} = G(s)$$

```
                    ┌──────────────┐
                    │   Transfer   │
                    │   function   │
──── Input (s) ────▶│              │──── Output (s) ───▶
                    │     G(s)     │
                    └──────────────┘
```

The Laplace form is used since it provides a method of handling the differential equations in an algebraic manner. The transfer function for the ac servomotor will now be developed.

A block diagram representing the motor characteristics is shown in Fig. 2.16. The motor torque gain K_m can be either calculated from Eq. (2.33) or obtained from hardware measurements since it is the slope of the stall torque vs. control phase voltage curve (Fig. 2.17). This shows that the motor torque gain is essentially linear over the rated operating range. The motor damping coefficient B_m can be calculated by using Eq. (2.34) or measured as the inverse slope of the speed-torque curve.

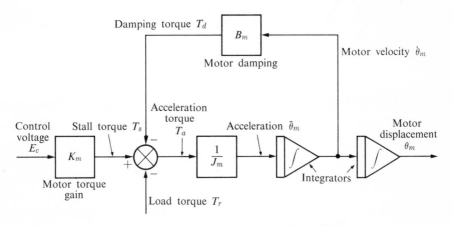

Fig. 2.16. Servomotor mathematical block diagram.

___

* The Laplace operator will be used frequently throughout the text. Readers unfamiliar with its usage should read the Appendix.

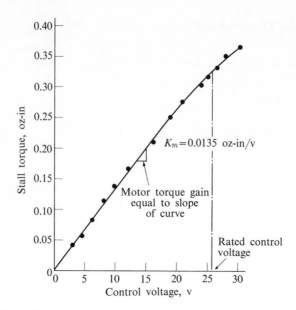

Fig. 2.17. Stall torque vs. control voltage for a typical ac servomotor.

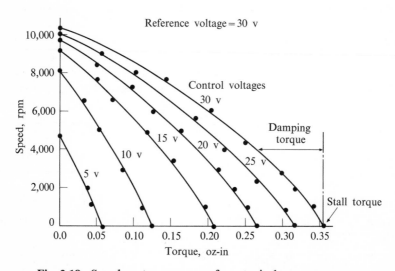

Fig. 2.18. Speed vs. torque curves for a typical ac servomotor.

Figure 2.18 shows the motor damping to be quite nonlinear. It varies with the operating point since the slopes of the speed-torque curves are not constant. However, normally B_m may be assumed constant with little loss in design accuracy. This is especially true when a generator is used since its damping usually overshadows that of the motor.

Using the block diagram, we may write equations which define the operation of the motor. These equations in the Laplace domain are:

$$\text{Stall torque} \qquad = K_m E_c, \qquad\qquad (2.49)$$

$$\text{Damping torque} \quad = B_m s \theta_m(s), \qquad\qquad (2.50)$$

$$\text{Acceleration torque} = J_m s^2 \theta_m(s). \qquad\qquad (2.51)$$

Since the acceleration torque must equal the stall torque minus the damping and load torques,

$$J_m s^2 \theta_m(s) = K_m E_c(s) - B_m s \theta_m(s) - T_r(s). \qquad\qquad (2.52)$$

Let us consider that the load torque is zero for the moment. The motor transfer function may then be determined directly from the above equation:

$$\frac{\theta_m(s)}{E_c(s)} = \frac{K_m/B_m}{s(\tau_m s + 1)}, \qquad\qquad (2.53)$$

where

τ_m is called the *motor mechanical time constant*,

$$\tau_m = J_m/B_m \text{ (sec)}. \qquad\qquad (2.54)$$

The motor mechanical time constant is the time required by the motor to reach 63.2% of its final speed for a step voltage input. For example, if a motor with the characteristics shown in Fig. 2.18 was at rest and suddenly a 20-v step was applied, a stall torque of 0.27 oz-in would be developed. This torque would instantly accelerate the motor inertia. Once the motor picks up speed, damping torque is developed which subtracts from the stall torque, thereby decreasing the acceleration until the damping torque equals the stall torque. At this point, there is zero torque available to accelerate the motor inertia and the motor speed remains constant. This steady state speed is called the *no-load speed*. The motor operating point has actually moved up the 20-v speed-torque curve, starting from the stall torque point and progressing along the curve to the no-load speed point. The motor will reach 63.2% of the no-load speed in τ_m sec.

Since motor damping is not constant, the motor time constant and associated response is not really a linear relationship. Good approximations may be made, or the exact curves may be used with computer simulation.

2.6. EQUIVALENT MOTOR CONNECTED AT LOAD

It is often most convenient to refer the motor to the load through the gear train. This is accomplished as shown in Fig. 2.19 by mathematically defining an equivalent motor which, if connected directly to the load, would produce the same relationships as the actual motor and gear train.

Let us consider that the gear train has a gear ratio N such that the motor turns N revolutions for each revolution of the load. The equivalent motor must produce N times the torque of the actual motor. The torque gain of the equivalent motor then must be NK_m.

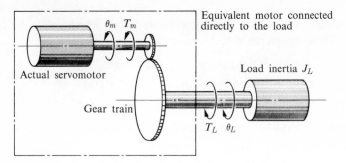

Fig. 2.19. Equivalent servomotor acting directly at the load.

The damping and inertia of the equivalent motor can be found, since the torque at the load is given by

$$T_L = J \frac{d^2\theta_L}{dt^2} + B \frac{d\theta_L}{dt},$$ (2.55)

where J and B are the inertia and damping of the equivalent motor at the load shaft. But the torque at the load shaft equals N times the actual motor torque

$$T_L = NT_m = NK_m E_m,$$ (2.56)

and the load shaft displacement, velocity, and acceleration equal N^{-1} times that of the motor shaft:

$$\theta_L = \frac{1}{N} \theta_m,$$ (2.57)

$$\frac{d\theta_L}{dt} = \frac{1}{N} \frac{d\theta_m}{dt},$$ (2.58)

$$\frac{d^2\theta_L}{dt^2} = \frac{1}{N} \frac{d^2\theta_m}{dt^2}.$$ (2.59)

Substituting the load velocity and acceleration expressions into the load torque equation and dividing through by N, we arrive at the following equation:

$$K_m E_c = \frac{J}{N^2} \frac{d^2\theta_m}{dt^2} + \frac{B}{N^2} \frac{d\theta_m}{dt}.$$ (2.60)

This must be identical to an equation written for the actual motor, that is,

$$K_m E_c = J_m \frac{d^2\theta_m}{dt^2} + B_m \frac{d\theta_m}{dt}.$$ (2.61)

Equating the coefficients of the derivative terms, we see that the equivalent motor must have an inertia and damping coefficient equal to N^2 times that of the actual motor. Therefore

$$J = N^2 J_m, \qquad B = N^2 B_m.$$ (2.62)

Since the equivalent motor is connected directly to the load, the equivalent motor inertia may be added to the load inertia. The total inertia J_T of the servo is then given by

$$J_T = N^2 J_m + J_L. \tag{2.63}$$

The gear train inertia may be reflected and added as part of the load inertia.

The gear train and load seldom exhibit any significant amount of viscous damping, and therefore load viscous damping is usually ignored. Gear train and load coulomb friction will be considered in Chapter 7.

The combined transfer function of the motor, gear train, and load may now be written as

$$\frac{\theta_L(s)}{E_c(s)} = \frac{NK_m/N^2 B_m}{s(\tau_T s + 1)}, \tag{2.64}$$

where τ_T is the mechanical time constant of the motor and load,

$$\tau_T = (N^2 J_m + J_L)/N^2 B_m. \tag{2.65}$$

In block diagram form:

Input $E_c(s)$	$\dfrac{NK_m/N^2 B_m}{s(\tau_T s + 1)}$	Output $\theta_L(s)$
(Control voltage)		(Load displacement)

The above mathematical representation of the motor, gear train, and load is completely linear and therefore can only approximate the actual characteristics. There are several limitations that do not appear in the above transfer function. These limitations are:

1. *Motor torque saturation.* Figure 2.17 shows the motor torque to be a linear function of voltage up to approximately 26 v, where the torque begins to saturate. Most servomotors are designed to have a linear torque gain throughout their rated operating range. Therefore, the motor torque saturation usually can be omitted from an analysis since the amplifier should be designed to saturate before the motor rating is exceeded.

2. *Electrical time constant.* A second lag term, caused by the motor winding reactance, is also present in the servomotor. The resulting time constant is usually much lower than the mechanical time constant. We can most often obtain sufficient accuracy without considering the additional lag, although, if desired, it may be included in a final design with little added labor required. The additional lag should be considered when checking for inner-loop stability (generator buzz) even though it is not significant relative to major loop performance.

3. *Nonlinear speed-torque curves.* Figure 2.18 shows that the servomotor speed-torque curves are not parallel straight lines. If the motor is to be analyzed by itself, either a nonlinear analysis is required or the curves should be approximated by parallel straight lines. If the motor is to be considered as part of a servo, the latter is normally adequate. This is especially true when a generator is included, since the damping created by the generator usually overshadows that provided by the motor.

4. *Motor starting voltage, cogging, or torque at zero control voltage.* Servomotors usually either require a small control phase voltage to start or produce a small torque with zero control phase voltage (single phasing). Both these effects cause a small steady state error but have little effect on dynamic performance. A cogging or jerking is also noticeable at slow speeds and sometimes causes difficulty, especially with low gear ratios.

The gear train also has the nonlinearities of backlash and friction and has finite stiffness and therefore was overly simplified. These simplifying assumptions will, however, be eliminated in the next chapter.

2.7. SUMMARY

In this chapter equations were derived to analytically describe the performance of the ac servomotor. We started by developing an analytical description of the ideal motor, described balanced operation, and demonstrated that under certain conditions, an increase in motor excitation could reduce the motor's speed.

Once the ideal motor was described, the effects of various losses were presented. The windage effect was shown to be negligible, but the effects of bearing friction and magnetic slot lock were found to be important and therefore were analyzed in detail.

An analytical procedure was then developed that enabled the designer to calculate the performance factors of torque, speed, gain, damping, and starting voltage under any excitation condition from the manufacturer's rated data. Furthermore, the effect of a center-tapped control winding was described and related to the case without a center tap.

The chapter was concluded by development of a mathematical block diagram and transfer function representing the motor. This transfer function was then modified to include the effects of the gear train by the definition of an equivalent motor acting at the load. To accomplish this, it was shown that the motor's inertia and damping coefficient are both reflected by the square of the gear ratio.

PROBLEMS

*2.1. Calculate the synchronous speeds of a four-pole and six-pole 400-cps servomotor.

*2.2. The following motor rated parameters are given:

$$Z_c = 103 + j\,102 \text{ ohms}, \qquad Z_r = 103 + j\,102 \text{ ohms}$$
$$E_c = 26 \text{ v}, \qquad E_r = 26 \text{ v}$$
$$T_s = 0.28 \text{ oz-in}, \qquad \theta_m(NL) = 10,000 \text{ rpm}$$
$$E_c(\text{start}) = 0.8 \text{ v}.$$

* *Note:* Problems whose numbers are preceded by an asterisk have answers printed in the back of the book.

Assume that the amplifier saturation level is only 19 v and calculate the following new parameters, considering the presence of 19 and 26 v on the control and reference phases, respectively:

a) stall torque,   b) no-load speed,
c) torque gain,   d) damping coefficient,
e) reference phase power,   f) control phase power,
g) starting voltage.

*2.3. Consider the same motor to be used as in Problem 2.2, with 19 v on the control phase. Calculate what reference phase voltage would be required to achieve the rated stall torque. With these conditions, what are the values of:

a) no-load speed,   b) torque gain,
c) damping coefficient,   d) reference phase power,
e) starting voltage?

*2.4. The following specification data for a center-tapped servomotor are given:

$$Z_r = 2150 + j\,2050 \text{ ohms}, \qquad Z_c(\text{end-to-end}) = 1400 + j\,1360 \text{ ohms}$$
$$Z_c(\text{CT-to-end}) = 510 + j\,340 \text{ ohms}, \qquad E_r = 115 \text{ v},$$
$$E_c(\text{CT-to-end}) = 26 \text{ v}.$$

Calculate the complex coupling factor and the corresponding end-to-end control voltage that will produce the same torque and no-load speed.

2.5. Using the inputs given in Table 2.1, calculate the following mean output parameters:

a) stall torque,   b) motor no-load speed,
c) motor torque gain,   d) motor damping coefficient.

2.6. How would the stall torque and no-load speed of a servomotor vary if the reference and control winding voltages were both reduced to 0.7 of their original values?

2.7. Consider a servomotor to have the following properties:

$$Z_c = 350 + j\,600 \text{ ohms},$$
$$Z_r = 1500 + j\,2500 \text{ ohms},$$
$$E_r = 60 \text{ v}.$$

Calculate the control voltage value that would result in maximum no-load speed.

2.8. A servomotor has the following values:

$$T_s = 0.12 \text{ oz-in},$$
$$\dot{\theta}_m(NL) = 10{,}000 \text{ rpm},$$
$$J_m = 0.8 \text{ gm-cm}^2.$$

Assume that a gear ratio of 100 is used. What are the following values of the equivalent motor at the load:

a) stall torque (oz-in),   b) no-load speed (rpm)
c) damping coefficient (oz-in/rad/sec),   d) inertia (gm-cm^2),
e) inertia (oz-in/rad/sec^2)?

2.9. The slot-lock torque loss varies as the square of the voltages applied. Describe physically why the motor starting voltage is proportional to the first power of the reference voltage for high reference voltage values.

BIBLIOGRAPHY

BAILEY, B., and J. GAULT, *Alternating Current Machinery*, McGraw-Hill, 1951, pp. 346–352.

DAVIS, S. A., "Converting Ideal to Working Data for Application of Two-Phase Servo Motors," *Electrical Manufacturing* (September 1956).

DAVIS, S. A., and B. K. LEDGERWOOD, *Electromechanical Components for Servomechanisms*, McGraw-Hill, 1961, Chapter 6.

DAVIS, S. A., and J. SPECTOR, "Application Factors for Two-Phase Servo Motors," *Electrical Manufacturing* (June 1955).

FENG, TAI NUN, "Servo Motor Performance Under Unbalanced Conditions," *Electrical Manufacturing* (November 1957).

GIBSON, J., and F. TUTEUR, *Control System Components*, McGraw-Hill, 1958, Chapter 7.

GLASBERG, M., "Get the Most Out of Your AC Servo Motor," *Electromechanical Design* (April 1962).

IVERY, K., *AC Carrier Control Systems*, Wiley, 1964.

KOOPMAN, R. J. W., "Operating Characteristics of Two-Phase Servomotors," *AIEE Transactions* **68**, 319–329 (1949).

McCLAY, M., "How Temperature Affects Servomotor Performance," *Electronic Equipment Engineering* (December 1959).

TRICKEY, P. H., "Calculating Servomotor Speed-Torque Curves," *Control Engineering* (March 1962).

"A-C Instrument Servomotors," *Electromechanical Components and System Design* **2**, 8 (October 1958), pp. 33–47.

CHAPTER 3

THE GEAR TRAIN

The gear train serves the purpose of coupling the load to the motor. It may be considered a "mechanical transformer" in that it converts the speed-torque characteristic of the motor to that desired at the load. The gear ratio N will be defined as the velocity developed at the servomotor divided by that produced at the output of the gear train. The ratio is therefore normally greater than unity.

3.1. TORQUE VS. DEFLECTION CURVE

The gear train is often considered an ideal component and simply represented by a transfer function N. This assumption is sometimes adequate. However, it often leads to later stability complications because of its optimism. To investigate gear train performance in detail, let us consider the following test. The input shaft is locked and torques are applied to the output shaft and the resulting deflections of the output shaft are measured. These deflections are usually only several minutes of arc and therefore some sort of magnification is required in making measurements. This measurement apparatus can be something as simple as a long pointer clamped on the output shaft or something more elaborate such as a toolmaker's microscope. The latter is recommended, if available, since it is very convenient to use and provides good accuracy. The torques can be applied by using a torque watch, torque wrench, or any type of force gage acting on a lever arm. An example of the plotted torque and deflection readings is shown in Fig. 3.1. Readings are taken in both directions. Special care must be taken not to disturb the initial zero setting. This enables us to obtain a true measurement of the actual gear train backlash as well as the stiffness. Parallel straight lines may be drawn through the data points as shown in Fig. 3.1. The slope of the lines is the gear train stiffness and the corresponding torque dead zone is the effective backlash.

3.2. CALCULATION OF GEAR TRAIN STIFFNESS

The test procedure for measuring the stiffness of a gear train was described previously. However, it is equally important that equations be developed so that the designer can predict the value of stiffness a proposed gear design should yield. Describing the stiffness analytically also provides insight into what factors should be

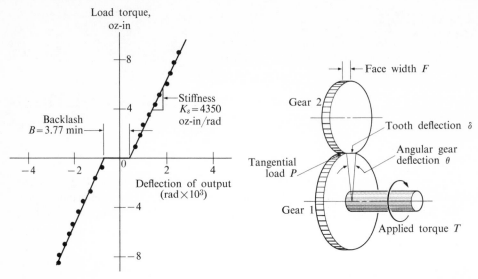

Fig. 3.1. Typical gear train torque vs. deflection curve.

Fig. 3.2. Nomenclature associated with stiffness calculation for a pair of spur gears.

considered to ensure that maximum stiffness is obtained. Let us first consider the stiffness associated with a pair of meshing spur gears (Fig. 3.2).

The deflection δ of the gear teeth for a pair of meshing spur gears, assuming one-tooth contact at the tooth center, is given by

$$\delta = \frac{P}{F} \frac{E_1 Z_1 + E_2 Z_2}{E_1 Z_1 E_2 Z_2}, \tag{3.1}$$

where

$Z =$ elasticity deformation factor for gear teeth, which is given by the equation

$$Z = \frac{y}{(0.242 + 7.25y)}, \tag{3.2}$$

$y =$ gear tooth Lewis form factor and is a function of the circular pitch, number of teeth, pressure angle, and tooth profile,

$E =$ modulus of elasticity of the gear material,

$\delta =$ total elastic deformation for the pair of mating tooth profiles,

$F =$ gear face width,

$P =$ applied tangential load.

The Lewis form factor is tabulated for various numbers of teeth in Table 3.1. The table is based upon a conventional 20-deg pressure angle full depth gear.

Table 3.1

LEWIS FORM FACTOR
20 DEGREE FULL DEPTH TOOTH

Number of Teeth	Lewis Form Factor	Number of Teeth	Lewis Form Factor
10	0.064	26	0.110
11	0.072	28	0.112
12	0.078	30	0.114
13	0.083	34	0.118
14	0.088	38	0.122
15	0.092	43	0.126
16	0.094	50	0.130
17	0.096	60	0.134
18	0.098	75	0.138
19	0.100	100	0.142
20	0.102	150	0.146
21	0.104	300	0.150
22	0.105	Rack	0.154
24	0.107		

Since the torsional spring constant is desired, Eq. (3.1) may be converted to the form

$$K_s = \frac{T}{\theta} = 4D_1^2 F \frac{E_1 Z_1 E_2 Z_2}{E_1 Z_1 + E_2 Z_2},\qquad(3.3)$$

where

K_s = stiffness (oz-in/rad) of the gear pass referred to gear 1,

T = torque at the gear under consideration corresponding to P,

$$T = P[D_1/2],$$

θ = torsional deflection corresponding to δ,

$$\theta = [2/D_1]\delta,$$

D_1 = pitch diameter (in.) of gear 1.

The spring constant computed by the preceding equation is based on one-tooth contact. Some texts multiply Eq. (3.3) by the tooth contact ratio to arrive at a more "accurate" stiffness value. However, practice has shown that even Eq. (3.3) results in values that are often higher than those experienced for actual hardware. This quite possibly is due to the neglected resilience of the housings, bearings, etc. For these reasons, it is recommended that the "more pessimistic" stiffness calculations which assume one-tooth contact be used in design.

The shafting associated with a gear train often contributes a significant amount to the total stiffness. Let us consider a solid, uniform circular shaft fixed at one end. The torsional stiffness of such a shaft is given by the equation

$$k_s = \frac{\pi G_s D^4}{2L}, \tag{3.4}$$

where

k_s = the shaft torsional stiffness (oz-in/rad),

G_s = the shear modulus of elasticity of the shaft material (lb/in²),

D = the shaft diameter (in.),

L = the shaft length (in.).

The designer must ensure adequate shaft stiffness. Let us consider the following example.

Example 3.1 Calculate the stiffness of a steel shaft 0.09 in. in diameter and 2.0 in. long. The shear modulus of elasticity for steel is 12.0×10^6 lb/in². Using Eq. (3.4), we obtain

$$k_s = \frac{\pi(12 \times 10^6)(0.09)^4}{2(2.0)}$$

$$= 620 \text{ oz-in/rad}.$$

The value of shaft stiffness calculated in the above example would have the most significant effect if it occurred near the output, in which case it might well cause instability of the servosystem, as will be discussed in later chapters.

Stiffness is reflected by the gear ratio squared, as we can illustrate by considering a spring coupled through an ideal gear train (infinite stiffness) as shown in Fig. 3.3. The stiffness constant K_{s1} desired at shaft 1 is by definition

$$K_{s1} = T_1/\theta_1. \tag{3.5}$$

But the torque and displacements at shaft 1 are related to those of shaft 2 by the gear ratio N through the following two equations:

$$T_1 = NT_2, \qquad \theta_1 = \theta_2/N. \tag{3.6}$$

Substituting these relationships into Eq. (3.5), we find

$$K_{s1} = N^2(T_2/\theta_2). \tag{3.7}$$

But by definition of K_{s2}, Eq. (3.7) can be written as

$$K_{s1} = N^2 K_{s2}, \tag{3.8}$$

which demonstrates that the stiffness varies as the square of the gear ratio.

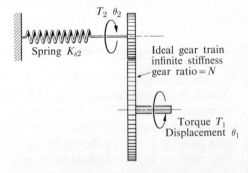

Spring K_{s2}

Ideal gear train infinite stiffness gear ratio = N

$T_2\ \theta_2$

Torque T_1
Displacement θ_1

Fig. 3.3. Reflection of a torsional spring.

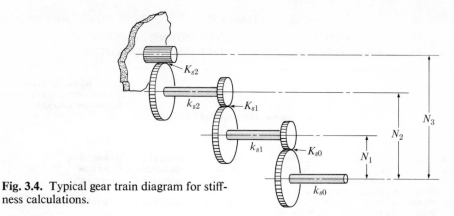

Fig. 3.4. Typical gear train diagram for stiffness calculations.

Figure 3.4 illustrates a typical gear train. Equations (3.3) and (3.4) are used to calculate the spring constant for each pair of gears and the associated shaft. The corresponding total stiffness K_{pi} of each pass is then given by the equation

$$K_{pi} = k_{si}K_{si}/(k_{si} + K_{si}). \qquad (3.9)$$

The torsional spring constant K_s of the total gear train is given by the reciprocal of the sum of the reciprocals of the individual spring constants referred to a common shaft. It is standard practice in servo design to refer all parameters to the load or output shaft. In equation form,

$$K_s = \frac{1}{1/K_{p0} + 1/N_1^2K_{p1} + 1/N_2^2K_{p2} + \cdots + 1/N_n^2K_{pn}}. \qquad (3.10)$$

To use the preceding equations we should take the pitch diameter of the gear nearest the load to calculate the constant for each stage. The value of N is the gear ratio measured from the gear nearest the load of the gear pair being considered to the load shaft.

We can implement Eqs. (3.3), (3.4), and (3.10) by using a digital computer program to calculate the effective total stiffness of a gear train. Table 3.2 is a sample output sheet from such a computer program used in standard servo design. The first group of data represents the inputs associated with each of the four gears in the train. The helix angle is shown as a possible input to include the helical antibacklash gear to be discussed in Section 3.4. The individual gear inputs are followed by the shaft data inputs associated with the two passes and the corresponding total stiffness of each pass.

The effective value of each pass is also shown reflected to the load shaft, and the total effective stiffness of the whole train is summarized at the bottom. Using this automated approach, the designer can obtain a complete stiffness analysis of a given gear train design in a matter of seconds. By printing out the effective stiffness value of each stage at the load, the designer can immediately detect any weak point and take corrective action.

Table 3.2*

EXAMPLE OF A COMPUTER OUTPUT SHEET
USED FOR GEAR TRAIN STIFFNESS CALCULATIONS

```
                                                         LEAR SIEGLER INC.
                                                         INSTRUMENT DIVISION
                                                         PROGRAM GR002A
                             GEAR TRAIN STIFFNESS


GEAR            FACE       HELIX       NO.     ELASTIC    DIAMETRAL
NO.            WIDTH       ANGLE       TEETH   MODULUS    PITCH
             (INCHES)    (DEGREES)            (LB/SQIN)  (1/INCHES)
       MAX   6.750E-02   0.000E-99
  1    MEAN  6.250E-02   0.000E-99   1.410E+02  1.020E+07  7.200E+01
       MIN   5.750E-02   0.000E-99


       MAX   1.300E-01   0.000E-99
  2    MEAN  1.250E-01   0.000E-99   2.200E+01  3.000E+07  7.200E+01
       MIN   1.200E-01   0.000E-99


       MAX   6.750E-02   0.000E-99
  3    MEAN  6.250E-02   0.000E-99   6.700E+01  3.000E+07  9.600E+01
       MIN   5.750E-02   0.000E-99


       MAX   2.550E-01   0.000E-99
  4    MEAN  2.500E-01   0.000E-99   1.000E+01  3.000E+07  9.600E+01
       MIN   2.450E-01   0.000E-99


               SHAFT       SHAFT     ELASTIC   STIFFNESS  STIFFNESS
              LENGTH     DIAMETER    MODULUS   AT PASS    AT LOAD
             (INCHES)    (INCHES)   (LB/SQIN) (OZIN/RAD) (OZIN/RAD)
       MAX   5.050E-01   1.050E-01             4.127E+03  4.127E+03
       MEAN  5.000E-01   1.000E-01   1.100E+07 3.440E+03  3.440E+03
       MIN   4.950E-01   9.500E-02             2.754E+03  2.754E+03


       MAX   1.300E-01   2.050E-01             1.056E+05  4.341E+06
       MEAN  1.250E-01   2.000E-01   1.100E+07 9.920E+04  4.074E+06
       MIN   1.200E-01   1.950E-01             9.271E+04  3.808E+06


       MAXIMUM        MEAN       MINIMUM
       4.123E+03    3.438E+03   2.752E+03 EFFECTIVE STIFFNESS AT LOAD (OZ-IN/RAD)

            E SIGNIFIES CONVENTIONAL POWER-OF-TEN NOTATION
```

* Reprinted by courtesy of Lear Siegler, Inc., Instrument Division, Grand Rapids, Michigan.

3.3. CALCULATION OF GEAR TRAIN BACKLASH

Backlash is the lost motion in a gear train. An accurate method of measurement using the torque-deflection diagram was presented in Section 3.1. For high-performance instrument servomechanisms, backlash or lost motion must be controlled and often reduced to a minimum. Insufficient control of backlash often results in instability of the servosystem. On the other hand, arbitrarily assigning excessively tight tolerances results in undue cost. It is important that the servo designer be able to calculate the backlash expected in a design as a function of the associated parameters.

For a theoretical set of perfectly mating gears, the tooth gap is equal to the tooth thickness on the line of contact and the backlash would be zero provided the center distance C was fixed at

$$C_s = (n_1 + n_2)/2P, \qquad (3.11)$$

where

C_s = the standard center distance (in.),

n_1, n_2 = the number of teeth for gears 1 and 2, respectively,

P = the diametral pitch associated with the gear pair (in.$^{-1}$).

Such a gear pair, however, is nonexistent because of discrepancies in manufacture. Moreover, the chance of "binding" even for a set of "perfect" gears is great because of the difference in thermal expansion rates for different materials. For these reasons, some backlash is built into conventional spur gears. This is accomplished by cutting the teeth thinner than the theoretical thickness, which is equal to half the circular pitch. Also, it is customary to increase the center distance by an amount equal to that resulting from differential thermal expansion. Because of this increase, there will be additional backlash at room temperature.

Let us first consider the backlash introduced by the nonideal tooth thickness. This is equal to the difference ΔT_t between the actual and the ideal tooth thickness:

$$\begin{aligned} \Delta T_t &= \frac{\pi}{2P} - T_1 + \frac{\pi}{2P} - T_2 \\ &= \frac{\pi}{P} - T_1 - T_2, \end{aligned} \qquad (3.12)$$

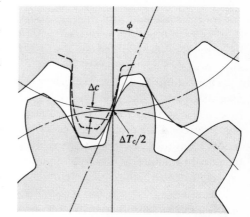

Fig. 3.5. Relationship between backlash and change in center distance.

where T_1, T_2 are the tooth thickness associated with gears 1 and 2, respectively.

The backlash ΔT_c introduced by a nonideal center distance is determined by the involute relationship illustrated in Fig. 3.5.

The following analytical relationship can be established for ΔT_c as a function of ΔC:

$$\Delta T_c = (2 \tan \phi) \Delta C + \left[\frac{2P}{(n_1 + n_2) \tan \phi} \right] (\Delta C)^2$$

$$+ \left[\frac{1 + 3 \tan^2 \phi}{3 \tan^3 \phi} \right] \left[\frac{2P}{n_1 + n_2} \right]^2 (\Delta C)^3 + \cdots \qquad (3.13)$$

where ϕ is the standard pressure angle and ΔC is the difference between the operating and standard center distance.

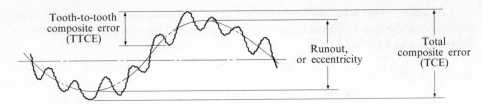

Tooth-to-tooth
composite error
(TTCE)

Runout,
or eccentricity

Total
composite error
(TCE)

Fig. 3.6. Typical gear error chart obtained by variable center distance test fixtures.

Equation (3.13) is an infinite series accounting for the effect of the involute curve. Calculations may be carried out to any desired accuracy by including a sufficient number of terms. For the typical precision gear train, ΔC is sufficiently small so that the higher-order terms may be neglected. Considering this to be the case, we calculate the backlash ΔT_c resulting from center distance variation as

$$\Delta T_c = 2 \tan \phi \left[C - \frac{n_1 + n_2}{2P} \right], \tag{3.14}$$

where C is the actual center distance (in.).

In this same category falls the radial play in the bearings. Running gears tend to force each other apart to the extent allowed by the bearing play. This tendency increases the operating center distance and can be included in the calculations by appropriately increasing ΔC.

One additional factor, the gear pitch diameter runout, or eccentricity, must be considered when one calculates backlash. In a perfect gear, the pitch circle would be concentric about the axis of rotation. In actuality, a curve drawn through all points of constant tooth thickness would be both eccentric and jagged. The latter results from tooth-to-tooth spacing and involute variations. The total variation of the curve is defined as the total composite error (TCE). The total composite error as well as the tooth-to-tooth composite error (TTCE) may be measured by the following test. The gear to be tested is rotated under spring tension around a fixed master gear, which is assumed to be perfect. The variation of the center distance is carefully recorded during the test. Figure 3.6 illustrates a typical curve obtained.

The run-out or eccentricity is given by the difference between the TCE and the TTCE. Since the eccentricity is representative of a center distance variation, it contributes to the total backlash in the same manner as the true center distance. Following the same approximation made in the center distance equation, we obtain

$$T_{\text{tce}} = 2[\tan \phi][\text{TCE}_1 - \text{TTCE}_1 + \text{TCE}_2 - \text{TTCE}_2]. \tag{3.15}$$

For any fixed collection of errors, Eq. (3.15) represents a "worst case" situation because it assumes that both gears are meshed at their low point of eccentricity. If we consider that a hunting tooth exists, however, we see that this point will always occur.

Combining the backlash components given by Eqs. (3.12), (3.14), and (3.15) results in the equation which defines the existing backlash of two mating gears in terms of each of their parameters and the center distance:

$$B = \left\{ 2 \tan \phi \left[\left(C - \frac{n_1 + n_2}{2P} \right) + \text{TCE}_1 - \text{TTCE}_1 + \text{TCE}_2 - \text{TTCE}_2 \right] \right.$$
$$\left. + (\pi/P - T_1 - T_2) \right\} \frac{6876P}{n_1}, \qquad (3.16)$$

where

B = the combined angular backlash (min) of gear 1 and 2 referred to gear 1, which is taken as the gear nearest the load,

C = the actual center distance (in.) between gear 1 and 2,

n_1, n_2 = the number of teeth for gears 1 and 2, respectively,

P = the diametral pitch associated with the gear pair,

$\text{TCE}_1, \text{TCE}_2$ = the total composite errors associated with gears 1 and 2, respectively,

$\text{TTCE}_1, \text{TTCE}_2$ = the tooth-to-tooth composite errors associated with gears 1 and 2, respectively,

T_1, T_2 = the tooth thickness associated with gears 1 and 2, respectively.

To calculate the total effective backlash for a whole gear train, one must

1. calculate the backlash $B_0, B_1, B_2, \ldots, B_k$ for each pass, using Eq. (3.16),
2. calculate the gear ratios $N_1, N_2, N_3, \ldots, N_k$ from each pass (gear side toward load) and the load,
3. calculate the total effective backlash B at the load, using the equation

$$B = B_0 + \frac{B_1}{N_1} + \frac{B_2}{N_2} + \frac{B_3}{N_3} + \cdots + \frac{B_k}{N_k}. \qquad (3.17)$$

We may implement Eqs. (3.16) and (3.17) by using a digital computer. Table 3.3 illustrates the typical output from such a program implementation. The first group of data represents the inputs associated with each of the four gears in the train. The face width and helix angle are shown as possible inputs to include the helical anti-backlash gear discussed in the following section. These are followed by the center distance and diametral pitch inputs associated with each pass, as well as the cal-culated backlash values. The total effective backlash of the whole train is summarized at the bottom.

Table 3.3*

EXAMPLE OF A COMPUTER OUTPUT SHEET
USED FOR GEAR TRAIN BACKLASH CALCULATIONS

```
                                                              LEAR SIEGLER INC.
                                                              INSTRUMENT DIVISION
                                                              PROGRAM GR001A
                              GEAR TRAIN BACKLASH


GEAR            FACE        TOOTH       TOT-COMP.   T-T COMP.   HELIX       NO.
NO.             WIDTH       THICKNESS   ERROR       ERROR       ANGLE       TEETH
                (INCHES)    (INCHES)    (INCHES)    (INCHES)    (DEGREES)
        MAX     7.800E-02   2.182E-02   1.000E-03   4.000E-04   0.000E-99
   1    MEAN    7.800E-02   2.157E-02   5.000E-04   2.000E-04   0.000E-99   1.410E+02
        MIN     7.800E-02   2.132E-02   0.000E-99   0.000E-99   0.000E-99


        MAX     7.800E-02   2.182E-02   1.000E-03   4.000E-04   0.000E-99
   2    MEAN    7.800E-02   2.157E-02   5.000E-04   2.000E-04   0.000E-99   2.200E+01
        MIN     7.800E-02   2.132E-02   0.000E-99   0.000E-99   0.000E-99


        MAX     7.800E-02   1.636E-02   1.000E-03   4.000E-04   0.000E-99
   3    MEAN    7.800E-02   1.611E-02   5.000E-04   2.000E-04   0.000E-99   6.700E+01
        MIN     7.800E-02   1.586E-02   0.000E-99   0.000E-99   0.000E-99


        MAX     7.800E-02   1.636E-02   1.000E-03   4.000E-04   0.000E-99
   4    MEAN    7.800E-02   1.611E-02   5.000E-04   2.000E-04   0.000E-99   1.000E+01
        MIN     7.800E-02   1.586E-02   0.000E-99   0.000E-99   0.000E-99


                CENTER      DIAMETRAL   BACKLASH    BACKLASH    BACKLASH
                DISTANCE    PITCH       AT PASS     AT PASS     AT LOAD
                (INCHES)    (1/INCHES)  (MILS)      (MINUTES)   (MINUTES)
        MAX     1.134E+00               2.621E+00   9.203E+00   9.203E+00
        MEAN    1.132E+00   7.200E+01   1.337E+00   4.696E+00   4.696E+00   (PASS  1)
        MIN     1.131E+00               5.399E-02   1.895E-01   1.895E-01


        MAX     4.010E-01               1.575E+00   1.552E+01   2.422E+00
        MEAN    4.010E-01   9.600E+01   9.134E-01   8.999E+00   1.404E+00   (PASS  2)
        MIN     4.010E-01               2.510E-01   2.473E+00   3.859E-01


        MAXIMUM         MEAN        MINIMUM
        1.162E+01    6.100E+00    5.755E-01  EFFECTIVE BACKLASH AT LOAD (MINUTES)

        E SIGNIFIES CONVENTIONAL POWER-OF-TEN NOTATION
```

* Reprinted by courtesy of Lear Siegler, Inc., Instrument Division, Grand Rapids, Michigan.

3.4. ANTIBACKLASH GEARING

In the previous section equations were presented for calculating the backlash of a
conventional spur gear train. These equations and the gear design they represent
are adequate for some instrument servo applications. However, as will be demonstrated later, additional techniques often must be applied to reduce the backlash in a
gear train. Two types of antibacklash gearing will be considered, the first one a
deflectable helical gear meshing with a straight spur and the second a split spring-
loaded gear meshing with a straight spur. The characteristics associated with each

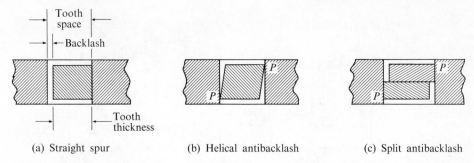

(a) Straight spur   (b) Helical antibacklash   (c) Split antibacklash

Fig. 3.7. Comparison between straight spur and antibacklash gearing cross sections.

type are presented as follows:

1. *Helical antibacklash gearing.* This gear design features a gear with a slight helix angle (typically 3 deg) in contact with a straight spur gear. Figure 3.7 illustrates the backlash of conventional spur gears and the effect of the helical design. The split antibacklash gear is also shown for comparison.

Figure 3.7 demonstrates the helical design in which the backlash is taken up by the helix angle of the mating tooth. By making this helical gear flexible (e.g., a thin metallic web or Delrin teeth), it is possible to achieve the positive pressure P shown in Fig. 3.7 between tooth and gap, thus eliminating all backlash. The amount of effective negative backlash caused by the face advance is given by the equation

$$B(\text{neg}) = \frac{(F)(P) \tan \psi}{n_1} 6876, \qquad (3.18)$$

where

F = face width of helical gear (in.),

ψ = helix angle (deg),

P = diametral pitch (in.$^{-1}$),

n_1 = number of teeth.

The value of backlash calculated from Eq. (3.16) must be reduced by the value obtained from Eq. (3.18). If we obtain a larger value from Eq. (3.18) than from Eq. (3.16), there is positive interference and the backlash is zero.

The main disadvantage of the helical gear approach is the reduction in stiffness due to the reduced effective face width and the flexible nature of the gear. However, there are many applications where stiffness is not a critical requirement and for these applications the helical gear provides an ideal solution for minimizing gear train backlash.

2. *Split spring loaded gearing.* The spring loaded antibacklash gear is actually constructed of two gears which can rotate one toward another as illustrated by Fig. 3.8. Coupling of the two is accomplished by means of a spring. The spring can be pre-

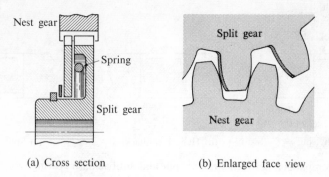

(a) Cross section   (b) Enlarged face view

Fig. 3.8. Split spring-loaded antibacklash gear.

loaded by rotating one gear relative to the other before mating them with the nest gear. This spring load forces the antibacklash gear in a "scissor action" and so takes up the backlash.

Figure 3.9 shows a torque vs. deflection curve of a gear train employing a split spring-loaded gear in the output stage. The torque dead zone at the null is the effective backlash of the stages other than the output. Torque is a linear function of deflection in the negative direction while in the positive direction the nonlinearity of the anti-backlash spring is readily apparent. The spring preload torque has caused an initial deflection of about 1.2×10^{-3} rad. Opposing torques merely take up this deflection until the preload is reached (5.9 oz-in) and then the antibacklash spring is deflected with little increase in torque until its "backlash" is taken up.

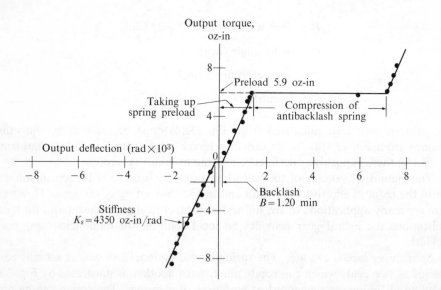

Fig. 3.9. Gear train torque vs. deflection curve with a split antibacklash gear in the output stage.

The split antibacklash gear is not effective in reducing the backlash unless the spring preload is selected to be greater than the torque level transmitted by the gear train. We calculate the maximum torque level transmitted at any point in a gear train by considering the equivalent diagram in Fig. 3.10, where

> M_1 represents the inertia of the gearing on the motor side of the antibacklash gear,
>
> M_2 represents the inertia of the gearing on the load side of the antibacklash gear,
>
> F_1 represents the torque applied to the gear train by the drive motor, and
>
> f_1 and f_2 represent the friction torques associated with M_1 and M_2.

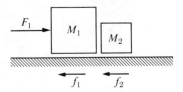

Fig. 3.10. Gear train equivalent diagram for calculating antibacklash gear spring preload.

The acceleration $\ddot{X}$ caused by an input force F_1 is given by the equation

$$\ddot{X} = \frac{F_1 - f_1 - f_2}{M_1 + M_2}. \tag{3.19}$$

Let us denote the force acting between the two masses by P. The force P represents the torque at the antibacklash gear. Setting the forces acting on M_2 equal to $M_2\ddot{X}$, substituting for $\ddot{X}$ using Eq. (3.19), and solving for P, we obtain

$$P = [M_2/(M_1 + M_2)][F_1 - f_1 - f_2] + f_2. \tag{3.20}$$

Converting back to rotational notation yields

$$T_R(\text{max}) = [J_2/(J_1 + J_2)][T_1(\text{max}) - t_1 - t_2] + t_2. \tag{3.21}$$

Considering the split antibacklash gear to be at the output shaft and that the maximum torque available from the motor is NT_s which is much greater than t_1, we may write Eq. (3.21) as

$$T_R(\text{max}) = [J_L/(J_L + N^2 J_m)][NT_s - T_f] + T_f. \tag{3.22}$$

3.5. GEAR AND LOAD INERTIA

Determination of system inertia is of major importance for instrument mechanism design and analysis. The value of inertia directly affects the system damping, stability, and response. Methods of calculating and measuring inertia are therefore essential to the servo design engineer.

Table 3.4

DENSITY OF COMMON INSTRUMENT MATERIALS

Material Description	Weight Density (lb/in³)
Acetal resin	0.0515
Magnesium	0.066
2024 aluminum alloy	0.100
Aluminum bronze	0.274
17–4 stainless steel	0.280
416 stainless steel	0.280
303 stainless steel	0.290
Beryllium copper	0.298
Brass	0.305
Phosphor bronze	0.320
Lead	0.401
Tungsten powder compacts	0.609

3.6. CALCULATION OF INERTIA

A great majority of servo rotating components are by nature symmetrical about the axis of rotation. For example, shafts, hubs, gears, data dials, etc., lend themselves to easy calculation. In fact, the inertia of most of these can be calculated by subdividing each component into hollow right circular cylinders. The general equation for calculating the inertia of a hollow right circular cylinder in terms of diameters is

$$J = \tfrac{1}{8}M(D^2 + d^2),\tag{3.23}$$

where

$$D = \text{outside diameter,}$$
$$d = \text{inside diameter,}$$
$$M = \text{mass of the cylinder.}$$

The mass of the cylinder is defined by the equation

$$M = (\pi/4g)\rho h(D^2 - d^2),\tag{3.24}$$

where

$$\rho = \text{weight density of the material,}$$
$$h = \text{height of cylinder, and}$$
$$g = \text{acceleration of gravity.}$$

Substituting Eq. (3.24) into Eq. (3.23) and combining the coefficients with the appropriate unit conversion factors, we find

$$J = 286.5h\rho(D^4 - d^4),\tag{3.25}$$

Table 3.5*

EXAMPLE OF A COMPUTER OUTPUT SHEET
USED FOR COMPONENT INERTIA CALCULATIONS

```
                                              LEAR  SIEGLER  INC.
                                              INSTRUMENT  DIVISION
                                              PROGRAM  SD019A


                 COMPONENT  INERTIA  TABULATION


            OUTSIDE      INSIDE     CYLINDER   MATERIAL    CYLINDER
            DIAMETER     DIAMETER   LENGTH     DENSITY     INERTIA
DETAIL      (INCHES)     (INCHES)   (INCHES)   (LB/CUIN)   (GM CMSQ)
  1    MAX  1.023E-00    2.870E-01  1.280E-01  2.830E-01   1.128E+01
       MIN  1.021E-00    2.850E-01  1.240E-01              1.092E+01

  2    MAX  5.150E-01    2.870E-01  2.600E-01  2.830E-01   1.293E-00
       MIN  4.850E-01    2.850E-01  2.400E-01              9.752E-01

  3    MAX  3.200E-01    2.870E-01  2.600E-01  2.830E-01   7.745E-02
       MIN  3.120E-01    2.850E-01  2.400E-01              5.590E-02


     MAXIMUM       MEAN       MINIMUM
    1.255E+01   1.230E+01   1.206E+01   TOTAL  INERTIA  (GM  CMSQ)


       E  SIGNIFIES  CONVENTIONAL  POWER-OF-TEN  NOTATION
```

* Reprinted by courtesy of Lear Siegler, Inc., Instrument Division, Grand Rapids, Michigan.

where

J = inertia (gm-cm^2),

D = outside diameter (in.),

d = inside diameter (in.),

ρ = weight density of material (lb/in^3),

h = height of cylinder (in.).

The densities for common instrument materials are listed in Table 3.4. The following procedure is used to determine the inertia of a symmetrical component.

1. The component is subdivided into the required right circular cylinders.

2. Equation (3.25) is used to calculate the inertia of each subdivided cylinder.

3. The various cylinder inertias are then summed to provide the total inertia for the component.

This procedure may be applied to determine the inertia of most servomechanism components. Equation (3.25) and the required summation may be programmed for application to a digital computer. Table 3.5 shows a typical computer output sheet obtained from such a program.

It was demonstrated in the previous chapter that inertia is reflected by the square of the gear ratio. Therefore, once the composite inertia about each shaft is determined, the total effective inertia for the system may be calculated by using the equation

$$J_T = J_o + N_1^2 J_1 + N_2^2 J_2 + \cdots + N_m^2 J_m, \tag{3.26}$$

where

J_T = total effective system inertia,

J_o = inertia at output shaft,

N_1 = gear ratio between shaft 1 and output,

J_1 = inertia at shaft 1,

N_2 = gear ratio between shaft 2 and output,

J_2 = inertia at shaft 2,

N_m = total gear ratio of system,

J_m = inertia at motor shaft.

3.7. TORSIONAL PENDULUM PRINCIPLE OF INERTIA MEASUREMENT

Sometimes a component is a collection of objects of complex shape and consequently it is extremely difficult and costly to calculate its inertia. The torsional pendulum principle provides an accurate, efficient, and economical method of measuring the inertia of such components.

If a mass is suspended from a wire and given a torsional displacement, the period of oscillation is independent of the amount of displacement, provided that the elastic limit of the wire is not exceeded. The inertia of the mass may be obtained directly from this period and the physical properties of the wire.

Let us first consider a mass suspended from a wire (Fig. 3.11). The restoring torque τ for any displacement θ is given by

$$\tau = K\theta, \tag{3.27}$$

where K is the torsional spring constant of the wire and depends on the wire material and physical dimensions. The resisting torque is given by

$$\tau = J[d^2\theta/dt^2], \tag{3.28}$$

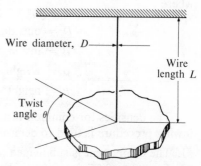

Fig. 3.11. Torsional pendulum.

where J is the inertia of the load suspended from the wire. By setting the restoring torque equal to the resisting torque, we derive the following differential equation:

$$K\theta = J[d^2\theta/dt^2], \tag{3.29}$$

$$d^2\theta/dt^2 - [K/J]\theta = 0. \tag{3.30}$$

This is the equation for simple harmonic motion, and the period T is given by

$$T = 2\pi\sqrt{J/K}. \tag{3.31}$$

The torsional spring constant K may be determined by either of two ways.

1. The inertia of a symmetrical mass such as a solid circular cylinder may be calculated by means of Eq. (3.25) developed in the previous section. This mass may then be suspended and given a torsional displacement. The period may be measured and the constant K computed by using Eq. (3.31) for the period.

2. The K may be calculated directly using the material characteristics and dimensions of the wire, as shown by Eq. 3.32.

$$K = \pi D^4 G/32L, \tag{3.32}$$

where

D = wire diameter,

G = shear modulus of elasticity of the wire material,

L = wire length.

The torsional spring constant K may also be separated into two terms, one term depending only on the wire material and the other depending only on the wire dimensions. This has been done for steel music wire, resulting in the period T depending on a constant, the wire length, wire diameter, and load inertia. For steel wire, the shear modulus of elasticity is

$$G = 12.0 \times 10^6 \text{ lb/in}^2.$$

Substituting Eq. (3.32) into Eq. (3.31), letting G equal the above value, and including the necessary unit conversion factors, we obtain the following two equations:

$$T = (5.4533)(\sqrt{J}\sqrt{L}/D^2), \tag{3.33}$$

$$J = (0.033626)(D^4 T^2/L), \tag{3.34}$$

where

J = inertia of the load under test (gm-cm^2),

T = period of oscillation (sec),

L = length of the wire (in.),

D = diameter of the wire (mil).

If we wish to determine the inertia J or the period T by using the preceding equations, we must not exceed the elastic limit of the wire. This limits the number of turns that we may twist the wire, and depends on the wire material, diameter, and length. The number of turns may be computed as follows.

Substituting Eq. (3.32) into (3.27) and solving for θ, we have

$$\theta = 32L\tau/\pi D^4 G. \tag{3.35}$$

The shear stress S_s caused by the torsional displacement is given by

$$S_s = 16\tau/\pi D^3. \tag{3.36}$$

Solving Eq. (3.36) for τ and substituting it into Eq. (3.35), we find

$$\theta = 2S_sL/DG = [2S_s/G](L/D). \tag{3.37}$$

Let

$$\theta = 2\pi N, \tag{3.38}$$

where N is the maximum number of turns allowable without exceeding the elastic limit of the wire. If we then substitute Eq. (3.38) into Eq. (3.37) and solve for N, we obtain

$$N = [S_s/\pi G](L/D). \tag{3.39}$$

For music wire with the maximum allowable elastic limit in shear of 100×10^3 psi,

$$N = (2.632) \frac{L}{D}, \tag{3.40}$$

where

$$N = \text{allowable number of turns,}$$
$$L = \text{length of wire (in.),}$$
$$D = \text{wire diameter (mil).}$$

Figure 3.12 provides a nomograph based on Eq. (3.40) such that it may be used to determine the allowable number of turns for a given set of wire dimensions. Another factor that should be used in selecting the wire size is the weight of the component that is to be tested.

The maximum weight P that may be suspended from the wire without exceeding the elastic limit is given by

$$P = (\pi SD^2/4) \times 10^{-6}, \tag{3.41}$$

where

$$P = \text{maximum weight (lb),}$$
$$D = \text{wire diameter (mil),}$$
$$S = \text{allowable elastic limit in tension (lb/in}^2\text{).}$$

In order to be able to neglect the combined stresses developed from both torsion and tension, the maximum allowable elastic limit in tension used in Eq. (3.41) must be smaller than that of the material. A value of 30,000 psi is commonly used for music wire.

The choice of the wire size is determined by the following considerations:

1. The wire diameter must be large enough to (a) support the weight of the load applied, and (b) result in a period that is reasonably short in duration so that the test does not consume an unnecessary amount of time.

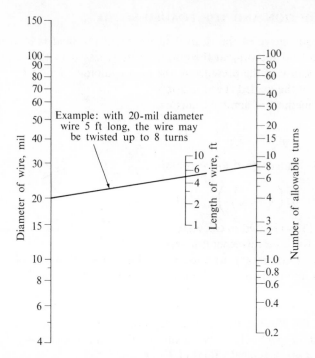

Fig. 3.12. Nomograph for number of turns permissible in torsional pendulum inertia test.

2. The wire diameter must be small enough to (a) result in a period that is reasonably long so that the period can be easily measured, and (b) allow at least half a turn of displacement with a reasonable length of wire without exceeding the elastic limit.

The axis of the wire in the preceding test will, by nature of the test, pass through the center of gravity of the component. Usually a component is mounted in the system so that its axis of rotation is through the center of gravity. If this is the case, the test method yields the correct inertia directly. If it is not the case, the inertia about the desired axis of rotation can be determined by using the parallel-axis theorem. The components being tested are suspended on an axis through the center of gravity parallel to the axis desired. The inertia is then determined, as already discussed, through the center of gravity. The inertia J of the component about the desired parallel axis may then be calculated by means of the equation

$$J = J_{cg} + \tfrac{1}{2}M\,d^2,\tag{3.42}$$

where

J = inertia of the load about the desired axis,

J_{cg} = inertia of the load through the center of gravity parallel to the axis desired,

M = mass of the load,

d = distance between the two parallel axes.

3.8. LOAD FRICTION AND THE LOADED SPEED

The speed-torque curve of the equivalent motor at the load is shown in Fig. 3.13. The maximum load speed $\dot\theta_L$ at the output shaft is less than the equivalent no-load speed $\dot\theta_m/N$ because of the presence of the load coulomb friction T_{fo}.

The value of the loaded speed is determined by the method of similar triangles:

$$\frac{\dot\theta_L}{NT_s - T_{fo}} = \frac{\dot\theta_m/N}{NT_s}. \qquad (3.43)$$

Solving for the loaded speed $\dot\theta_L$, we obtain

$$\dot\theta_L = \frac{\dot\theta_m}{N}\left(1 - \frac{T_{fo}}{NT_s}\right). \qquad (3.44)$$

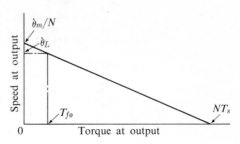

Equation (3.44) is used to calculate the followup rate for a motor-generator servo as a function of the motor torque-speed characteristics, the gear ratio, and amount of load friction.

Fig. 3.13. Motor speed vs. torque curve reflected to the output shaft.

For the cases where T_{fo} is greater than NT_s, Eq. (3.44) yields negative loaded speed values, thereby signifying that the motor does not have enough torque to move the load. Figure 3.14 shows a plot of the loaded speed as a function of the gear ratio for a set of typical values of T_{fo}, $\dot\theta_m$, and T_s.

A normal design requirement is that the servo be capable of following a specified velocity. It is possible to meet this specification requirement with a given motor only over a limited range of gear ratios. Since the gear ratio must lie between these limits, it is advantageous to calculate them directly.

Let us consider the family of reflected speed-torque curves for various gear ratio values illustrated in Fig. 3.15. We must calculate the two values of N that result in the reflected curve intersecting the specification point defined by $\dot\theta_L$ (required) and T_{fo}. This may be accomplished by cross multiplying the terms in Eq. (3.43), the

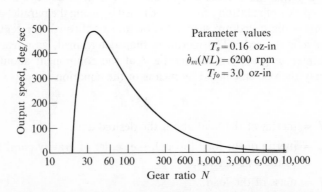

Fig. 3.14. Servo output speed as a function of gear ratio.

result being the following quadratic equation in terms of the gear ratio N:

$$(\dot{\theta}_L)N^2 - (\dot{\theta}_m)N + (T_{fo}/T_s)\dot{\theta}_m = 0. \tag{3.45}$$

Solving this equation for N, we obtain

$$N = \frac{\dot{\theta}_m \pm \sqrt{\dot{\theta}_m^2 - 4\dot{\theta}_L\dot{\theta}_m(T_{fo}/T_s)}}{2\dot{\theta}_L}. \tag{3.46}$$

Equation (3.45) yields the two limiting values of gear ratio directly, namely, N_1 and N_2.

It is possible that the reflected speed-torque curve will not lie above the specifications point for any value of gear ratio. This indicates that the motor does not provide adequate mechanical power to drive the load. The maximum power available from a servomotor is given by the equation

$$P_a = (0.1849 \times 10^{-3})(\dot{\theta}_m)(T_s), \quad (3.47)$$

where

P_a = power available (watts),

$\dot{\theta}_m$ = motor no-load speed (rpm),

T_s = motor stall torque (oz-in).

The power required to drive the load of a rotational output servo is given by the equation

$$P_r = (0.7395 \times 10^{-3})(\dot{\theta}_L)(T_{fo}), \quad (3.48)$$

where

P_r = power required (watts),

$\dot{\theta}_L$ = followup rate (rpm),

T_{fo} = load friction (oz-in).

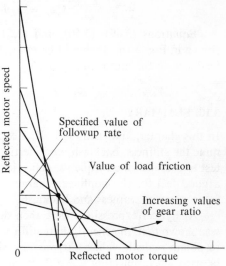

Fig. 3.15. Motor reflected speed-torque curves as a function of gear ratio.

3.9. NONLINEAR BLOCK DIAGRAM REPRESENTATION

Torque is transmitted through the gear train by the spring rate K_s to the load. In equation form,

$$T_r = K_s\theta_k, \tag{3.49}$$

where θ_k is the deflection of the gear train and is defined by the equations

$$\theta_k = \{|\theta_m - \theta_L| - B\} \, \text{sgn} \, (\theta_m - \theta_L), \quad \text{for} \quad |\theta_m - \theta_L| \geq B \tag{3.50}$$

$$\theta_k = 0, \quad \text{for} \quad |\theta_m - \theta_L| \leq B.$$

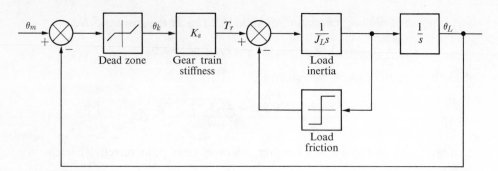

Fig. 3.16. Equivalent block diagram representing the gear stiffness, backlash, and load.

Equating the gear train torque T_r to the torque acting on the load T_L, we find

$$K_s\theta_k = J_L\ddot{\theta}_L + T_{fo}(\dot{\theta}_L/|\dot{\theta}_L|). \qquad (3.51)$$

Equations (3.49), (3.50), and (3.51) can be represented by the block diagram shown in Fig. 3.16. It should be noted that the torque T_r is equal to the load torque feedback to the motor in Fig. 2.16.

3.10. SUMMARY

In this chapter, analytical as well as experimental methods were developed to determine the stiffness, backlash, and inertia of a gear train. We started by introducing a test to establish the torque vs. deflection curve for a gear train. This curve provided a good feel for the nonlinear characteristics of a gear train as well as an accurate measure of its stiffness and backlash.

Analytical expressions were then developed to calculate gear train stiffness. It was shown that, in general, shaft stiffness must be included along with tooth deflection to obtain realistic values. It was also shown that the square of the gear ratio must be used when reflecting the stiffness at each stage to the load. Because of this fact, it is normally only the stiffness of the last couple of stages nearest the load that is of importance.

A procedure was then developed to predict analytically the amount of backlash in a given gear train design based on such factors as tooth thickness, center distance, composite error, etc. Backlash reflects as the first power of gear ratio and becomes less important as one approaches the motor. Therefore, if antibacklash gearing is to be used, it should be placed near the load. Two types of antibacklash gears were considered, namely, helical and spring loaded. Equations were written to calculate the "negative backlash" attributed by the former and the preload required to make the latter exhibit zero effective backlash.

Inertia plays an important part in servo response. Fortunately, the inertia of most components can be calculated by subdivision and by means of the equation developed for a hollow right circular cylinder. For shapes that are not easily cal-culable, the torsional pendulum was introduced as a means of measurement.

Most servo systems must be designed to follow a specified input velocity. An equation was therefore derived to determine the followup capability as a function of the motor, gear ratio, and load friction. Limiting equations were also derived which established the range of allowable gear ratio, and power relationships were derived as an aid in motor selection.

The chapter was concluded by the development of a mathematical block diagram to represent the gear train including the effects of stiffness, backlash, inertia, and coulomb friction.

PROBLEMS

*3.1. Consider a motor with the characteristics

$$T_s = 0.12 \text{ oz-in}, \qquad \dot{\theta}_m(NL) = 8500 \text{ rpm}.$$

a) Calculate the maximum mechanical power that is available.
b) Assume that a servo friction load is to be 1.0 oz-in and that a followup rate of 360 deg/sec is required. Can the above motor be used to drive this servo?
c) What is the allowable range of gear ratio?
d) For a gear ratio of 120, what followup rate is to be expected?

*3.2. Given the gear cross section in Fig. 3.17,

a) calculate the inertia in $gm\text{-}cm^2$;
b) calculate the inertia in $oz\text{-}in\text{-}sec^2$.

*3.3. Assume that a test performed to measure the inertia of a component by the torsional pendulum principle gave the following data:

$$\text{wire diameter} = 0.020 \text{ in.,}$$
$$\text{wire length} = 42.5 \text{ in.,}$$
$$\text{period of oscillation} = 5.74 \text{ sec.}$$

What is the inertia of the component tested?

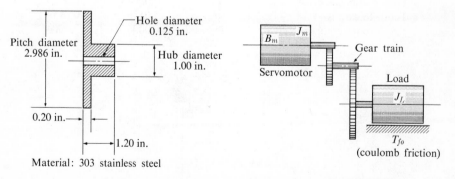

Figure 3.17

Figure 3.18

3.4. Explain the difference between the constant (0.1849×10^{-3}) in Eq. (3.47) and the constant (0.7395×10^{-3}) in Eq. (3.48).

*3.5. The values for the system shown in Fig. 3.18 are:

$$J_m = 1 \text{ gm-cm}^2, \qquad J_L = 5000 \text{ gm-cm}^2,$$

$$N = 100, \qquad T_{fo} = 3 \text{ oz-in},$$

$$B_m = 0.0003 \text{ oz-in/rad/sec}.$$

Consider the system to be running at a steady-state load velocity of 300 deg/sec at $t = 0$ when the control winding is shorted. Derive and solve an equation for the time it takes the system to come to a stop. What would be the time required if both windings were suddenly opened?

*3.6. A gear pass (Fig. 3.19) is to be added to a standard commercial gear head in an attempt to increase stiffness and decrease backlash. The data pertaining to the commercial gear head are:

gear ratio = 100,

inertia = 0.17 gm-cm^2 (referred to input shaft),

backlash = 30 min (at gear head output shaft),

stiffness = 1200 oz-in/rad (at gear head output shaft), and

friction = 0.0004 oz-in (referred to input shaft).

Parameter	Units	Gear Number	
		1	2
Number of teeth	—	67	10
Diametral pitch	in.$^{-1}$	96	96
Pressure angle	deg	20	20
Modulus of elasticity	lb/in^2	10.2×10^6	30×10^6
Face width	in.	0.062	0.250
Total composite error	in.	0.0008	0.0008
Tooth thickness	in.	0.0159	0.0159
Tooth-tooth composite error	in.	0.0004	0.0004

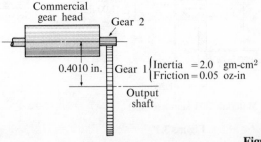

Figure 3.19

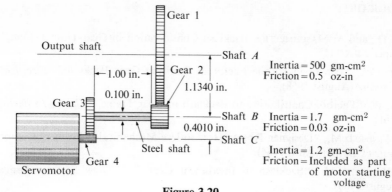

Figure 3.20

Calculate the following characteristics for the over-all gearing configuration:

a) gear ratio,
b) total effective inertia at output (gm-cm²),
c) total effective friction at output (oz-in),
d) total effective backlash at output (min),
e) total effective stiffness at output (oz-in/rad).

3.7. Sketch how the required antibacklash spring preload varies with load inertia J_L. Define the two asymptotes in terms of the physical parameters.

3.8. Derive an equation for the gear ratio N that yields the maximum followup rate. Check this with Fig. 3.14.

***3.9.** Given the gear train layout in Fig. 3.20 and the following spur gear data tabulation:

Parameter	Units	Gear number			
		1	2	3	4
Number of teeth	—	141	22	67	10
Pitch diameter	in.	1.958	0.3055	0.698	0.104
Diametral pitch	in.⁻¹	72	72	96	96
Pressure angle	deg	20	20	20	20
Modulus of elasticity	lb/in²	10.2×10^6	30×10^6	30×10^6	30×10^6
Face width	in.	0.125	0.375	0.187	0.375
Lewis form factor	—	0.145	0.105	0.136	0.064
Tooth thickness	in.	0.0213	0.0213	0.0159	0.0159
TCE	in.	0.001	0.001	0.001	0.001
TTCE	in.	0.0004	0.0004	0.0004	0.0004

Calculate the following characteristics:

a) gear ratio,
c) total effective friction at output,
e) total effective stiffness at output.

b) total effective inertia at output,
d) total effective backlash at output, and

BIBLIOGRAPHY

ACKER, D., and A. MASCHMEYER, "Backlash Consideration in Gear-Train Design," *ASME* Paper 54-A-111.

AKSAMIT, W., "The Load-Torque Factor in Precision Gear Backlash," *Electrical Manufacturing* (August 1958).

BENSON, R., "Factors Contributing to Backlash in Gear Trains," *Electro-Technology* (July 1961).

BERG, WINIFRED M., "Designer Tips on How to Use Mechanical Instrument Components," *Systems Design* (April 1964).

BERG, WINIFRED M., "Backlash in Instrument Gears," *Military Systems Design* (July-August 1960).

GIBSON, J., and F. TUTEUR, *Control System Components*, McGraw-Hill, 1958, Chapter 8.

GITLIN, R., "Design Charts for Precision Gears," *Product Engineering* (October 1955).

GOODMAN, T., "How to Calculate Dynamic Effects of Backlash," *Machine Design* (May 23, 1963).

GUTMANN, F., "Fine Pitch Gear Trains," *Electrical Manufacturing* (March 1960).

HALSTENBERG, R., and P. RUSSELL, "Backlash in Servo Systems," *Electrical Manufacturing* (September 1958).

MICHALEC, G., "Critical Criteria for Precision Gears," *Electrical Manufacturing* (July 1960).

MICHALEC, G., "Methods of Specifying Precision Spur Gears," *Product Engineering* (November 1956).

MICHALEC, G., "Precision Gearing," *Machine Design* (January 1955).

THOEN, R., "High-Grade Fine-Pitch Gearing," *Machine Design* (January 19, 1961).

THOEN, R., "How to Find Exact Values of Backlash in Spur Gears for Changes in Tooth Thickness or Center Distance," *Machine Design* (January 1958).

WADSWORTH, R., "Lost Motion in Precision Gear Trains, Part I," *Machine Design* (October 2, 1958).

WADSWORTH, R., "Lost Motion in Precision Gear Trains, Part II," *Machine Design* (October 16, 1958).

WIEGAND, W., "7 Rules Simplify Instrument Gear Specifications," *Product Engineering* (November 25, 1958).

CHAPTER 4

THE OTHER SERVO COMPONENTS

The two previous chapters detailed the motor and the gear train as components for instrument servomechanisms. The purpose of this chapter is to complete the necessary component definitions by describing analytically the followup, generator, amplifier, and summing circuit. This is followed by a discussion of inner-loop stability. The chapter is concluded by the introduction of two special components, inertial and viscous dampers.

4.1. SYNCHRO FOLLOWUP

Instrument positional servos are built to follow either mechanical or electrical input signals. By its basic nature a servomechanism must have a component that measures or "follows up" the output position. This component is called the followup. The most conventional followup used for the mechanical input case is the synchro. The concept of the synchro followup was introduced in Fig. 1.4, which is a pictorial diagram of a typical servo with a mechanical input.

The synchro followup system represented consists of a control transmitter (CX) and a control transformer (CT) which can be schematically illustrated as shown in Fig. 4.1. The command or input is connected mechanically to the CX rotor, and the servo output is connected mechanically to the CT rotor. The CX rotor winding is excited by a fixed reference voltage. An electrical signal is transmitted from the stator of the CX to indicate the angular position of its rotor. This signal is coupled through the CT to provide a voltage output from the CT rotor, which is a function

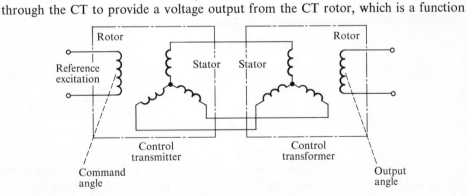

Fig. 4.1. Synchro followup.

61

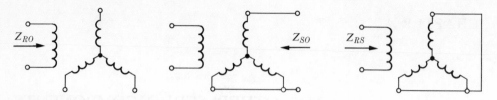

Fig. 4.2. Synchro impedance definition.

of the difference between the CX and CT rotor angular position. Since this angular difference is the positional error of the servo, the synchro system not only follows the output but it generates the error signal directly.

The characteristics of the CX and CT are defined by their respective impedance values:

Z_{RO} = rotor impedance with the stator open circuited,

Z_{SO} = stator impedance with the rotor open circuited,

Z_{RS} = rotor impedance with the stator short circuited.

These values are specified by the manufacturer and are readily measured. The impedances are defined with maximum coupling between the rotor and stator. Therefore two of the stator terminals have equal potential and may be tied together. Figure 4.2 illustrates the impedances as defined for both the CX and CT.

The CX and the CT may be represented as three terminal components using a T equivalent circuit notation (Fig. 4.3). This enables the servo designer to couple any desired CX and CT together and obtain the total gain, phase shift, and output impedance.

We can find the values for the T equivalent circuit impedances (Z_A, Z_B, and Z_C) in terms of Z_{RO}, Z_{SO}, and Z_{RS} by applying the definitions of the latter to the circuit of Fig. 4.3. In the case of the CX,

Z_{RO} = rotor impedance with open stator

$$= \frac{V_R}{I_R}\bigg|_{I_S=0} = \frac{E_{in}}{I_{in}}\bigg|_{I_{out}=0} = Z_A + Z_C, \tag{4.1}$$

Z_{SO} = stator impedance with the rotor open

$$= \frac{V_S}{I_S}\bigg|_{I_R=0} = \frac{E_{out}}{I_{out}}\bigg|_{I_{in}=0} = Z_B + Z_C, \tag{4.2}$$

$$Z_{RS} = \frac{V_R}{I_R}\bigg|_{V_S=0} = \frac{E_{in}}{I_{in}}\bigg|_{E_{out}=0} = Z_A + \frac{Z_B Z_C}{Z_B + Z_C}. \tag{4.3}$$

There is one point here which should be noted carefully. All these impedances are assumed to be line-to-line measurements. In the case of Z_{SO}, however, this is not strictly true. Figure 4.2 shows that Z_{SO} is measured with two of the stator windings shorted. Assume that the impedances of the three "legs" of the wye are equal and

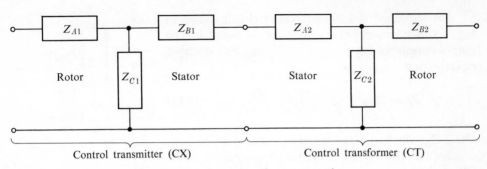

Fig. 4.3. Synchro network representation.

let this impedance be Z. With two windings shorted as shown, Z_{SO} is given by

$$Z_{SO} = Z + \frac{Z \times Z}{Z + Z} = \frac{3Z}{2}. \tag{4.4}$$

But the true line-to-line impedance $Z_{SO'}$ is given by

$$Z_{SO'} = 2Z.$$

The ratio is then

$$\frac{Z_{SO'}}{Z_{SO}} = [2Z]\left[\frac{2}{3Z}\right] = \frac{4}{3}. \tag{4.5}$$

Therefore, before we use the measured value of Z_{SO} in the T equivalent, we must take this factor into account. Instead of using Z_{SO}, we take

$$Z_{SO'} = \tfrac{4}{3}Z_{SO}. \tag{4.6}$$

Equation 4.6 in conjunction with Eqs. 4.1, 4.2, and 4.3, yield the following conversion formulas:

For control transmitter (CX),

$$Z_{A1} = Z_{RO} - Z_{C1}, \tag{4.7}$$

$$Z_{B1} = \tfrac{4}{3}Z_{SO} - Z_{C1}, \tag{4.8}$$

$$Z_{C1} = \sqrt{\tfrac{4}{3}Z_{SO}(Z_{RO} - Z_{RS})}. \tag{4.9}$$

These expressions can be used to define the equivalent T impedances for the control transmitter in terms of standard measurements. In a similar manner the corresponding equation can be generated for the CT as follows:

For control transformer (CT),

$$Z_{A2} = \tfrac{4}{3}Z_{SO} - Z_{C2}, \tag{4.10}$$

$$Z_{B2} = Z_{RO} - Z_{C2}, \tag{4.11}$$

$$Z_{C2} = \sqrt{\tfrac{4}{3}Z_{SO}(Z_{RO} - Z_{RS})}. \tag{4.12}$$

The combined synchro equivalent circuit shown as Fig. 4.3 may be represented as shown in Fig. 4.4. The output impedance $(Z_f = R_f + j\,X_f)$ may be calculated directly from Fig. 4.3 as

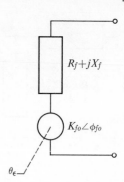

$$Z_f = Z_{B2} + \frac{(Z_{\text{in}} + Z_{A2})Z_{C2}}{Z_{\text{in}} + Z_{A2} + Z_{C2}}, \qquad (4.13)$$

where Z_{in}, which can be viewed as either the input impedance that the CT sees or the output impedance of the CX, is given by

$$Z_{\text{in}} = Z_{B1} + \frac{Z_{A1}Z_{C1}}{Z_{A1} + Z_{C1}}. \qquad (4.14)$$

Fig. 4.4. Followup represented as a voltage source and an output impedance.

From Fig. 4.3, the open circuit output voltage E_o at maximum coupling may be written in terms of the excitation e_i as

$$E_o = \left[\frac{Z_{C2}Z_{C1}}{Z_{C1}Z_{A1} + Z_{C1}Z_{C2} + Z_{B1}Z_{A1} + Z_{B1}Z_{C1} + Z_{A2}Z_{A1} + Z_{A2}Z_{C1} + Z_{C2}Z_{A1}}\right]e_i. \qquad (4.15)$$

Equation (4.15) expresses maximum coupling. Actually the synchro followup yields an electrical signal e_o proportional to the sine of the angular difference θ_ϵ between the CX and the CT:

$$e_o = E_o \sin \theta_\epsilon. \qquad (4.16)$$

Differentiating Eq. (4.16) with respect to θ_ϵ and evaluating at null $(\theta_\epsilon = 0)$, we see that the open circuit followup gain K_{fo} is given by the magnitude of the bracketed quantity in Eq. (4.15) times e_i. For example, a synchro pair that has an output voltage of 22.5 v at maximum coupling also has a gain of 22.5 v/rad. The open circuit carrier phase shift ϕ_{fo} is given as the phase angle associated with Eq. (4.15). The effective open circuit output e_o can thus be written as

$$e_o = K_{fo} \sin \phi_{fo} \sin \theta_\epsilon, \qquad (4.17)$$

where

$$K_{fo} = \text{open circuit gain of the followup (v/rad), and}$$

$$\phi_{fo} = \text{carrier phase shift (degrees)}.$$

However, for small angles about null, $\sin \theta_\epsilon \simeq \theta_\epsilon$, and the voltage output e_o may be represented by

$$e_o = (K_{fo} \sin \phi_{fo})\theta_\epsilon. \qquad (4.18)$$

The tracking accuracy of the synchro followup is defined as the difference between electrical and mechanical zero. It is important in evaluations of the total accuracy of the instrument system and will be denoted by θ_f.

Table 4.1*

EXAMPLE OF A COMPUTER OUTPUT SHEET
USED FOR SYNCHRO FOLLOWUP PERFORMANCE CALCULATIONS

```
                                                         LEAR SIEGLER INC.
                                                         INSTRUMENT DIVISION
                                                         PROGRAM SD014A


              SYNCHRO (CX-CT) PERFORMANCE DATA TABULATION


                    CX IMPEDANCE DATA (OHMS)

              R-RO        X-RO        R-SO        X-SO        R-RS        X-RS
     MEAN    2.500E+01  1.150E+02  5.900E-00  2.100E+01  2.450E+01  1.670E+01
   PCT TOL   1.000E+01  1.000E+01  1.000E+01  1.000E+01  1.000E+01  1.000E+01


                    CT IMPEDANCE DATA (OHMS)

              R-RO        X-RO        R-SO        X-SO        R-RS        X-RS
     MEAN    4.700E+02  1.960E+03  7.200E+01  3.340E+02  5.820E+02  2.210E+02
   PCT TOL   1.000E+01  1.000E+01  1.000E+01  1.000E+01  1.000E+01  1.000E+01


                    EXCITATION CONDITIONS

                          VOLTAGE        FREQUENCY
             MAXIMUM    2.860E+01        4.200E+02
                MEAN    2.600E+01        4.000E+02
             MINIMUM    2.340E+01        3.800E+02


                   K-FO        PHI-FO       R-F         X-F
        MAXIMUM   2.598E+01   1.534E+01   6.584E+02   2.666E+02
           MEAN   2.285E+01   1.286E+01   6.007E+02   2.413E+02
        MINIMUM   1.971E+01   1.038E+01   5.430E+02   2.161E+02


         E SIGNIFIES CONVENTIONAL POWER-OF-TEN NOTATION
```

* Reprinted by courtesy of Lear Siegler, Inc., Instrument Division, Grand Rapids, Michigan.

Manual solution of the equations developed in this section to define the performance characteristics of a synchro pair is tedious because of the complex number manipulations required. However, they can be easily programmed on a digital computer. Table 4.1 illustrates a typical output sheet from such a program. The first two groups of data represent the rated impedance values associated with the CX and CT. The third data group represents the line excitation condition. The calculated outputs of open circuit gain K_{fo}, phase shift ϕ_{fo}, and output impedance $(R_f + j\,X_f)$ are tabulated at the bottom. The tolerances of all the inputs are shown as well as the mean. The resulting distributions of the performance parameters are determined from the component and excitation tolerances by the process explained in Chapter 6.

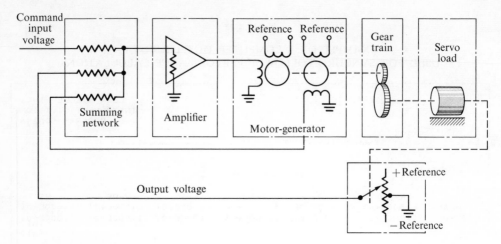

Fig. 4.5. Pictorial diagram of an ac motor-generator servo with an electrical input.

4.2. POTENTIOMETER FOLLOWUP

Positional servos are built to follow either a mechanical input (synchro rotor position, etc.) or an electrical input signal. A pictorial diagram of a typical ac motor generator servo with an electrical input signal is shown in Fig. 4.5. The resistor network sums the command voltage, voltage developed by the followup potentiometer, and the generator feedback voltage. The resulting voltage is amplified, in turn, to energize the motor to position the output in such a manner that the voltage developed by the followup equals the command input voltage.

From an analytical standpoint, both the mechanical and electrical input servos are identical and may be represented by the block diagram in Fig. 4.6. This identity holds because there is only one relationship between displacement (either input, output, or error) and the corresponding voltage. This relationship is the gain of the followup device (v/rad displacement).

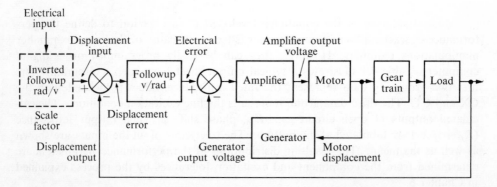

Fig. 4.6. Component block diagram of an ac motor-generator servo.

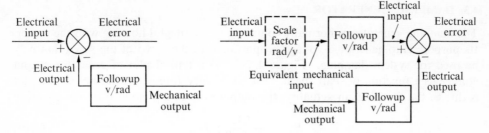

(a) Servo with electrical input   (b) Multiplying and dividing input by followup

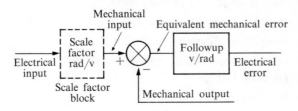

(c) Block diagram converted to form of mechanical
input servo with conversion block equivalent

Fig. 4.7. Block diagram manipulation to achieve a unity feedback system.

For the mechanical input servo, the block diagram follows directly from Fig. 1.4 (the dashed scale factor block may be ignored). For the electrical input servo, one can arrive at the same servo loop block diagram with unity feedback by first deriving an equivalent input displacement using the scale factor block. Figure 4.7 illustrates the block diagram manipulation required for the electrical input servo loop so that it becomes identical to the mechanical input servo. We see that the basic servo loops for the electrical and mechanical inputs are identical and therefore the same analysis may be used directly for both servos. The followup gain K_{fo} is calculated from the potentiometer excitation divided by the corresponding travel expressed in radians. Note that the scale factor of the input voltage (rad/v) does not necessarily equal the reciprocal of the followup gain (v/rad). In any event, the gain inside the loop is that of the potentiometer; outside the loop it is the scale factor of the servo.

The tracking accuracy θ_f is determined directly from the linearity of the potentiometer, which is normally expressed as a percentage of full scale. Depending on the loading effects on the potentiometer; an additional term that is a function of the servo position may be required.

One additional factor must be considered when using a wire-wound potentiometer for the followup device. Careful measurements of a conventional wire-wound potentiometer show that a graph of the output voltage vs. angular displacement forms a staircase, with the angular distance between each voltage step given by the ratio of total travel divided by the number of wires. The resolution of such a potentiometer must be smaller than the dead zone or resolution of the servomechanism (to be derived in Chapter 8). If it is not, then an oscillation referred to as "wirehopping" will occur as the servo attempts to seek a null between adjacent wire turns.

4.3. DAMPING GENERATOR

The damping generator is normally contained in an integral housing with the motor. Its purpose is to generate a voltage proportional to the speed of the servo that may be used for system damping. Figure 4.8 shows a typical plot of generator output voltage as a function of shaft speed. The slight curvature of the hardware data plot is due to the fact that, in actuality, the output voltage E_{go} is given by the equation

$$E_{go} = \frac{Av}{1 + Bv^2}\, E_{in}, \qquad (4.19)$$

where

E_{in} = voltage applied to primary winding,

A = complex generator gradient,

B = complex nonlinearity coefficient,

v = ratio between actual rpm ($\dot{\theta}_g$) and synchronous rpm given by $120f/p$,

f = line frequency,

p = number of generator poles.

At low speeds, v is small, making the B^2v-term negligible. The output voltage is essentially proportional to the actual speed $\dot{\theta}_g$ and the line is straight. As the speed is increased, the Bv^2-term eventually becomes significantly large, thereby accounting for the curvature. However, the value of B is usually made small, and the operating range is far enough below synchronous speed so that the Bv^2-term can be neglected. This is especially true when the generator is used only for damping, since a fairly wide gain change can be tolerated.

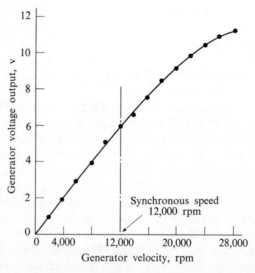

Fig. 4.8. Output voltage vs. shaft speed curve for a typical four-pole size 8 damping generator.

Assuming the above conditions, we may consider the generator to produce an open circuit voltage E_{go} that is proportional to the generator shaft speed. However, as in the synchro system, the output impedance $(R_g + j X_g)$ must be specified as a parameter in order to include loading effects. The generator may therefore be represented as shown in Fig. 4.9. The K_{go}-term is called the *open circuit gain* and is usually given in v/1000 rpm, and the ϕ_{go}-term corresponds to the phase shift between the reference excitation and the output voltage. Neglecting the Bv^2-term in Eq. (4.19), we see that ϕ_{go} corresponds to the phase angle associated with A, and K_{go} equals the magnitude of A times the excitation voltage divided by the synchronous speed.

The parameters shown in Fig. 4.9 are those required to adequately represent a generator in a system and should be specified. In addition, the open circuit in-phase null voltage of the generator is important in calculating the accuracy of the total system. This is defined as E_{go} (null) and will be used in Chapter 8. Numerical values for the parameters K_{go}, ϕ_{go}, R_g, X_g, and E_{go} (null) are normally provided directly by the generator manufacturer. Thus the servo engineer is seldom required to make any additional calculations. An exception to this is that the tolerance on K_{go} must be widened to account for any changes in line voltage excitation.

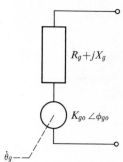

Fig. 4.9. Damping generator represented as a voltage source and an output impedance.

4.4. SUMMING CIRCUIT

The summing circuit is an electrical network used to add the followup and the generator voltages. The followup voltage is proportional to the system error and the generator voltage is proportional to the output velocity. The algebraic sum of these voltages is applied to the amplifier input to drive the servomotor.

Two basic types of summing networks are used. They are called series and parallel networks and are illustrated in their simplest form in Fig. 4.10. Both circuits result in a loading or attenuation of the followup and generator signals as seen by the amplifier input. Thus the open circuit characteristics developed in the previous sections must be modified to account for this effect. The values of the gain, null, and phase shift effective at the amplifier are the desired parameters. Let us define these parameters as follows:

$$K_f = \text{followup gain effective at the amplifier (v/rad),}$$

$$\phi_f = \text{followup carrier phase shift effective at amplifier (deg),}$$

$$K_g = \text{generator gain effective at amplifier (v/1000 rpm),}$$

$$E_g \text{ (null)} = \text{generator null voltage effective at amplifier (mv),}$$

$$\phi_g = \text{generator carrier phase shift effective at amplifier (deg).}$$

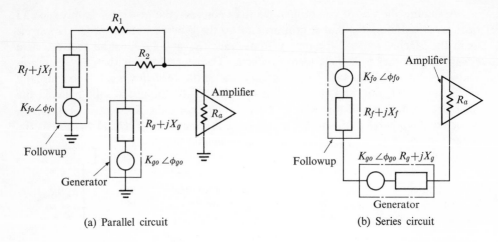

Fig. 4.10. Series and parallel summing networks.

These parameters can be determined in terms of the open-circuit values of the generator and followup, and the various circuit impedances. Let us consider the following simple examples.

Example 4.1 Generate the effective summing circuit parameter equations for the parallel network shown in Fig. 4.10(a).

Consider the generator parameters. The followup impedances R_1 and Z_f can be lumped in parallel with the amplifier to arrive at an effective input value Z_{af}:

$$Z_{af} = \frac{R_a(R_1 + Z_f)}{R_a + R_1 + Z_f}.$$

The generator gain K_g is then

$$K_g = \left| \frac{Z_{af}}{Z_g + R_2 + Z_{af}} \right| K_{go}.$$

The effective generator null is given by

$$E_g(\text{null}) = \left[\frac{K_g}{K_{go}} \right] E_{go}(\text{null}),$$

and the generator carrier phase shift is the sum of the phase angle associated with the magnitude term of the K_g expression ϕ_{gc} and ϕ_{go} for the generator, $\phi_g = \phi_{gc} + \phi_{go}$. The expressions for the followup parameters may be derived in a similar manner.

Example 4.2 Generate the effective summing circuit parameter equations for the series network shown in Fig. 4.10(b). The followup gain K_f is given by

$$K_f = \left| \frac{R_a}{Z_g + Z_f + R_a} \right| K_{fo},$$

and the followup carrier phase shift is the sum of the phase angle associated with the magnitude term ϕ_{fc} and the open circuit value ϕ_{fo}, that is, $\phi_f = \phi_{fc} + \phi_{fo}$. Due

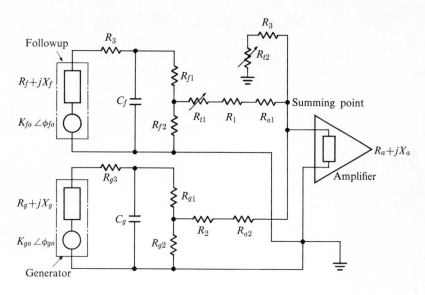

Fig. 4.11. Parallel summing network.

to the simplicity of the circuit, we obtain the generator gain K_g, by using the same attenuation ratio as we used for the followup:

$$K_g = \left| \frac{R_a}{Z_g + Z_f + R_a} \right| K_{go}$$

and

$$\phi_g = \phi_{gc} + \phi_{fo},$$

where $\phi_{gc} = \phi_{fc}$. The effective null voltage is given by

$$E_g(\text{null}) = \left[\frac{K_g}{K_{go}} \right] E_{go}(\text{null}).$$

The circuits shown in Fig. 4.10 and the preceding examples, although simple, are in some instances adequate and are used in instrument servo designs. However, often the circuits are complicated, with tuning capacitors, attenuation resistors, voltage dividers, and additional bias type inputs. Figure 4.11 illustrates a general summing network that includes most specific parallel circuits. The equations for such a circuit can be programmed on a digital computer. Table 4.2 illustrates a typical computer output sheet from such a program. By setting unused components to either zero or infinity (or more specifically some large value such as 1.E10), the majority of reduced circuits may be formulated.

The first and largest group of data represents the input parameters for the followup, generator, amplifier input impedance, frequency, and circuit resistor-capacitor components. The bottom group of data represents the computed output parameters for K_f, ϕ_f, K_g, E_g (null), and ϕ_g.

Table 4.2*

EXAMPLE OF A COMPUTER OUTPUT SHEET
USED FOR SUMMING NETWORK CALCULATIONS

```
                                                          LEAR SIEGLER INC
                                                          INSTRUMENT DIVISION
                                                          PROGRAM SD009B


                      PARALLEL SUMMING NETWORK CALCULATIONS



               K-FO        PHI-FO        R-F         X-F        K-GO        E-GO
              (V/RAD)       (DEG)       (OHMS)      (OHMS)   (V/1000RPM)     (MV)
  MAXIMUM    2.582E+01    1.621E+01    6.812E+02   3.217E+02   3.780E-01   1.500E+01
     MEAN    2.224E+01    1.272E+01    5.724E+02   2.473E+02   3.460E-01   7.500E-00
  MINIMUM    1.866E+01    9.245E-00    4.637E+02   1.730E+02   3.140E-01   0.000E-99


               PHI-GO        R-G         X-G         R-A         X-A      FREQUENCY
               (DEG)       (OHMS)      (OHMS)      (OHMS)      (OHMS)       (CPS)
  MAXIMUM    1.000E+01    1.644E+03    1.944E+03   1.126E+03   0.000E-99   4.200E+02
     MEAN    0.000E-99    1.430E+03    1.690E+03   9.680E+02   0.000E-99   4.000E+02
  MINIMUM   -1.000E+01    1.216E+03    1.436E+03   8.100E+02   0.000E-99   3.800E+02


               R-F1         R-F2        R-F3        C-F         R-T         R-1
              (OHMS)       (OHMS)      (OHMS)      (MF)        (OHMS)      (OHMS)
     MEAN    0.000E-99    1.000E+10    0.000E-99   0.000E-99   0.000E-99   1.000E+04
  PCT TOL    0.000E-99    0.000E-99    0.000E-99   0.000E-99   0.000E-99   5.000E-00


               R-A1         R-G1        R-G2        R-G3        C-G         R-2
              (OHMS)       (OHMS)      (OHMS)      (OHMS)      (MF)        (OHMS)
     MEAN    4.320E+03    0.000E-99    1.000E+10   0.000E-99   0.000E-99   1.000E+04
  PCT TOL    5.000E-00    0.000E-99    0.000E-99   0.000E-99   0.000E-99   5.000E-00


               R-A2         R-3
              (OHMS)       (OHMS)
     MEAN    0.000E-99    1.000E+10
  PCT TOL    0.000E-99    0.000E-99



               K-F          PHI-F        K-G         E-G         PHI-G
              (V/RAD)       (DEG)    (V/1000RPM)     (MV)        (DEG)
  MAXIMUM    1.467E-00    1.593E+01   2.782E-02   1.095E-00    2.344E-00
     MEAN    1.259E-00    1.244E+01   2.525E-02   5.473E-01   -7.745E-00
  MINIMUM    1.051E-00    8.945E-00   2.267E-02  -5.092E-04   -1.783E+01

         E SIGNIFIES CONVENTIONAL POWER-OF-TEN NOTATION
```

* Reprinted by courtesy of Lear Siegler, Inc., Instrument Division, Grand Rapids, Michigan.

4.5. SERVO AMPLIFIER

Amplifier design is a separate field in itself and is covered in many other books. Thus little will be said about it here except to mention the parameters that the servo engineer needs for his design. We have already seen from the previous section that the input impedance is one of these parameters.

The most fundamental property of the amplifier is its transfer characteristic. That is the relationship between the input voltage E_{in} and the corresponding output

Table 4.3*

EXAMPLE OF A COMPUTER OUTPUT SHEET
USED FOR OBTAINING SERVO AMPLIFIER DATA

```
                                              LEAR SIEGLER INC
                                              INSTRUMENT DIVISION
                                              PROGRAM SD007B


               SERVO AMPLIFIER APPLICATION DATA

                        LIBRARY DATA
              AMPLIFIER PART NUMBER-139009.01
              TEMPERATURE CONDITION- 25 DEG C.

                  MOTOR IMPEDANCE DATA (OHMS)
            CENTER TAP-TO-END              END-TO-END
            REAL      IMAGINARY        REAL      IMAGINARY
  MAXIMUM   8.490E+02  3.580E+02      1.955E+03  1.425E+03
  MEAN      7.075E+02  3.110E+02      1.630E+03  1.238E+03
  MINIMUM   5.660E+02  2.640E+02      1.305E+03  1.051E+03

              AMPLIFIER EXCITATION CONDITIONS
                     VOLTAGE     FREQUENCY
                     (VOLTS)       (CPS)
            MAXIMUM  1.270E+02    4.200E+02
            MEAN     1.150E+02    4.000E+02
            MINIMUM  1.030E+02    3.800E+02

         EFFECTIVE AMPLIFIER PERFORMANCE DATA
            K-A       E-NULL       PHI-A       E-SAT
            (V/V)     (MV)        (DEGREES)   (VOLTS)
  MAXIMUM  1.104E+02  1.500E-00    5.000E-00   4.040E+01
  MEAN     9.600E+01  7.500E-01   -1.000E+01   3.640E+01
  MINIMUM  8.160E+01  0.000E-99   -2.500E+01   3.240E+01

      E SIGNIFIES CONVENTIONAL POWER-OF-TEN NOTATION
```

* Reprinted by courtesy of Lear Siegler, Inc., Instrument Division, Grand Rapids, Michigan.

voltage E_c developed across the motor terminals. This relationship is usually considered to be linear over some operating range of the device, and thus the transfer function can be written as

$$E_c/E_{\text{in}} = K_a \cos \phi_a, \tag{4.20}$$

where K_a is called the *amplifier gain* (v/v) and ϕ_a is the corresponding phase shift associated with the carrier. The amplifier output voltage is proportional to the input only up to some limit, which is called the *saturation level* of the amplifier E_{sat}. This value, when used in the motor calculations presented in Chapter 2, determines the followup rate capabilities of the servo.

Since most amplifiers have an appreciable output impedance, the values of K_a, E_a (null), ϕ_a, and E_{sat} are a function of the impedance of the motor that the amplifier is driving. Thus the amplifier is ordinarily specified with a given motor load, and revised characteristics must be obtained when the load is changed. If the amplifier design is automated, then the corresponding characteristics can be readily

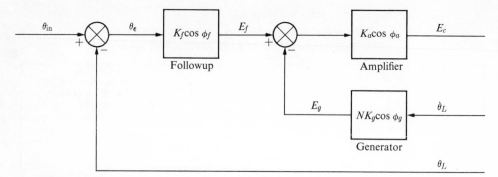

Fig. 4.12. Block diagram representation of the followup, generator, summing circuit, and amplifier.

determined for any given load. An output sheet from such a program is illustrated as Table 4.3. The first set of data constitutes the part number used to identify the amplifier followed by the temperature condition at which the data are to be generated. The next block of inputs, labeled motor impedance data, represents the load on the amplifier to be used in the calculations. These are followed by the amplifier excitation conditions to be used. The last block of data shows the effective amplifier performance data which are the program outputs.

4.6. BLOCK DIAGRAM REPRESENTATION

We can represent the followup, generator, summing circuit, and amplifier in block diagram form by using transfer function notation, as shown by Fig. 4.12. The gear ratio N has been included as part of the generator transfer function to refer the generator to the load in the same manner as the motor.

4.7. INNER LOOP STABILITY

The motor transfer function developed previously (Eq. 2.52) can be multiplied by the Laplace operator (s) to obtain velocity and combined with the block diagram generated in the previous section. From this, one obtains a complete loop called the *generator* or *inner loop*, shown in Fig. 4.13. It should be noted that Fig. 4.13 and the subsequent analysis do not include the effects of the load. That is, the gear ratio N is omitted and τ_m is used instead of τ_T. The reason for this is that instability of the inner loop usually takes place entirely within the backlash region of the gear train. Thus, the load does not move and hence has no effect upon the system. However, if it should move, it would tend to decrease the oscillation. Therefore the design as presented without the load represents the worst case.

    The loop in Fig. 4.13 represents a stable system since there is a maximum possible phase shift of 90 deg. However, let us consider the case where the loop gain $(K_g K_a K_m)$ is raised to such a value that phase shifts which we would neglect ordinarily

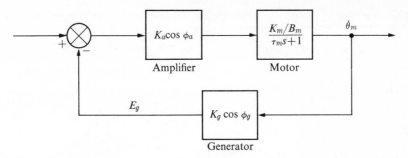

Fig. 4.13. Inner loop mathematical block diagram.

now contribute appreciably to the total phase shift. Under this condition, it is possible to have an unstable inner loop. This instability is called "generator buzz" since it is characterized by a buzzing noise originating in the motor generator. This phenomenon is particularly troublesome in high-gain loops which contain additional phase shifts resulting from quadrature stripping and filtering. We can easily analyze this type of instability by using a conventional Bode frequency response diagram, as shown by the following examples.

Example 4.3 Consider the analysis of a high gain loop that has the following parameters:

$$K_g = 0.262 \text{ v}/1000 \text{ rpm},$$
$$K_a = 2000 \text{ v/v},$$
$$K_m = 3.5 \times 10^{-3} \text{ oz-in/v},$$
$$B_m = 3.5 \times 10^{-4} \text{ oz-in/rad/sec},$$
$$J_m = 0.49 \text{ gm-cm}^2.$$

Converting K_g and J_m values to obtain a consistent set of units yields

$$K_g = (0.262 \times 10^{-3})[60/2\pi] = 0.0025 \text{ v/rad/sec},$$
$$J_m = (0.49)(1.42 \times 10^{-5}) = 0.695 \times 10^{-5} \text{ oz-in/rad/sec}^2.$$

The gain K_G of the inner loop is thus calculated to be

$$K_G = \frac{K_g K_a K_m}{B_m} = \frac{(0.0025)(2000)(0.0035)}{(0.00035)} = 50.$$

Converting this to decibels, we have

$$K_G = 20 \log (50) = 34 \text{ db}.$$

The time constant τ_m and corresponding break frequency are calculated as

$$\tau_m = \frac{J_m}{B_m} = \frac{0.695 \times 10^{-5}}{3.5 \times 10^{-4}} = 0.01987 \text{ sec},$$
$$\omega_m = 50.3 \text{ rad/sec} = 8.0 \text{ cps}.$$

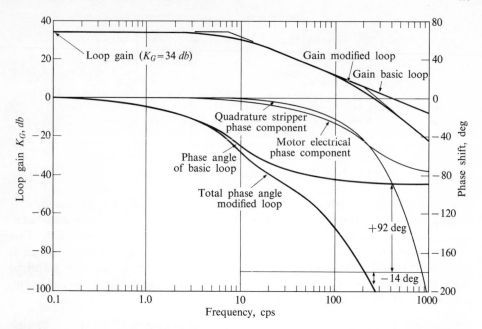

Fig. 4.14. Open-loop frequency response diagram showing instability resulting from quadrature stripper and added motor lag.

Using these values, we can construct a Bode plot as shown in Fig. 4.14. As we should expect, we see that the loop is stable with a phase margin of about 92 deg. However, if one then adds a quadrature stripper represented by a quarter cycle time delay and includes a 200-cps corner associated with the motor electrical time constant, the loop becomes unstable. Figure 4.15 illustrates the block diagram for the modified loop. The effect of the added lag and time delay functions on the original Bode plot is shown in Fig. 4.14. As can be seen by the −14 deg phase margin, the modified loop is unstable and would continually oscillate or "buzz" at a frequency of around 200 cps.

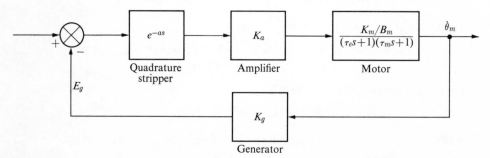

Fig. 4.15. Modified inner loop including quadrature stripper and motor electrical time constant.

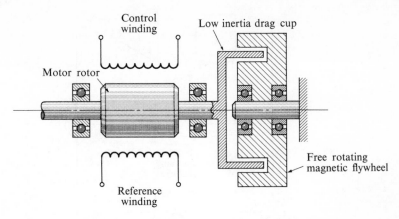

Fig. 4.16. Mechanical schematic of inertially damped servomotor.

4.8. INERTIAL DAMPER

Before progressing to the next chapter and assembling the components already described to make a system, we should consider two special types of dampers. The first one, the inertial damper, will be discussed in this section.

The inertial damper, like the generator, is connected to the motor in one integral assembly. Structurally, the damper consists of a low inertia drag cup of conducting material rigidly connected to the motor shaft and a freely rotating magnetic flywheel mounted as shown in Fig. 4.16. The drag cup is located in the field of the permanent magnet flywheel so that a viscous torque is developed proportional to the relative velocity between the drag cup and flywheel. This torque acts as a drag on the motor to provide the desired damping and at the same time accelerate the flywheel. During transient periods the high inertia flywheel tries to remain stationary, thus providing heavy viscous damping on the motor. However, during slewing or constant-velocity operation the flywheel eventually accelerates to the same speed as the drag cup, and there is no reduction in motor speed or power except for the bearing friction losses. Thus the inertial damper provides negligible damping under constant-velocity steady state conditions. This characteristic will be shown (Chapter 5) to be highly desirable for many applications.

The inertially damped servomotor can be represented by the mathematical block diagram shown in Fig. 4.17. From this figure we can directly derive the following transfer function for the inertially damped servomotor:

$$\frac{\theta_m(s)}{E_c(s)} = \frac{K_m(\tau_d s + 1)/B_m}{s[(\tau_m\tau_d)s^2 + (\tau_m + \tau_d + \tau_{md})s + 1]},\tag{4.21}$$

where

$$\tau_d = J_d/B_d, \qquad \tau_{md} = J_d/B_m, \qquad \tau_m = J_m/B_m,$$

$$J_d = \text{flywheel inertia}, \qquad B_d = \text{viscous coupling coefficient}.$$

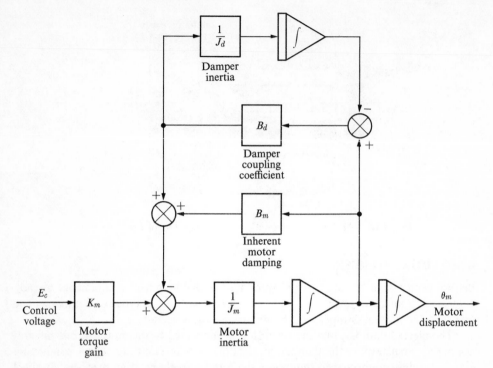

Fig. 4.17. Mathematical block diagram of inertially damped servomotor.

The J_d/B_d term is called the *damper time constant,* which is similar to the motor time constant τ_m.

The quadratic in the denominator of Eq. (4.21) can be expressed by two single-order time constants to yield the transfer function in the following form:

$$\frac{\theta_m(s)}{E_c(s)} = \frac{K_v(\tau_2 s + 1)}{s(\tau_1 s + 1)(\tau_3 s + 1)}, \qquad (4.22)$$

where τ_1 and τ_3 = the two solutions obtained from the quadratic equation

$$\tau^2 - (\tau_m + \tau_d + \tau_{md})\tau + \tau_m \tau_d = 0,$$

$$\tau_2 = \tau_d = J_d/B_d,$$

$$K_v = K_m/B_m.$$

The K_v-term is normally called the *velocity constant* of the motor. To get a feel for the relative magnitudes of τ_1 and τ_2, we can solve the quadratic in general terms and after eliminating the less significant terms, obtain the following approximate relationships for the three time constants:

$$\tau_1 \simeq J_d \left[\frac{B_m + B_d}{B_m B_d} \right], \qquad \tau_2 = \frac{J_d}{B_d}, \qquad \tau_3 \simeq \frac{J_m}{B_m + B_d}. \qquad (4.23)$$

The three corner frequencies ω_1, ω_2, ω_3 of the inertially damped servomotor are given by the reciprocal of the corresponding time constant and exhibit the relationship

$$\omega_1 < \omega_2 < \omega_3. \tag{4.24}$$

These three parameters are used by the servo engineer to select the optimum motor damper combination to stabilize any particular system, as will be shown in Chapter 5.

4.9. VISCOUS DAMPER

The viscous damper is similar to the inertial damper described in the previous section, but instead of the magnet being mounted on bearings as a flywheel, it is rigidly mounted to the motor case. Ordinarily two magnets are used, one fixed and the other adjustable by means of a screwdriver slot in a shaft extending from the rear of the motor housing. This permits the damping to be adjusted to any desired value within the range of the device.

The viscous damper does not adversely affect the motor starting voltage or stall torque, but does increase its inertia and reduces the system slew speed. Since the addition of a viscous damper simply lowers the motors "no-load speed," its effect can be analyzed by an appropriate increase in the B_m-term defined previously. The application of the viscous damper to system design will be shown in Chapter 5.

4.10. SUMMARY

In this chapter, analytical descriptions were obtained for the followup, generator, servo amplifier, and summing circuit. We started by developing a complete mathematical representation of the synchro followup from its characteristic impedance parameters. Expressions were then obtained for the open circuit values of gain and phase shift as well as for the output impedance and accuracy. It was shown that an electrical input servo with a potentiometer followup is mathematically equivalent to a synchro. Thus one can use the same system design procedure for either case.

A mathematical representation of the generator was obtained and it was demonstrated that the nonlinear term could be safely neglected. The generator was thereby represented by specifying the open circuit values of gain, phase shift, and null as well as the output impedance.

The summing circuit was introduced as a means of adding the signal voltages from the followup and generator. Both the parallel and series type were shown and sample calculations were made for each. This was followed by a discussion of the servo amplifier.

The followup, generator, summing circuit, and amplifier were combined to form an equivalent block diagram representation. This diagram was combined with that for the motor obtained in Chapter 2 to form the generator loop. The stability of this inner loop was then investigated and the destabilizing effects of a quadrature stripper and added time constants were illustrated.

The chapter was concluded by describing the characteristics of inertial and viscous dampers. Complete mathematical expressions were derived for the inertial damper and approximations were made so that the designer could obtain a physical feel for the manner in which the added time constants varied with the motor damper parameters. On the other hand, it was shown that the effect of a viscous damper could be included by simply increasing the apparent value of the inherent motor damping B_m.

PROBLEMS

*4.1. A synchro CX and CT combination, which is excited with 26 v, has the following characteristics:

	CX data	CT data
	$Z_{RO} = 25 + j\,115$	$Z_{RO} = 470 + j\,1960$
	$Z_{SO} = 5.9 + j\,21$	$Z_{SO} = 72 + j\,334$
	$Z_{RS} = 24.5 + j\,16.7$	$Z_{RS} = 582 + j\,221$

Calculate the following data:

a) CX T-equivalent circuit impedance Z_{A1}, Z_{B1}, Z_{C1},

b) CT T-equivalent circuit impedances Z_{A2}, Z_{B2}, Z_{C2},

c) Open circuit gain K_{fo},   d) Open circuit phase angle ϕ_{fo},

e) Output impedance $Z_f = R_f + jX_f$.

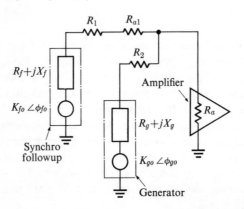

Figure 4.18

*4.2. Consider the parallel type summing circuit in Fig. 4.18. The following component parameters are given:

$K_{fo} = 22.52$ v/rad,	$R_g = 300$ ohms,
$\phi_{fo} = 13.59$ deg,	$X_g = 260$ ohms,
$R_f = 589$ ohms,	$R_a = 2140$ ohms,
$X_f = 209.4$ ohms,	$R_1 = 2610$ ohms,
$K_{go} = 0.411$ v/1000 rpm,	$R_2 = 4320$ ohms,
$E_{go} = 10$ mv,	$R_{a1} = 4320$ ohms.
$\phi_{go} = -16$ deg,	

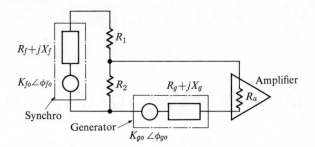

Figure 4.19

Calculate the following parameter values effective at the amplifier input:

a) followup gain K_f,
b) followup phase angle ϕ_f,
c) generator gain K_g,
d) generator phase angle ϕ_g,
e) generator null voltage E_g.

*4.3. Consider the series type summing circuit in Fig. 4.19. The following component parameters are given:

$$K_{fo} = 22.5 \text{ v/rad}, \qquad \phi_{go} = 10 \text{ deg},$$
$$\phi_{fo} = 13.0 \text{ deg}, \qquad R_g = 650 \text{ ohms},$$
$$R_f = 1850 \text{ ohms}, \qquad X_g = 325 \text{ ohms},$$
$$X_f = 711 \text{ ohms}, \qquad R_a = 10{,}000 \text{ ohms},$$
$$K_{go} = 0.244 \text{ v/1000 rpm}, \qquad R_1 = 11{,}300 \text{ ohms},$$
$$E_{go} = 15.0 \text{ mv}, \qquad R_2 = 7100 \text{ ohms}.$$

Calculate the following parameter values effective at the amplifier input:

a) followup gain K_f,
b) followup phase angle ϕ_f,
c) generator gain K_g,
d) generator phase angle ϕ_g,
e) generator null voltage E_g.

4.4. Show the derivation of Eq. (4.15) in the text.

4.5. Show the relationships that must exist between J_m, B_m, B_d, and J_d for the approximations given as Eqs. (4.23) in the text to be valid.

BIBLIOGRAPHY

DAVIS, S., and B. LEDGERWOOD, *Electromechanical Components for Servomechanisms*, McGraw-Hill, 1961, Chapter 3.

DIAMOND, A., "Inertially Damped Servomotors: Performance Analysis," *Electro-Technology* pp. 28–32 (July 1965).

GIBSON, J., and F. TUTEUR, *Control System Components*, McGraw-Hill, 1958, Chapter 5.

GILLE, J. C., M. J. PELEGRIN, and P. DECAULNE, "Components of Servo Systems," in *Feedback Control Systems*, McGraw-Hill, 1959, Part IV.

PARVIN, R. H., "Getting the Most Out of Synchros," *Electronic Equipment Engineering* (October 1958).

TRUXAL, J. G., *Control Engineers Handbook*, McGraw-Hill, 1958, Section 17, "Signal Transducers."

CHAPTER 5

CHARACTERISTICS OF TOTAL SERVO SYSTEM

The first four chapters presented a background and developed mathematical models for the various components that constitute an instrument servo. Analytic formulas were developed to help the designer determine numeric values for the parameters describing each component. To predict the behavior of a servo in terms of the component descriptions, we must interconnect the various component models as in the hardware so that we can generate a mathematical representation of the total system. Once we have accomplished this, we will be in a position to vary the numerous component parameter values and evaluate the corresponding effects on the total system. The purpose of this chapter is to show how the various components of a motor generator servo can be combined to formulate total system block diagrams and characteristics. Stability requirements as well as response will be discussed.

5.1. SYSTEM NONLINEAR AND LINEAR BLOCK DIAGRAM

The individual models developed in the previous chapters for the followup, generator, amplifier, motor, gear train, and load may now be combined to develop a complete mathematical block diagram for the motor-generator servo, as shown in Fig. 5.1. The load and motor inertias are separated and the effect of finite gear train stiffness is included. The nonlinearities of amplifier saturation, motor starting voltage, backlash, and load coulomb friction are considered. Figure 5.1 represents the servo in its mathematically complete form and will be used extensively in Chapter 7. However, for now, let us consider a linearized form obtained directly from Fig. 5.1 by letting (1) load coulomb friction be replaced by viscous damping, (2) motor starting voltage equal zero, (3) amplifier saturation limits become large, and (4) backlash equal zero. The resulting system can be represented by the block diagram shown as Fig. 5.2. Although this linear model represents a significant deviation from the actual hardware, it is mathematically tractable, and much can be learned by it.

5.2. DERIVATION OF CLOSED-LOOP TRANSFER FUNCTION

The linearized block diagram of the complete instrument servo was developed as Fig. 5.2. By first rearranging the blocks to combine the motor and generator damping loops and then substituting the series equivalent for the load damping loop, we obtain

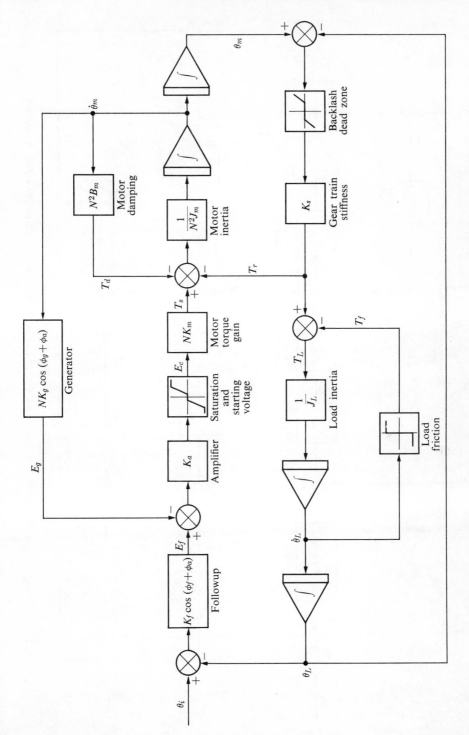

Fig. 5.1. Complete mathematical block diagram of motor-generator instrument servomechanism.

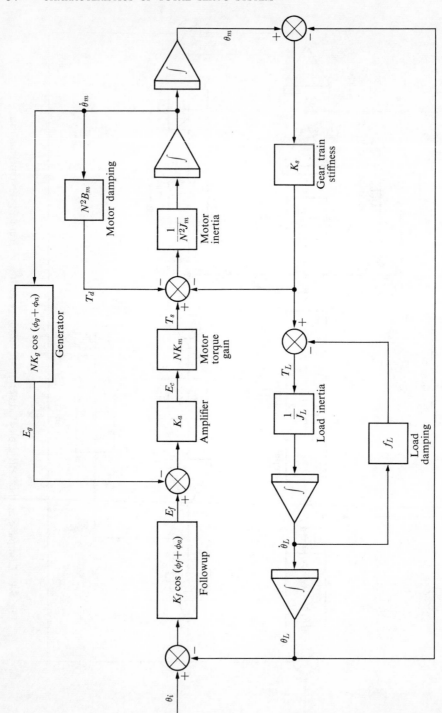

Fig. 5.2. Complete linearized mathematical block diagram of motor-generator instrument servomechanism.

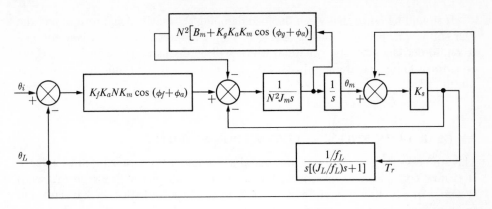

Fig. 5.3. Reduced version of Fig. 5.2.

the reduced diagram shown as Fig. 5.3. By defining the quantities

$$K_T = K_f K_a N K_m \cos (\phi_f + \phi_a), \qquad J_T = N^2 J_m + J_L,$$
$$f_T = N^2 [B_m + K_g K_a K_m \cos (\phi_g + \phi_a)] \tag{5.1}$$

and moving the torque feedback loop to the load position and substituting the series equivalent for the damping loop and the innermost load position feedback, we accomplish the further reduction shown by Fig. 5.4.

Using standard block diagram algebra, we compute the complete open-loop transfer function as

$$\frac{\theta_L(s)}{\theta_\epsilon(s)} = \frac{K_T K_s}{s[(N^2 J_m J_L)s^3 + (f_L N^2 J_m + J_L f_T)s^2 + (K_s J_T + f_L f_T)s + K_s(f_L + f_T)]}. \tag{5.2}$$

From this, the closed-loop transfer function is given by

$$\frac{\theta_L(s)}{\theta_i(s)} = \frac{1}{\left(\dfrac{N^2 J_m J_L}{K_T K_s}\right)s^4 + \left(\dfrac{f_T J_L + f_L N^2 J_m}{K_T K_s}\right)s^3 + \left(\dfrac{f_T f_L}{K_T K_s} + \dfrac{J_T}{K_T}\right)s^2 + \left(\dfrac{f_T + f_L}{K_T}\right)s + 1} \tag{5.3}$$

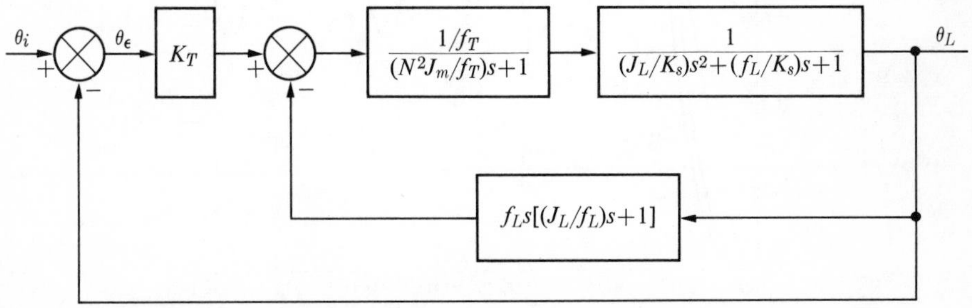

Fig. 5.4. Reduced version of Fig. 5.3.

It should be noted that when the load damping f_L is made equal to zero and the gear stiffness K_s becomes infinite, Eq. (5.3) simply reduces to the more conventional second-order characteristic equation, which will be discussed in detail later. However, for a finite gear train stiffness, Eq. (5.3) shows that the resulting system is of fourth order.

5.3. GEAR TRAIN STIFFNESS EFFECT UPON STABILITY

This stiffness of a gear train was introduced as a component parameter in Chapter 3. It is now convenient to investigate the effects of finite gear stiffness on the servo system. In actuality, the stiffness effect is interrelated with that of backlash and friction; however, it is of interest to consider first just the stiffness effects. The associated nonlinearities will be introduced in Chapter 7.

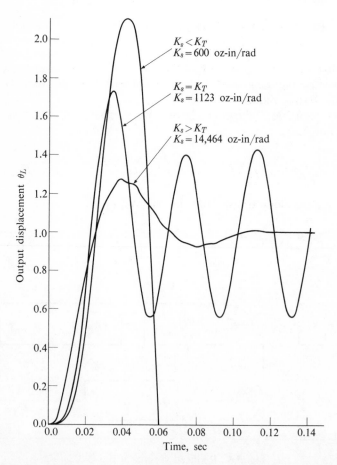

Fig. 5.5. Response to a unit step for various values of gear stiffness.

Figure 5.2 shows a mathematical block diagram representing the servo including gear train stiffness. Using standard block diagram algebra, we derived the closed-loop transfer function for the system as Eq. (5.3). Let us consider the theoretical case of no friction or damping at the load. The only damping in the system is a result of the motor and the generator feedback.

Letting all the load damping be zero ($f_L = 0$) and multiplying both the numerator and denominator of Eq. (5.3) by the quantity $K_T K_s / N^2 J_m J_L$ yields

$$\frac{\theta_L(s)}{\theta_i(s)} = \frac{K_T K_s / N^2 J_m J_L}{s^4 + \left(\dfrac{f_T}{N^2 J_m}\right) s^3 + \left(\dfrac{K_s}{J_L} + \dfrac{K_s}{N^2 J_m}\right) s^2 + \left(\dfrac{K_s f_T}{N^2 J_m J_L}\right) s + \left(\dfrac{K_T K_s}{N^2 J_m J_L}\right)}.$$

(5.4)

The corresponding system stability requirements can be obtained by using a conventional Routh test. Constructing a triangular array from the polynomial coefficients of Eq. (5.4), we obtain

s^4	1	$\dfrac{K_s}{J_L} + \dfrac{K_s}{N^2 J_m}$	$\dfrac{K_s K_T}{N^2 J_m J_L}$
s^3	$\dfrac{f_T}{N^2 J_m}$	$\dfrac{f_T K_s}{N^2 J_m J_L}$	
s^2	$\dfrac{K_s}{N^2 J_m}$	$\dfrac{K_s K_T}{N^2 J_m J_L}$	
s^1	$\dfrac{K_s f_T}{N^2 J_m J_L} - \dfrac{K_T f_T}{N^2 J_m J_L}$		
s^0	$\dfrac{K_s K_T}{N^2 J_m J_L}$		

For the system to be stable, all the coefficients in the first column must have the same sign. Therefore, the condition required for stability is that

$$K_s f_T / N^2 J_m J_L > K_T f_T / N^2 J_m J_L,$$

or more simply,

$$K_s > K_T. \tag{5.5}$$

Equation (5.5) shows that for the system to be stable, the gear train stiffness K_s must be greater than the servo forward-loop static gain or torque constant K_T. This fact is demonstrated by Fig. 5.5, which shows a transient response to a step input for various values of gear stiffness K_s and the following typical values for the other parameters:

$$K_f = 18 \text{ v/rad}, \qquad K_g = 0.140 \text{ v/1000 rpm},$$
$$K_a = 240 \text{ v/v}, \qquad K_m = 2.60 \times 10^{-3} \text{ oz-in/v},$$
$$B_m = 2.0 \times 10^{-4} \text{ oz-in/rad/sec}, \qquad J_m = 1.0 \text{ gm-cm}^2,$$
$$J_L = 3000 \text{ gm-cm}^2, \qquad N = 100,$$
$$\phi_f = 0 \text{ deg}, \qquad \phi_g = 0 \text{ deg}, \qquad \phi_a = 0 \text{ deg}.$$

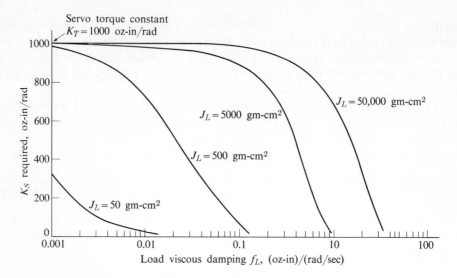

Fig. 5.6. Gear stiffness required as a function of load viscous damping.

The three solutions are shown with the above parameters held constant and letting K_s assume values greater than, equal to, and less than K_T, which is given by

$$K_T = K_f K_a K_m N \cos (\phi_f + \phi_a) = (18)(240)(0.0026)(100) = 1123.2 \text{ oz-in/rad}.$$

It should be remembered that the above requirement, that the gear stiffness K_s be greater than the servo torque constant K_T, is based on the assumption of zero damping or friction at the load. In actuality this represents a sufficient condition for stability and not a necessary one. We can demonstrate this by considering viscous damping f_L to exist at the load. The same procedure may be carried out by using a Routh test to determine the stability requirement, but not letting f_L go to zero results in the requirement that

$$K_s > \frac{K_T f_T^2 J_L^2 + 2 f_T f_L J_L N^2 J_m K_T + K_T f_{L}^2 N^4 J_m^2 - f_T^3 f_L J_L - f_T^2 f_{L}^2 N^2 J_m - f_T^2 f_{L}^2 J_L - f_T f_{L}^3 N^2 J_m}{f_T^2 J_L^2 + f_T f_L N^4 J_m^2 + f_L f_T J_L^2 + f_{L}^2 N^4 J_m^2}. \qquad (5.6)$$

Figure 5.6 shows a plot of the right-hand side of Eq. (5.6), which represents the value of K_s required for neutral stability as a function of load viscous damping for a system with the parameters

$$K_T = 1000 \text{ oz-in/rad}, \qquad f_T = 20 \text{ oz-in/rad/sec}, \qquad N^2 J_m = 10000 \text{ gm-cm}^2.$$

Curves for four values of load inertia are shown. It is seen that for values of f_L approaching zero all curves asymptotically approach the value of K_T. This is also evident from Eq. (5.6) since for $f_L = 0$ the inequality reduces to the previous require-ment that $K_s > K_T$. However, as we can see from Fig. 5.6, for $f_L > 0$, K_s can be less than the torque constant. In fact, for small values of load inertia J_L, the system is stable for all practical values of f_L and K_s.

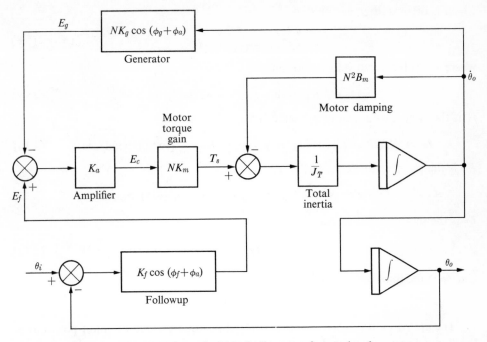

Fig. 5.7. Linear mathematical block diagram of second-order system.

A similar relationship will be shown to exist when the presence of load coulomb friction is considered in Chapter 7. The latter is of more practical value since load damping is normally more coulomb than viscous in nature.

5.4. REDUCED SYSTEM CHARACTERISTIC EQUATIONS

There are applications for which it is sufficient to consider the gear train stiffness to be infinite or at least so high that the effects may be neglected. This is especially true during the early design phase of selecting feasible parameters. This assumption is also of special interest because with infinite stiffness the system reduces to the conventional second-order system. On the basis of what we already know about the second-order system, we can learn much about the instrument servomechanism.

Considering the gear train stiffness to be infinite, we can reduce the system linear block diagram to that shown in Fig. 5.7. We obtain the open-loop transfer function (output position divided by system error) by writing the series equivalent for the minor loop and then combining this with the followup gain, obtaining the following relationship:

$$\frac{\theta_o(s)}{\theta_\epsilon(s)} = \frac{\dfrac{K_f K_a N K_m \cos(\phi_f + \phi_a)}{K_a N K_m N K_g \cos(\phi_g + \phi_a) + N^2 B_m}}{s\left[\dfrac{J_T}{K_a N K_m N K_g \cos(\phi_g + \phi_a) + N^2 B_m} s + 1\right]}, \qquad (5.7)$$

which is often written as

$$\frac{\theta_o(s)}{\theta_\epsilon(s)} = \frac{K_V}{s(\tau_T s + 1)},$$
(5.8)

where K_V is the servo velocity constant

$$K_V = K_T/f_T \qquad \text{(rad/sec)},$$
(5.9)

f_T is the system total damping coefficient

$$f_T = K_a N K_m N K_g \cos(\phi_g + \phi_a) + N^2 B_m \qquad \text{[(oz-in)/(rad/sec)]},$$
(5.10)

K_T is the servo torque constant

$$K_T = K_f K_a N K_m \cos(\phi_f + \phi_a) \qquad \text{(oz-in)/rad},$$
(5.11)

τ_T is the servo time constant

$$\tau_T = J_T/f_T \quad \text{(sec)},$$
(5.12)

and J_T is the total servo inertia

$$J_T = N^2 J_m + J_L \qquad \text{[(oz-in)/(rad/sec}^2\text{)]}.$$
(5.13)

The closed-loop transfer function (output position divided by input position) of the complete servo may be determined directly from the open-loop transfer function:

$$\frac{\theta_o(s)}{\theta_i(s)} = \frac{1}{\left[\dfrac{J_T}{K_f K_a N K_m \cos(\phi_f + \phi_a)}\right]s^2 + \left[\dfrac{K_a N K_m N K_g \cos(\phi_g + \phi_a) + N^2 B_m}{K_f K_a N K_m \cos(\phi_f + \phi_a)}\right]s + 1},$$
(5.14)

which can be written in terms of the system torque constant and damping coefficient as

$$\frac{\theta_o(s)}{\theta_i(s)} = \frac{1}{(J_T/K_T)s^2 + (f_T/K_T)s + 1}.$$
(5.15)

As we can see from Eq. (5.15), the closed-loop transfer function for the reduced system is of second order and is equivalent to that obtained for the conventional spring mass damper.

5.5. SYSTEM LINEAR COEFFICIENTS AND THEIR PHYSICAL SIGNIFICANCE

The system linear coefficients have been introduced and each has been defined by an appropriate equation. However, it is important that we develop a thorough understanding for all these coefficients since they are the main parameters on which a design is based.

1. Servo torque constant K_T. The servo torque constant is a measure of the "mechanical stiffness" of the servo. It is a figure of merit for *all* positional servos. Higher

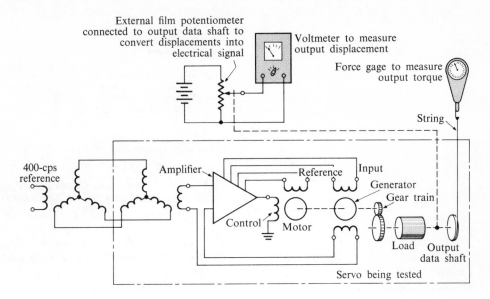

Fig. 5.8. Typical test setup for measuring servo torque constant.

values of K_T represent greater servo stiffness and therefore greater ability to overcome friction and external loads. The torque constant is the most meaningful and perhaps the simplest parameter to measure. It yields the static gain of the complete forward loop considering all the loading and interactions between components. The test is conducted by applying a torque to the output shaft and measuring this torque and the resulting displacement. Figure 5.8 shows a typical test setup that can be used to measure the torque constant. The torque is applied to the output shaft by wrapping a string around the output shaft and then applying a measured force with a gram gauge. The torque could also be applied directly using a torque wrench or a torque watch. A film potentiometer (infinite resolution) is connected to the output shaft so that displacement can be read by applying a dc voltage across the potentiometer and recording the voltage developed at the wiper with a dc voltmeter. The synchro output could be used to measure the displacement, provided that its loaded gain into the amplifier is known and enough significant readings about null can be made. However, this method is not recommended since one has to rely on one of the components being measured for the calibration of the test. This is certainly not a good test procedure. Another method of measuring the load displacement is to use a tool-maker's microscope. This method is preferable since it provides a direct and accurate displacement measurement, thereby eliminating all scale and conversion factors.

Figure 5.9 shows a typical curve of torque vs. displacement. The torque developed is a linear function of displacement up to the saturation level, which, for this case, is approximately 0.55 deg. The servo torque constant K_T is the slope of the curve and may be computed to be 2800 oz-in/rad. This is a measure of the stiffness of the servo as given by the product $K_f K_a N K_m \cos(\phi_f + \phi_a)$.

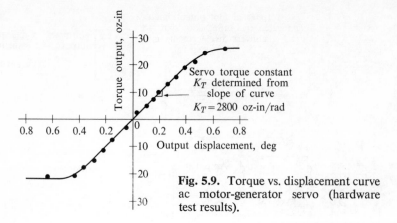

Fig. 5.9. Torque vs. displacement curve ac motor-generator servo (hardware test results).

2. Damping coefficients. From the linear block diagram (Fig. 5.7) we see that the generator loop can be eliminated by replacing the motor damping block with the quantity $N^2[B_m + K_g K_a K_m \cos (\phi_g + \phi_a)]$. Therefore, disregarding saturation effects, we see that the generator has simply supplemented the inherent motor damping. Consequently, the servo damping can be divided into two components: that supplied by the motor and that supplied by the generator. The total damping coefficient is a measure of the amount of negative torque developed at the output due

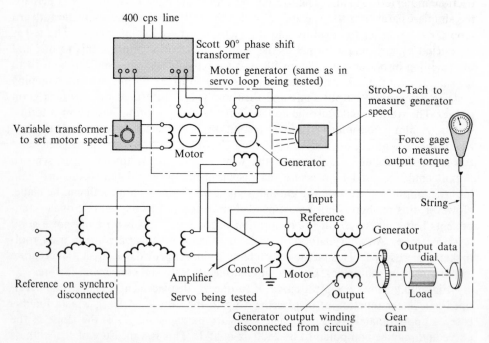

Fig. 5.10. Typical test setup for measuring amount of servo damping due to generator.

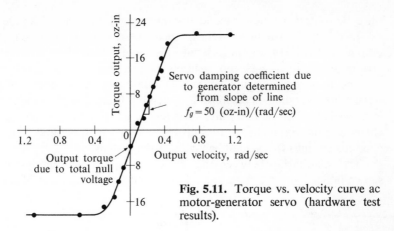

Fig. 5.11. Torque vs. velocity curve ac motor-generator servo (hardware test results).

to a given output velocity. A most informative test can be conducted to measure the amount of damping that is present because of the generator loop. Figure 5.10 shows a typical test setup used to measure the generator damping. The generator output leads in the servo being tested are disconnected and an external "standard" generator of the same type is connected in its place. The motor portion of the external motor-generator set is connected to a Scott 90-deg phase-shift transformer with a variable transformer in one phase. The external motor voltage is set and the resulting no-load speed is recorded with a Strob-O-Tach or a digital counter with a photo pickup. The torque is recorded with the force gage and string arrangement as in the torque-constant test. It should be noted that the Strob-O-Tach readings must be divided by the gear ratio N in the servo being tested since the velocity desired is that of the output shaft.

Figure 5.11 shows the torque vs. velocity curve. We see that the damping torque is a linear function of speed up to the saturation level. The damping coefficient f_g is given by the slope of the curve as 50 oz-in/(rad/sec). This also includes all loading effects and interaction between components and defines the total product $NK_g K_a NK_m \cos(\phi_g + \phi_a)$. Figure 5.11 also shows the effect of the total null voltage in producing a torque at zero generator speed. In this test, the null voltage produces a negative torque. As the generator speed increases, the developed positive torque overcomes the negative torque. This null torque is most important in defining the accuracy of the servo, which will be discussed in more detail later.

5.6. TRANSIENT RESPONSE

Of utmost concern to the servo system designer is the answer to the question, "How authentically does the output of the servo represent the command input?" For a perfect servomechanism, the output would be in exact correspondence with the input under all conditions, both static and dynamic. In actuality, however, this goal cannot be reached. This is especially true during rapid changes of the input command, since the output cannot respond instantaneously because of its inertia. Thus the designer is interested in answers to such questions as, "How long will it take the output to obtain correspondence with the input?" and "Will it overshoot, and if so, how far, and will successive overshoots dampen out?"

The most conventional method of qualifying the response of the instrument servo is to determine its response to a step input. Although response to a step input is somewhat academic in nature, since few actual systems are required to follow step changes in the command, it does provide a convenient method of measurement and good insight into the general behavior of the system.

The relationship between the input and output for the simplified system was shown in Section 5.4 to be a second-order differential equation of the form

$$J_T \frac{d^2\theta_o}{dt^2} + f_T \frac{d\theta_o}{dt} + K_T\theta_o = K_T\theta_i. \tag{5.16}$$

The general solution for this equation is given by

$$\theta_o(t) = C_o + C_1 e^{r_1 t} + C_2 e^{r_2 t}, \tag{5.17}$$

where C_o is the steady-state displacement and C_1 and C_2 are the coefficients for the transient terms corresponding to the roots r_1 and r_2. The characteristic equation of the simplified system is

$$J_T \frac{d^2}{dt^2} + f_T \frac{d}{dt} + K_T = 0, \tag{5.18}$$

and thus the two roots r_1 and r_2 are given by the quadratic formula as

$$r_1, r_2 = \frac{-f_T \pm \sqrt{f_T^2 - 4J_T K_T}}{2J_T}. \tag{5.19}$$

For all practical systems ($f_T > 0$), the roots r_1 and r_2 may be (1) complex conjugates with negative real parts, (2) equal, negative, and real, or (3) unequal, negative, and real, depending on the values of J_T, f_T, and K_T.

It is most convenient to introduce two new parameters, namely, the undamped natural frequency ω_N and the damping ratio ζ. By using these parameters we may express the roots r_1 and r_2 in terms of two quantities instead of three. The quantity ω_N is given by the characteristic equation when the damping coefficient is zero. That is,

$$J_T \frac{d^2}{dt^2} + K_T = 0, \tag{5.20}$$

giving roots

$$r_1, r_2 = \pm j\sqrt{K_T/J_T} = \pm j\omega_N. \tag{5.21}$$

Thus the natural frequency is defined as

$$\omega_N = \sqrt{K_T/J_T}. \tag{5.22}$$

The damping ratio ζ is given by the ratio of the actual damping coefficient f_T to that value required for critical damping. The latter occurs when the radical in Eq. (5.19) is zero. Thus the critical damping f_c is equal to $\sqrt{4J_T K_T}$ and the damping ratio is defined as

$$\zeta = \frac{f_T}{2\sqrt{J_T K_T}}. \qquad (5.23)$$

If one substitutes for f_T, J_T, and K_T in Eqs. (5.9), (5.12), and (5.10), ω_N and ζ are defined directly in terms of the component parameters:

$$\omega_N = \sqrt{[K_f K_a N K_m \cos(\phi_f + \phi_a)]/(N^2 J_m + J_L)}, \qquad (5.24)$$

$$\zeta = \frac{N^2(K_g K_a K_m \cos(\phi_g + \phi_a) + B_m)}{2\sqrt{K_f K_a K_m N \cos(\phi_f + \phi_a)(N^2 J_m + J_L)}}. \qquad (5.25)$$

Using these new parameters, we can write the closed-loop transfer function, Eq. (5.15),

$$\frac{\theta_o(s)}{\theta_i(s)} = \frac{1}{(1/\omega_N)^2 s^2 + (2\zeta/\omega_N)s + 1}. \qquad (5.26)$$

Dividing Eq. (5.18) by J_T and using ω_N and ζ, we can write the characteristic equation as

$$\frac{d^2}{dt^2} + (2\zeta\omega_N)\frac{d}{dt} + \omega_N^2 = 0, \qquad (5.27)$$

from which the two roots are

$$r_1 = -(\zeta - \sqrt{\zeta^2 - 1})\omega_N, \qquad r_2 = -(\zeta + \sqrt{\zeta^2 - 1})\omega_N. \qquad (5.28)$$

Thus the class of the roots depends only on the numerical value of ζ. Each form of the roots yields a different form to the time solution. When $\zeta < 1$, the roots are conjugate complex with negative real parts and the system is said to be *underdamped*. For a suddenly applied input θ_i the corresponding solution is found by substituting the r_1 and r_2 equations into Eq. (5.17) and writing the complex exponentials in terms of their equivalent sine and cosine expressions as follows:

$$\theta_o(t) = \theta_i + e^{-\zeta\omega_N t}[C_1 t \cos \omega_N \sqrt{1 - \zeta^2} + C_2 t \sin \omega_N \sqrt{1 - \zeta^2}]. \qquad (5.29)$$

The coefficients C_1 and C_2 are evaluated by using the initial conditions that

$$\theta_o(0+) = 0, \qquad \dot{\theta}_o(0+) = 0. \qquad (5.30)$$

By substituting these conditions, we find C_1 and C_2 to be

$$C_1 = -\theta_i, \qquad C_2 = -[\zeta/\sqrt{1 - \zeta^2}]\theta_i. \qquad (5.31)$$

The underdamped transient response to a step input can thus be written as

$$\theta_o(t) = \left[1 - e^{-\zeta\omega_N t}\left(\cos \omega_N \sqrt{1 - \zeta^2}\, t + \frac{\zeta}{\sqrt{1 - \zeta^2}} \sin \omega_N \sqrt{1 - \zeta^2}\, t\right)\right]\theta_i, \qquad (5.32)$$

which is often expressed in a more compact form as

$$\theta_o(t) = \left[1 - \frac{e^{-\zeta\omega_N t}}{\sqrt{1 - \zeta^2}} \sin(\omega_N t\sqrt{1 - \zeta^2} + \psi)\right]\theta_i, \qquad (5.33)$$

where

$$\psi = \tan^{-1}\left(\frac{\sqrt{1 - \zeta^2}}{\zeta}\right).$$

Thus for $\zeta < 1$ the solution is seen to be oscillatory due to the sine term, but the oscillations continually diminish in amplitude with time due to the negative exponential, and $\theta_o(t)$ approaches the step input θ_i. The frequency of the oscillation ω_D is constant and equal to

$$\omega_D = \omega_N \sqrt{1 - \zeta^2}, \qquad (5.34)$$

where ω_D is the *damped natural frequency*. Figure 5.12 shows a plot of the ratio of ω_D/ω_N as a function of the damping ratio.

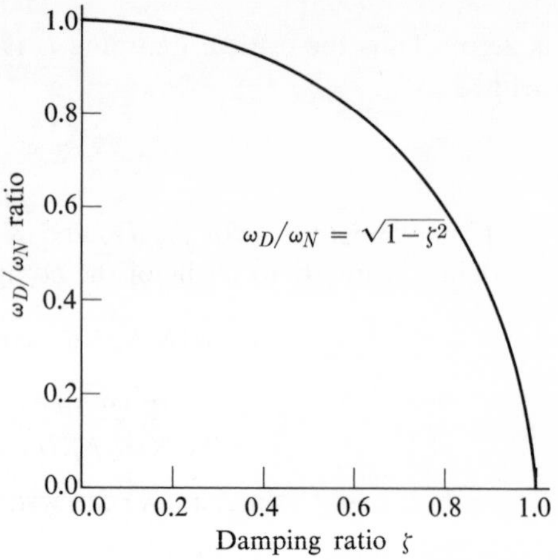

Expressions similar to Eq. (5.33) may be derived for the *critically damped* ($\zeta = 1$)

Fig. 5.12. Ratio of damped natural frequency ω_D to undamped natural frequency ω_N vs. damping ratio ζ for a linear second-order system.

and the *overdamped* ($\zeta > 1$) conditions.   Instead of the step input, one can also use a suddenly applied ramp input with a velocity $\dot{\theta}_i$.   The response $\theta_o(t)$ for each of

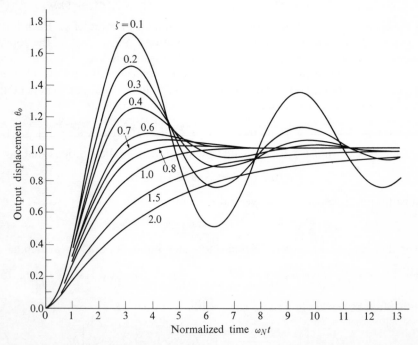

Fig. 5.13. Normalized linear transient response to a unit step input for a linear second-order system.

Table 5.1

OUTPUT RESPONSE EXPRESSIONS FOR SECOND-ORDER SYSTEM

Con-dition	Step input position θ_i
$\zeta < 1$	$\theta_o(t) = \left\{1 - \dfrac{e^{-\zeta\omega_N t}}{\sqrt{1-\zeta^2}} \sin\left[\omega_N t\sqrt{1-\zeta^2} + \psi\right]\right\}\theta_i$
	where $\psi = \tan^{-1}\left[\sqrt{1-\zeta^2}/\zeta\right]$
$\zeta = 1$	$\theta_o(t) = \{1 - e^{-\omega_N t}[1 + \omega_N t]\}\theta_i$
$\zeta > 1$	$\theta_o(t) = \left\{1 - e^{-\zeta\omega_N t}\left[\cosh \omega_N t\sqrt{\zeta^2-1} + \dfrac{\zeta}{\sqrt{\zeta^2-1}}\sinh \omega_N t\sqrt{\zeta^2-1}\right]\right\}\theta_i$

Con-dition	Step input velocity $\dot{\theta}_i$
$\zeta < 1$	$\theta_o(t) = \left\{\left[t - \dfrac{2\zeta}{\omega_N}\right] - \dfrac{e^{-\zeta\omega_N t}}{\omega_N\sqrt{1-\zeta^2}}\sin\left[\omega_N t\sqrt{1-\zeta^2} + \phi\right]\right\}\dot{\theta}_i$
	where $\phi = \tan^{-1}\left[\dfrac{2\zeta\sqrt{1-\zeta^2}}{2\zeta^2-1}\right]$
$\zeta = 1$	$\theta_o(t) = \left\{\left[t - \dfrac{2\zeta}{\omega_N}\right] + \dfrac{2\zeta}{\omega_N}\left[e^{-\omega_N t}\left(1 + \dfrac{\omega_N t}{2}\right)\right]\right\}\dot{\theta}_i$
$\zeta > 1$	$\theta_o(t) = \left\{\left[t - \dfrac{2\zeta}{\omega_N}\right] + \dfrac{2\zeta}{\omega_N}e^{-\zeta\omega_N t}\left[\cosh \omega_N t\sqrt{\zeta^2-1} + \dfrac{2\zeta^2-1}{2\zeta\sqrt{\zeta^2-1}}\sinh \omega_N t\sqrt{\zeta^2-1}\right]\right\}\dot{\theta}_i$

these conditions is summarized in Table 5.1. Figure 5.13 shows the output response to a step input for various values of damping ratio ζ. The time axis has been normalized by multiplying the time by the natural frequency ω_N. We see that the most desirable response (response to values near the step value desired, in the least possible time) requires damping ratios between about 0.4 and 0.8. However, in instrument systems, a linear damping ratio of between 0.6 and 1.0 is often considered more desirable due to the nonlinear effects of saturation and backlash.

As we can see from Fig. 5.13, the amount of overshoot depends only on the damping ratio ζ. For the overdamped and critically damped case ($\zeta \geq 1$), there is no overshoot. For the underdamped case ($\zeta < 1$), the output does overshoot. The time t_p at which the peak overshoot occurs can be found by differentiating Eq. (5.33) with respect to time:

$$\frac{d\theta_o}{dt} = \zeta\omega_N e^{-\zeta\omega_N t} \sin(\omega_N t\sqrt{1-\zeta^2} + \psi)$$
$$- \omega_N t\sqrt{1-\zeta^2}\, e^{-\zeta\omega_N t} \cos(\omega_N t\sqrt{1-\zeta^2} + \psi) = 0. \qquad (5.35)$$

This derivative is zero when $\omega_N t\sqrt{1-\zeta^2} = 0,\ \pi,\ 2\pi,\ \ldots,\ k\pi$. Since the peak overshoot is the first overshoot, it occurs at the first value after zero; therefore

$$t_p = \frac{\pi}{\omega_N\sqrt{1-\zeta^2}}. \qquad (5.36)$$

Substituting t_p back into Eq. (5.32) gives the magnitude of the first overshoot M_p:

$$M_p = (1 + e^{-\zeta\pi/\sqrt{1-\zeta^2}})\theta_i. \qquad (5.37)$$

The overshoot per unit step is shown in Fig. 5.14 as a function of damping ratio.

The time required for the oscillations to decrease to a specified absolute percentage of the final value and thereafter remain less than this value is normally called the *settling time*. The size of the oscillation at any instant of time is never greater than the envelope defined by the exponential term $e^{-\zeta\omega_N t}$, which has the following tabulated values:

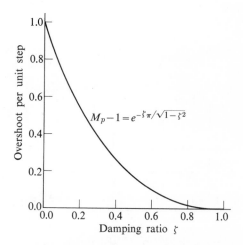

Fig. 5.14. Peak overshoot vs. damping ratio for a linear second-order system.

$\zeta\omega_N t$	$e^{-\zeta\omega_N t}$	Percental of final value
1	0.368	63.2
2	0.135	86.5
3	0.050	95.0
4	0.018	98.2
5	0.007	99.3

Thus, for example, an underdamped system will reach 95% of its final value for a step input when $\zeta\omega_N t = 3$ or when the true time is given by $t = 3/\zeta\omega_N$.

Figure 5.15 shows the normalized response $\omega_N\theta_o(t)/\dot{\theta}_i$ as a function of dimensionless time ($\omega_N t$), based on the equations shown in Table 5.1 for a step-velocity input. It can be seen that a constant positional error or lag exists between the input and output once the servo has reached steady-state conditions. This positional error is ordinarily called the *velocity lag error*, since it is the lag that exists for constant velocity conditions. Using the equations shown in Table 5.1 and letting t take on large values, we see that the magnitude of this error is given by

$$\epsilon_{VL} = (2\zeta/\omega_N)\dot{\theta}_i. \qquad (5.38)$$

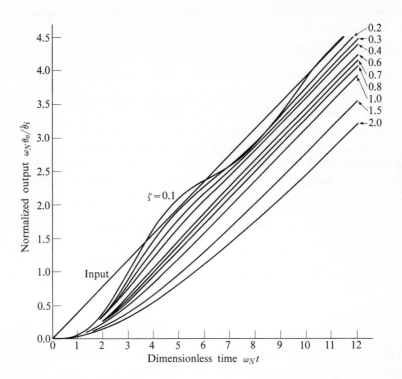

Fig. 5.15. Normalized linear transient response to a step velocity input for a linear second-order system.

Equation (5.38) represents a steady-state condition. Thus, instead of using the transient equation (Table 5.1), we could have derived the velocity lag error directly from the transfer function by using the final value theorem, as follows.

The servo error is expressed by using the Laplace operator as

$$\theta_\epsilon(s) = \theta_i(s) - \theta_o(s). \tag{5.39}$$

Substituting for $\theta_o(s)$, using the transfer function given by Eq. (5.26), and rearranging terms, we obtain

$$\theta_\epsilon(s) = \left[\frac{(1/\omega_N)^2 s + (2\zeta/\omega_N)}{(1/\omega_N)^2 s^2 + (2\zeta/\omega_N)s + 1}\right] s\theta_i(s). \tag{5.40}$$

But, since $s\theta_i(s)$ is simply $\dot{\theta}_i(s)$, by applying a step velocity input $\dot{\theta}_i$ and using the final value theorem

$$\lim_{s \to 0} sF(s) = \lim_{t \to \infty} f(t), \tag{5.41}$$

one has

$$\epsilon_{VL} = \lim_{s \to 0}\left[\frac{(1/\omega_N)^2 s + (2\zeta/\omega_N)}{(1/\omega_N)^2 s^2 + (2\zeta/\omega_N)s + 1}\right]\dot{\theta}_i, \qquad \epsilon_{VL} = (2\zeta/\omega_N)\dot{\theta}_i. \tag{5.42}$$

If Eqs. (5.22) and (5.23) are substituted for ω_N and ζ, respectively, then the velocity lag error can be written as

$$\epsilon_{VL} = f_T \dot{\theta}_i / K_T. \tag{5.43}$$

But since the velocity constant K_V was defined as the ratio K_T/f_T, Eq. (5.43) can be written simply

$$\epsilon_{VL} = \dot{\theta}_i / K_V. \tag{5.44}$$

Thus for the linear system, the velocity lag error is given by the input velocity divided by the velocity constant of the servo. The physical significance of the velocity constant is apparent, and K_V should be kept as high as possible to minimize the lag error.

So far this section has dealt only with the transient response of the reduced or second-order system. This study provides an insight to the general behavior of the system and is adequate for some applications, but it does neglect any effects that might result from finite gear stiffness. As was shown in Section 5.3, this neglect could be most disastrous.

Since with finite gear stiffness the order of the system increases to four, a solution for $\theta_o(t)$ in general terms, using classical methods, becomes most unwieldy. A solution is best generated directly from component parameters by means of a computer. If a digital computer is to be used, the transient solution is most easily obtained if the one fourth-order differential equation is replaced by four first-order differential equations. We can write these four differential equations directly from the system block diagram shown in Fig. 5.2 by writing expressions for θ_o, $\dot{\theta}_o$, θ_m, and $\dot{\theta}_m$ in terms of themselves and the excitation function θ_i. These are:

$$\dot{\theta}_m = \frac{1}{N^2 J_m} \int \{K_f K_a N K_m \cos(\phi_f + \phi_a)\theta_i - K_f K_a N K_m \cos(\phi_f + \phi_a)\theta_o$$
$$- K_a N K_m N K_g \cos(\phi_g + \phi_a)\dot{\theta}_m - N^2 B_m \dot{\theta}_m - K_s \theta_m + K_s \theta_o\} \, dt, \tag{5.45}$$

$$\theta_m = \int \dot{\theta}_m \, dt, \tag{5.46}$$

$$\dot{\theta}_o = \frac{1}{J_L} \int (K_s \theta_m - K_s \theta_o - f_L \dot{\theta}_o) \, dt, \tag{5.47}$$

$$\theta_o = \int \dot{\theta}_o \, dt. \tag{5.48}$$

Taking the derivative of both sides, using the previous definitions for K_T and f_T, and placing the equations in matrix notation, one can write these equations in the following format:

$$\frac{d}{dt}\begin{bmatrix} \dot{\theta}_m \\ \theta_m \\ \dot{\theta}_o \\ \theta_o \end{bmatrix} = \begin{bmatrix} -f_T/N^2 J_m & -K_s/N^2 J_m & 0 & \dfrac{K_s - K_T}{N^2 J_m} \\ 1 & 0 & 0 & 0 \\ 0 & K_s/J_L & -f_L & -K_s/J_L \\ 0 & 0 & 1 & 0 \end{bmatrix}\begin{bmatrix} \dot{\theta}_m \\ \theta_m \\ \dot{\theta}_o \\ \theta_o \end{bmatrix} + \begin{bmatrix} \dfrac{K_T}{N^2 J_m} \\ 0 \\ 0 \\ 0 \end{bmatrix} \theta_i. \tag{5.49}$$

The above set of equations is called the *state model* of the system, whose general form is

$$\frac{d}{dt}(\boldsymbol{\theta}) = (\boldsymbol{\alpha})(\boldsymbol{\theta}) + (\boldsymbol{\beta})\theta_i, \tag{5.50}$$

where $(\boldsymbol{\theta})$ is defined as the state vector and $(\boldsymbol{\alpha})$ and $(\boldsymbol{\beta})$ are coefficient matrices. It is important to note that each component of the state vector represents the output of an integrator in Fig. 5.2. Thus, if one knows the values for $[\boldsymbol{\theta}(t)]$, the state of the system is completely defined, since all other points are related to the state vector by algebraic equations. The complete problem solution is obtainable by simultaneously solving the four first-order differential equations. Since the system as described so far is linear, the solution to the Eqs. (5.49) and (5.50) is given by the matrix equation

$$(\boldsymbol{\theta}(t)) = e^{(\boldsymbol{\alpha})t}\boldsymbol{\theta}(0) + \int_o^t e^{(\boldsymbol{\alpha})(t-\tau)}(\boldsymbol{\beta})\theta_i(\tau)\,d\tau, \tag{5.51}$$

where $e^{(\boldsymbol{\alpha})t}$ is called the *transition matrix* and is a matrix function defined by the infinite series

$$e^{(\boldsymbol{\alpha})t} = (\mathbf{u}) + (\boldsymbol{\alpha})t + (\boldsymbol{\alpha})^2\frac{t^2}{2!} + \cdots + (\boldsymbol{\alpha})^n\frac{t^n}{n!} + \cdots, \tag{5.52}$$

where $(\mathbf{u})$ is the unit matrix.

One can program Eq. (5.51) on a digital computer using either a finite series approximation for the series definition for $e^{(\boldsymbol{\alpha})t}$ or the Sylvester expansion theorem:

$$e^{(\boldsymbol{\alpha})t} = \sum_{j=1}^n \frac{(\boldsymbol{\alpha} - \lambda_1\mathbf{u})\cdots(\boldsymbol{\alpha} - \lambda_{j-1}\mathbf{u})(\boldsymbol{\alpha} - \lambda_{j+1}\mathbf{u})\cdots(\boldsymbol{\alpha} - \lambda_n\mathbf{u})e^{\lambda_j t}}{(\lambda_j - \lambda_1)\cdots(\lambda_j - \lambda_{j-1})(\lambda_j - \lambda_{j+1})\cdots(\lambda_j - \lambda_n)}, \tag{5.53}$$

where the λ's are the eigenvalues of the coefficient matrix $\boldsymbol{\alpha}$, which are the roots of the characteristic equation of the system. They may be determined directly by solving for the values of λ for which the determinant of $(\lambda\mathbf{u} - \boldsymbol{\alpha})$ is equal to zero.

It is interesting to note that, using the state model approach, one not only obtains the output response $\theta_o(t)$, but its derivative, the output velocity, as well as motor response and velocity. Because of this and the convenience of using the state-model approach in digital computer programming, it is often desirable to treat the second-order system in the same manner. This will become readily apparent when the ease of adding nonlinearities is demonstrated in Chapter 7. It will suffice for now to simply list the corresponding state model for the second-order system as

$$\frac{d}{dt}\begin{bmatrix}\dot{\theta}_o \\ \theta_o\end{bmatrix} = \begin{bmatrix}-f_T/J_T & -K_T/J_T \\ 1 & 0\end{bmatrix}\begin{bmatrix}\dot{\theta}_o \\ \theta_o\end{bmatrix} + \begin{bmatrix}K_T/J_T \\ 0\end{bmatrix}\theta_i, \tag{5.54}$$

which is often written in the form

$$\frac{d}{dt}\begin{bmatrix}\dot{\theta}_o \\ \theta_o\end{bmatrix} = \begin{bmatrix}-2\zeta\omega_N & -\omega_N^2 \\ 1 & 0\end{bmatrix}\begin{bmatrix}\dot{\theta}_o \\ \theta_o\end{bmatrix} + \begin{bmatrix}\omega_N^2 \\ 0\end{bmatrix}\theta_i. \tag{5.55}$$

An alternative solution to the transient response problem is obtained by means of an analog computer. The analog computer diagram for the fourth-order system follows directly from Fig. 5.2 and is shown in Fig. 5.16. The computer diagram as

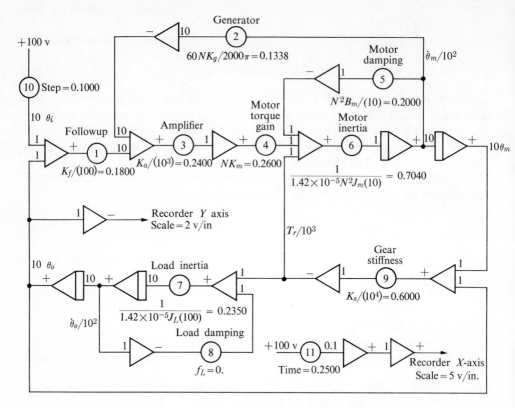

Fig. 5.16. Analog computer diagram for linear fourth-order system.

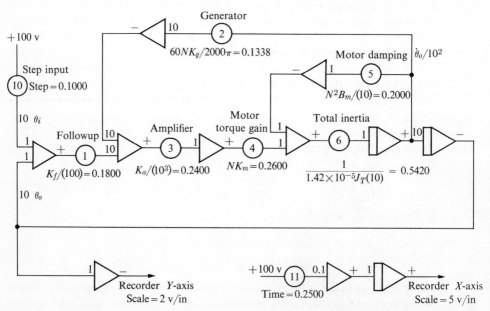

Fig. 5.17. Analog computer diagram for linear second-order system.

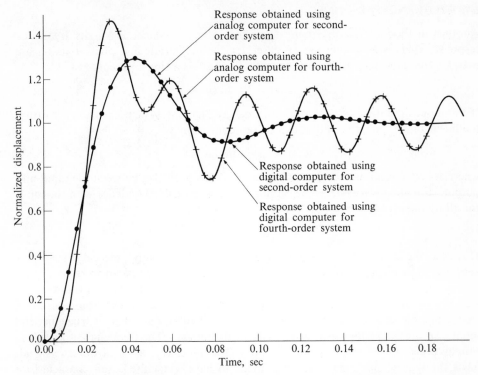

Fig. 5.18. Comparison of response curves obtained for second- and fourth-order system using both digital and analog computers.

shown is scaled for the following component parameters:

$$K_f = 18 \text{ v/rad}, \qquad K_a = 240 \text{ v/v},$$
$$K_g = 0.14 \text{ v/1000 rpm}, \qquad K_m = 0.0026 \text{ oz-in/v},$$
$$B_m = 0.0002 \text{ oz-in/rad/sec}, \qquad J_m = 1.0 \text{ gm-cm}^2,$$
$$J_L = 3000 \text{ gm-cm}^2, \qquad K_s = 6000 \text{ oz-in/rad}, \qquad N = 100.$$

The calculations required for each potentiometer setting are shown directly on the schematic diagram. The scale factor required to provide each potentiometer setting with a value less than unity is shown in parentheses, and any unit conversion factors are shown without parentheses. The problem is scaled to run at a speed that is $\frac{1}{100}$ of the speed of the actual servo. This is accomplished by considering each integrator to have an effective gain of 100 during the problem scaling.

The analog computer diagram corresponding to the reduced or second-order system is shown as Fig. 5.17. It is scaled for the same parameters as above except that by its nature the gear train stiffness is assumed to be infinite.

Figure 5.18 shows plots of $\theta_o(t)$ obtained from each analog simulation along with the corresponding solutions from the digital computer. The correlation between the two approaches and the effect of the finite gear train stiffness is readily apparent.

5.7. FREQUENCY RESPONSE

Another method of characterizing the behavior of a system is via its frequency response. This is accomplished by observing the magnitude and phase relationship between the input and the output when the input θ_i is a sinusoid represented by

$$\theta_i(t) = A \sin \omega t. \tag{5.56}$$

If the input amplitude A is sufficiently small so that the system excursion is within the linear range, then the output can be represented by

$$\theta_o(t) = B \sin (\omega t + \psi), \tag{5.57}$$

where B is the amplitude of the output and ψ is the phase lag between the input and output. For the ideal system, the output would be in correspondence with the input for all frequencies $0 \le \omega \le \infty$; thus

$$A = B, \quad \psi = 0.$$

However, the energy storage and dissipation properties of any physical system prevent it from achieving this condition. The capability of any system to respond uniformly to all frequencies is equivalent to that required to reproduce an instantaneous step disturbance. Fortunately, such performance is neither possible nor desirable since some filtering of the actual input signal is advantageous. This is true since the input $\theta_i(t)$ always contains spurious signals called *noise*. The frequency of the noise usually occurs in the spectrum slightly above the upper frequency of the true signal. Thus the typical instrument system is made to have a definite cutoff characteristic above a limiting frequency.

Let us now consider the frequency response of the reduced system. The corresponding closed-loop transfer function was shown previously to be

$$\frac{\theta_o(s)}{\theta_i(s)} = \frac{1}{(1/\omega_N)^2 s^2 + (2\zeta/\omega_N)s + 1}. \tag{5.58}$$

The frequency response is obtained by substituting $j\omega$ in place of s:

$$\frac{\theta_o}{\theta_i} (j\omega) = \frac{1}{[1 - (\omega/\omega_N)^2] + j(2\zeta\omega/\omega_N)}. \tag{5.59}$$

If a new dimensionless frequency variable u is defined as

$$u = \omega/\omega_N, \tag{5.60}$$

then Eq. (5.60) can be written as

$$\frac{\theta_o}{\theta_i} (ju) = \frac{1}{(1 - u^2) + j(2\zeta u)}. \tag{5.61}$$

The magnitude (M) and phase (ψ) relationships are thus given by

$$M = \frac{\theta_o}{\theta_i} (ju) = \frac{1}{\sqrt{(1 - u^2)^2 + (2\zeta u)^2}}, \tag{5.62}$$

$$\psi = -\tan^{-1} [2\zeta u/(1 - u^2)]. \tag{5.63}$$

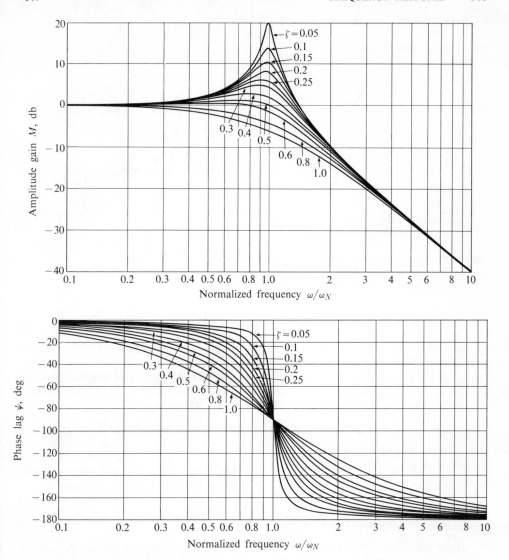

Fig. 5.19. Normalized linear frequency response for a second-order system.

Figure 5.19 shows the linear frequency response of the servo for various values of damping ratio. The amplitude response is obtained by taking the output magnitude $\theta_o(u)$ divided by the input magnitude $\theta_i(u)$ and converting the ratio to decibels:

$$\text{Gain (db)} = 20 \log \left| \frac{\theta_o}{\theta_i} (j u) \right|. \tag{5.64}$$

The phase angle is the angle by which the output differs from the input command and is given by ψ in Eq. (5.63).

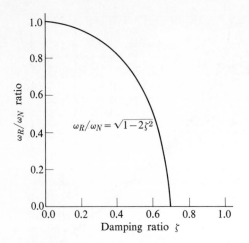

Fig. 5.20. Ratio of resonant frequency ω_R to undamped natural frequency ω_N vs. damping ratio ζ for a linear second-order system.

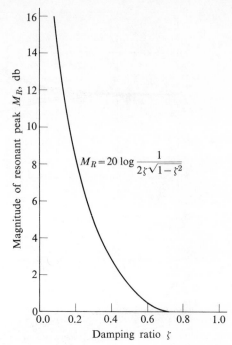

Fig. 5.21. Magnitude of resonant peak M_R vs. damping ratio ζ for a linear second-order system.

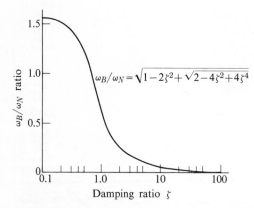

Fig. 5.22. Ratio of bandwidth frequency ω_B to undamped natural frequency ω_N vs. damping ratio ζ for a linear second-order system.

It is seen that for low input frequencies, the output equals the input (gain of unity or zero decibels; phase lag of zero degrees), since the servo can follow the input command exactly. At high frequencies the output lags behind in phase and is attenuated in amplitude. For damping ratios smaller than 0.707, the output peaks (reaches greater values than the input command) due to resonance before it attenuates. The frequency at which the peak occurs can be found by differentiating Eq. (5.62) with respect to u and setting it equal to zero:

$$\frac{dM}{du} = -\frac{4u^3 - 4u + 8\zeta^2 u}{2(u^4 + 1 - 2u^2 + 4\zeta^2 u^2)^{3/2}} = 0. \tag{5.65}$$

The derivative vanishes when $4u^3 - 4u + 8\zeta^2 u = 0$ or when $u = \sqrt{1 - 2\zeta^2}$.

Since $u = \omega/\omega_N$, the frequency at which peak resonance occurs is given by

$$\omega_R = \omega_N\sqrt{1 - 2\zeta^2}. \tag{5.66}$$

A plot of the ratio ω_R/ω_N is shown as a function of damping ratio in Fig. 5.20.

The magnitude of the resonant peak M_R is found by substituting $u = \sqrt{1 - 2\zeta^2}$ into Eq. (5.62). The corresponding value for M is M_R and is given by

$$M_R = \frac{1}{2\zeta\sqrt{1 - \zeta^2}}. \tag{5.67}$$

A plot of M_R in decibels vs. ζ is given in Fig. 5.21.

The bandwidth ω_B of the system is defined as the maximum frequency at which the closed-loop gain is 3 db below the gain value at zero frequency. Substituting this value into Eq. (5.62) along with the corresponding value of $u = \omega_B/\omega_N$, we obtain the following equation:

$$-3 = 40 \log \omega_N - 10 \log [(\omega_N^2 - \omega_B^2)^2 + (2\zeta\omega_B\omega_N)^2]. \tag{5.68}$$

Solving this equation for the bandwidth frequency ω_B, we obtain:

$$\omega_B = \omega_N\sqrt{1 - 2\zeta^2 + \sqrt{2 - 4\zeta^2 + 4\zeta^4}}. \tag{5.69}$$

A plot of the ratio of ω_B/ω_N is shown as a function of ζ in Fig. 5.22.

The closed-loop transfer function for the fourth-order system representation was shown in Section 5.2 to be

$$\frac{\theta_L(s)}{\theta_i(s)} = \left[\left(\frac{N^2 J_m J_L}{K_T K_s}\right)s^4 + \left(\frac{f_T J_L + f_L N^2 J_m}{K_T K_s}\right)s^3 \right.$$
$$\left. + \left(\frac{f_T f_L}{K_T K_s} + \frac{J_T}{K_T}\right)s^2 + \left(\frac{f_T + f_L}{K_T}\right)s + 1\right]^{-1} \tag{5.70}$$

The corresponding closed-loop frequency response characteristics are found, as before, by substituting $j\omega$ for s and separating real and imaginary parts. That is,

$$\frac{\theta_L}{\theta_i}(j\omega) = \left[\left(\frac{N^2 J_m J_L \omega^4}{K_T K_s} - \frac{f_T f_L \omega^2}{K_T K_s} - \frac{J_T \omega^2}{K_T} + 1\right)\right.$$
$$\left. + j\left(\frac{(f_T + f_L)\omega}{K_T} - \frac{(f_T J_L + f_L N^2 J_m)\omega^3}{K_T K_s}\right)\right]^{-1} \tag{5.71}$$

The resulting values for gain and phase shift are thus given by

$$M = \left[\sqrt{\left(\frac{N^2 J_m J_L \omega^4}{K_T K_s} - \frac{f_T f_L \omega^2}{K_T K_s} - \frac{J_T \omega^2}{K_T} + 1\right)^2} \right.$$
$$\left. + \left(\frac{(f_T + f_L)\omega}{K_T} - \frac{(f_T J_L + f_L N^2 J_m)\omega^3}{K_T K_s}\right)^2\right]^{-1}, \tag{5.72}$$

$$\psi = -\tan^{-1}\left[\frac{(f_T + f_L)\omega/K_T - (f_T J_L + f_L N^2 J_m)\omega^3/K_T K_S}{N^2 J_m J_L \omega^4/K_T K_S - f_T f_L \omega^2/K_T K_S - J_T \omega^2/K_T + 1}\right]. \tag{5.73}$$

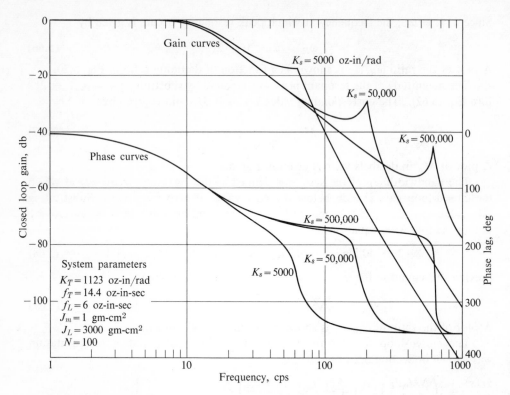

Fig. 5.23. Closed-loop frequency response of fourth-order system for various values of gear train stiffness.

Figure 5.23 shows a plot of the closed-loop frequency response obtained from typical parameter values. Curves are shown for various values of gear train stiffness to demonstrate its effect upon the response. Note that as K_s becomes large, the response approaches that of the second-order system.

5.8. DESIGN USING A VISCOUS DAMPER

The viscous damper, as described in Section 4.9, sometimes can be used to obtain system stability in place of the damping generator. The addition of a viscous damper simply lowers the motor "no-load speed." The additional damping is thereby achieved by the corresponding increase in B_m. Thus the mathematical descriptions generated in the previous sections for the more general motor generator servo still apply. The generator parameters (for example, K_g, E_g, ϕ_g) are simply set to zero, and the motor no-load speed ($\dot{\theta}_m$) and damping (B_m) terms are altered to include the effect of the viscous damper. Once these alterations are accomplished, all the same design techniques can be applied. However, if we use the viscous damper approach, we must pay special attention to parameter selection to obtain a satisfactory design. This becomes apparent if we study the general equation for the linear damping ratio developed in Section 5.6:

$$\zeta = \frac{N^2[K_g K_a K_m \cos(\phi_g + \phi_a) + B_m]}{2\sqrt{K_f K_a K_m N \cos(\phi_f + \phi_a)(N^2 J_m + J_L)}}. \tag{5.74}$$

A typical instrument servo, which uses a damping generator, has the gain product $K_g K_a K_m \cos(\phi_g + \phi_a)$ much greater than B_m and nearly all the damping is obtained from the generator. At first glance, one might say that B_m should be increased by the amount required to keep the numerator unchanged when the generator term is dropped. This, however, is usually impractical, because (1) the space requirement for the required damper becomes excessive, and (2) the servo slew capability becomes too low [damping created by the viscous damper lowers $\dot{\theta}_m$ and the slew speed of the servo given by Eq. (3.44)]. On the other hand, adding generator damping has no effect on $\dot{\theta}_m$ and thus no effect on the maximum speed capabilities of the system. Therefore, if the generator is to be removed, a significant change in design approach is required. We can best determine the changes required by considering what happens when the generator is removed.

The damping ratio with the generator gain set to zero is given by the equation

$$\zeta = \frac{N^2 B_m}{2\sqrt{K_f K_a K_m N \cos(\phi_f + \phi_g)(N^2 J_m + J_L)}}. \tag{5.75}$$

The rate of increase of ζ with respect to the gear ratio N is thus affected by the relationship between $N^2 J_m$ and J_L. For discussion purposes, let us consider the more typical case where the reflected motor inertia $N^2 J_m$ is large compared to the load inertia J_L. Under this assumption, the damping ratio equation becomes

$$\zeta = \frac{B_m}{2\sqrt{K_f K_a K_m \cos(\phi_f + \phi_a) J_m}} \sqrt{N}. \tag{5.76}$$

Thus to maintain an adequate damping ratio without a generator, one must

1) minimize the gains $K_f K_a$ and K_m as well as the motor inertia J_m, and

2) maximize the gear ratio N and the motor damping coefficient B_m.

There is, however, some interaction between the motor damping coefficient and the maximum gear ratio. The motor damping coefficient B_m is defined as the inverse slope of the speed-torque curve, which may be approximated by the relationship

$$B_m = T_s / \dot{\theta}_m, \tag{5.77}$$

and the followup rate of the servo $\dot{\theta}_L$, as derived in Section 3.8, is given by the equation

$$\theta_L = \dot{\theta}_m (1 - T_f / N T_s) / N. \tag{5.78}$$

Let us assume for comparison purposes only that the load friction T_f is small compared to the reflected stall torque NT_s. Under this condition, the maximum possible gear ratio that could be used is

$$N = \dot{\theta}_m / \dot{\theta}_L. \tag{5.79}$$

Substituting Eqs. (5.77) and (5.79) into Eq. (5.76), we see that the equation for damping ratio (considering N to be a maximum) becomes

$$\zeta = \frac{T_s}{2\sqrt{K_f K_a K_m \cos\,(\phi_f + \phi_a) J_m \dot{\theta}_m \dot{\theta}_L}}. \tag{5.80}$$

Therefore to maximize the amount of damping one must proceed as follows.

1) Maintain a high stall torque T_s. (Since the damping ratio is directly proportional to stall torque, it has the most significant influence upon the design.)

2) Maintain a low product gain $K_f K_a K_m$. This, of course, is limited by the accuracy requirements.

3) Maintain a low motor inertia J_m and no-load speed $\dot{\theta}_m$. Actually the optimum motor is one with a maximum value of the "damping performance factor:"

$$\mathrm{DPF} = T_s / \sqrt{J_m \dot{\theta}_m}. \tag{5.81}$$

The gain K_m is quite arbitrary since the $K_f K_a$ product compensates for any variations in gain.

4) Maintain a minimum followup rate $\dot{\theta}_L$. In addition, the gear ratio must be maximum since this is required by Eq. (5.80).

The preceding discussion and Eq. (5.80) show that the viscous damped motor is best suited for applications which provide for a low followup rate. Thus $\dot{\theta}_L$ can be minimized by using the maximum possible gear ratio. In fact, for some applications, if the followup rate requirement is small enough, one can obtain a satisfactory design by using only the inherent damping of the motor. Thus the viscous damper, as well as the generator, can be eliminated. This approach does have additional merit since J_m can be made an absolute minimum.

5.9. DESIGN USING AN INERTIAL DAMPER

The inertial damper was described as a component in Section 4.8. Since the inertial damper is usually connected to the motor in one integral assembly, the state model diagram and transfer function were derived for the combined motor and damper. Unlike the viscous damper described in the previous section, an inertial damper does change the characteristic equations that describe the system. Therefore, the design approach is considerably different.

The open-loop transfer function for the basic system is obtained by including the followup, amplifier, gear ratio, and load effects along with the transfer function derived as Eq. (4.20). This results in the open-loop transfer function for the total system:

$$\frac{\theta_o(s)}{\theta_\epsilon(s)} = \frac{K_f K_a K_m N \cos(\phi_f + \phi_a)(\tau_d s + 1)/N^2 B_m}{s[(\tau_m \tau_d)s + (\tau_m + \tau_d + \tau_{md})s + 1]}, \qquad (5.82)$$

where

$$\tau_d = J_d/B_d, \qquad \tau_{md} = J_d/B_m, \qquad \tau_m = J_T/N^2 B_m,$$

$$J_d = \text{flywheel inertia}, \qquad B_d = \text{flywheel coupling coefficient}.$$

Using the relationship for the system velocity constant

$$K_V = \frac{K_f K_a K_m N \cos(\phi_f + \phi_a)}{N^2 B_m}, \qquad (5.83)$$

we obtain the transfer function for the closed loop from Eq. (5.82):

$$\frac{\theta_o(s)}{\theta_i(s)} = \frac{\tau_d s + 1}{(\tau_m \tau_d/K_V)s^3 + [(\tau_m + \tau_d + \tau_{md})/K_V]s^2 + (\tau_d + 1/K_V)s + 1}. \qquad (5.84)$$

From this closed-loop transfer function, we see that the basic inertially damped system is of third order. Thus the damping ratio ζ which was derived for the second-order system has no meaning, and one has to resort to the system phase margin as a measure of stability. Although the phase margin can be most readily calculated by means of a subroutine to automatically iterate the frequency in Eq. (5.82) for unity gain, it is most easily visualized from the open-loop frequency response plot. Let us consider the following set of typical component parameters to construct such a plot:

$$K_f = 18 \text{ v/rad}, \qquad K_a = 240 \text{ v/v},$$

$$K_m = 0.0026 \text{ oz-in/v}, \qquad B_m = 0.00012 \text{ oz-in/rad/sec},$$

$$J_m = 1.0 \text{ gm-cm}^2 = 1.42 \times 10^{-5} \text{ (oz-in)/(rad/sec}^2),$$

$$J_L = 3000 \text{ gm-cm}^2 = 0.0426 \text{ (oz-in)/(rad/sec}^2),$$

$$N = 100, \qquad B_d = 0.0015 \text{ (oz-in)/(rad/sec)},$$

$$J_d = 5 \text{ gm-cm}^2 = 7.10 \times 10^{-5} \text{ (oz-in)/(rad/sec}^2),$$

$$\phi_f = 0 \text{ deg}, \qquad \phi_a = 0 \text{ deg}.$$

From these we can calculate the component time constant and break frequencies as follows:

$$\tau_d = J_d/B_d = (7.10 \times 10^{-5})/0.0015 = 0.0474 \text{ sec},$$

$$\omega_d = 1/\tau_d = 21.1 \text{ rad/sec} = 3.36 \text{ cps},$$

$$\tau_m = J_T/N^2 B_m = 0.1846/[(100)^2(0.00012)] = 0.1540 \text{ sec},$$

$$\omega_m = 1/\tau_m = 6.5 \text{ rad/sec} = 1.035 \text{ cps},$$

$$\tau_{md} = J_d/B_m = (7.10 \times 10^{-5})/0.00012 = 0.591 \text{ sec},$$

$$\omega_{md} = 1/\tau_{md} = 169 \text{ rad/sec} = 27.0 \text{ cps}.$$

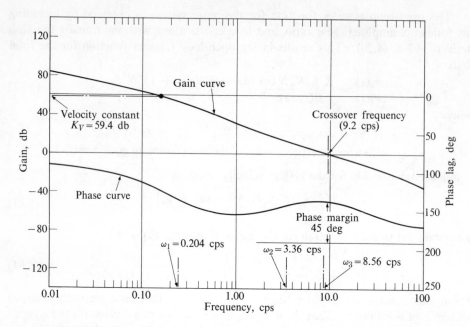

Fig. 5.24. Open-loop frequency response of inertially damped servo.

Substituting the above values for the component time constants, along with the system velocity constant, which is

$$K_V = \frac{(18)(240)(0.0026)(100)}{(100)^2(0.00012)} = 936 \text{ sec}^{-1} = 59.4 \text{ db},$$

into Eq. (5.82), one obtains

$$\frac{\theta_o(s)}{\theta_\epsilon(s)} = \frac{936(0.0474s + 1)}{s(0.0073s^2 + 0.7924s + 1)}. \qquad (5.85)$$

Figure 5.24 shows a frequency response plot of this function. The gain curve has a value equal to K_V at a frequency of 1 rad/sec (0.159 cps). It decreases with increasing frequency by 20 db/decade due to the factored s-term in the denominator until it is influenced by the additional system break frequencies. These frequencies can be calculated exactly by factoring the denominator of Eq. (5.85) into two time constants, yielding

$$\frac{\theta_o(s)}{\theta_\epsilon(s)} = \frac{K_V(\tau_2 s + 1)}{s(\tau_1 s + 1)(\tau_3 s + 1)} = \frac{936(0.0474s + 1)}{s(0.783s + 1)(0.0186s + 1)}. \qquad (5.86)$$

The corresponding break frequencies are then summarized as

$$\omega_1 = 1/\tau_1 = 1.278 \text{ rad/sec} = 0.204 \text{ cps},$$
$$\omega_2 = 1/\tau_2 = 21.1 \text{ rad/sec} = 3.36 \text{ cps},$$
$$\omega_3 = 1/\tau_3 = 53.8 \text{ rad/sec} = 8.56 \text{ cps}.$$

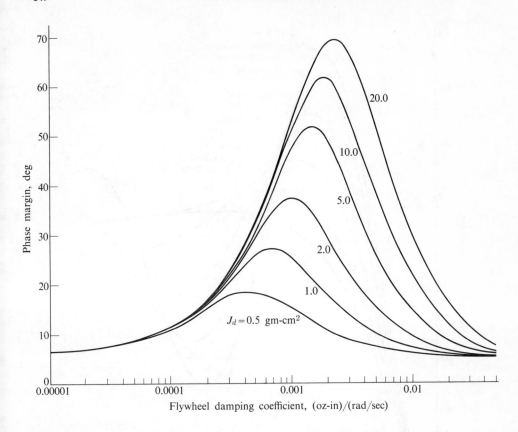

Fig. 5.25. Inertially damped servo phase margin vs. flywheel damping for various values, of flywheel inertia.

These frequencies are noted on Fig. 5.24. The function of the ω_1-term is to lower the gain crossover frequency, and the lead term ω_2 pulls the phase curve up to minimize the phase shift at crossover. This in turn increases the system phase margin, which is defined as 180 deg minus the phase lag at zero gain. The phase margin must be positive for the linear system to be stable. The case in Fig. 5.24 is stable since the phase margin is a positive 45 deg.

We can maximize the phase margin for any given design by optimally positioning the corner frequencies ω_1, ω_2, and ω_3 or, more directly, by properly selecting the values for the damper inertia J_d and coupling coefficient B_d. Figure 5.25 demonstrates how this can be accomplished by showing a plot of system phase margin vs. the flywheel coupling coefficient for various values of damper inertia. We see from the figure that the larger the value of J_d the larger the phase margin, but for each value of J_d there is one value of B_d that maximizes the phase margin. For the particular value of $J_d = 5.0$ gm-cm^2 selected, the optimum value of B_d is seen to be 0.0015 oz-in-sec, which also corresponds to the value used in Fig. 5.24.

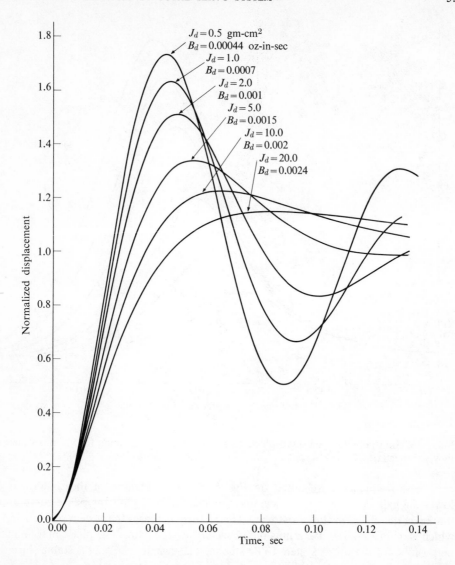

Fig. 5.26. Inertially damped servo step response for various values of flywheel inertia and flywheel viscous coupling selected for optimum phase margin.

The correlation between phase margin and adequate damping of the system transient response is illustrated in Fig. 5.26, which shows the response of the inertially damped servo to a unit step input for various values of flywheel inertia and viscous coupling coefficient. Each combination of parameters shown corresponds to the peaks in the previous phase margin curves. Thus Fig. 5.26 represents the response that can be obtained with the system optimally stabilized for each value of J_d. Cross correlating this response with that shown in Fig. 5.25, we see that a phase margin of

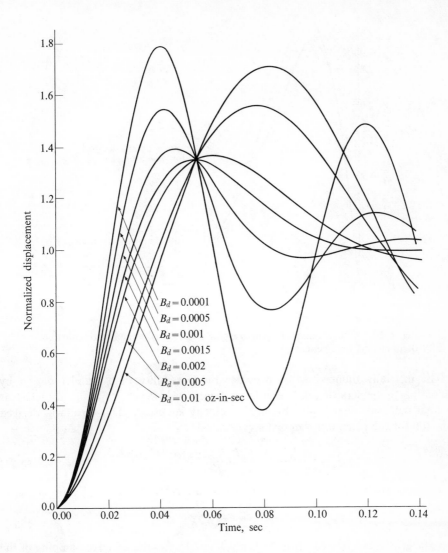

Fig. 5.27. Inertially damped servo step response for constant flywheel inertia and various values of flywheel viscous coupling coefficient.

at least 40 deg must exist to provide what is normally considered good transient behavior.

Figure 5.27 demonstrates the importance of operating at the point of maximum phase margin. Step response curves are shown for J_d held constant at 5.0 gm-cm^2 and B_d varied above and below the optimum value of 0.0015 oz-in-sec. The response becomes very oscillatory as the viscous coupling coefficient is varied in either direction from this optimum value.

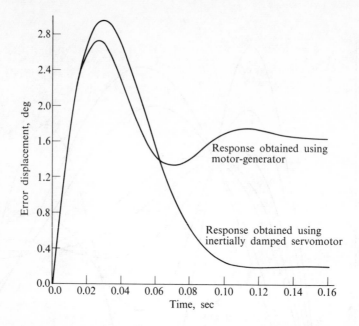

Fig. 5.28. Comparison of ramp response curves obtained with inertial damper and with generator.

The inertially damped servo provides the possibility of a simpler design by eliminating the generator and summing network. However, its main attraction is the great reduction that is possible in the velocity lag error. This error was derived on p. 100 for the generator-damped servo as follows:

$$\epsilon_{VL} = \frac{N^2[B_m + K_gK_aK_m \cos(\phi_g + \phi_a)]\dot{\theta}_i}{K_T}. \tag{5.87}$$

It can be shown that the corresponding equation for the inertially damped servo is simply

$$\epsilon_{VL} = N^2 B_m \dot{\theta}_i / K_T. \tag{5.88}$$

Since the generator often contributes as much as 10 times the effective damping of the motor, we see that for the same value of system torque constant, a greatly reduced value of velocity lag is possible. This is illustrated by Fig. 5.28, which shows the error response $(\theta_o - \theta_i)$ for a typical inertially damped system as well as for a system using a generator. The curves are shown for a 90 deg/sec input signal. Each servo has essentially the same component parameters, namely torque constant K_T and inertia J_T, which are listed on pp. 87 and 111. Although the transient peaks are essentially the same, it is seen that the steady-state error is greatly reduced for the inertially damped case. On the other hand, Fig. 5.29 demonstrates that the settling time for a step input has remained about the same. Thus one has obtained this reduced steady-state error for velocity inputs without any loss in transient capability.

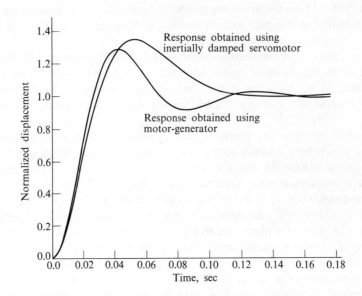

Fig. 5.29. Comparison of step response curves obtained with inertial damper and with generator.

The main limitation of the inertially damped servo is that the physical size of the inertial damper element becomes excessive if one tries to adequately stabilize a load with too high an inertia value.

5.10. SUMMARY

In this chapter, a linear mathematical model representing the total system was generated. First we obtained a state model diagram of the system by combining the previously derived expressions for the individual components. Then we reduced this block diagram to a form which would readily yield the system transfer functions.

Using the characteristic equation for the fourth-order system, we showed that a lower bound exists on the gear train stiffness for the linear system to be stable. For the case where the load damping and friction are zero, this lower bound is simply the system torque constant. An equation was also derived which demonstrated that gear stiffness could be less than the torque constant when damping was present at the load. It was demonstrated that the instrument servo becomes equivalent to the conventional second-order system for high values of gear stiffness. Tests were then described for measuring the system torque constant and damping coefficient.

The response equations of the second-order system to both step and ramp inputs were obtained. This was accomplished by first defining the natural frequency and damping ratio of the system and then solving the characteristic equation in terms of these parameters. From the resulting response equations, expressions were derived for such quantities as damped natural frequency, time and magnitude of the first overshoot, settling time, and velocity lag.

Once the response of the second-order system was thoroughly understood, the state model of the fourth-order system was derived. Using this model, we obtained transient solutions on both the digital and analog computer. We compared the second- and fourth-order response curves, thereby illustrating the effect of finite gear stiffness.

The steady-state frequency response characteristics were obtained by replacing s by $j\omega$ in the closed-loop transfer function of the system. Equations were then generated for system bandwidth and the frequency and magnitude of peak resonance. Next, frequency response plots were obtained, and it was demonstrated that an additional resonance occurs in the system as a result of gear train stiffness.

Analytical expressions were derived to show how a viscous damped servomotor could be used in place of a motor-generator. This was accomplished by treating the viscous damped servo as a special case of the previously derived theory. Relationships maximizing the damping ratio were then derived with the generator gain set to zero.

The incorporation of an inertially damped servomotor in a design was described. Since the inertial damper increased by one the order of the system characteristic equation and state model, the damping ratio expression for the second-order system no longer applied. Therefore, phase margin was used as a measure of system stability. It was shown that we should, in general, select as large a value of the inertia of the damper unit as possible. Once this is accomplished, there is only one value of viscous coupling coefficient that should be used, the value that maximizes the system phase margin. Comparisons were made between the response obtained using an inertial damper and that obtained by means of the more conventional generator approach. The main advantage of the inertial approach was seen to be the reduced steady-state error for constant-velocity inputs.

PROBLEMS

5.1. Sketch the damping ratio ζ as a function of the amplifier gain for a motor-generator servo. Derive an equation for the amplifier gain, in terms of the other system parameters, that yields the minimum damping ratio. Show how the original curve would be modified if the generator signal were disconnected.

*5.2. It is desired to design an instrument servo without a damping generator. To maximize the damping ratio, would you select the following parameters to be as high or low as possible? Why?

   a) Amplifier gain.
   b) Gear ratio.
   c) Motor inertia.

*5.3. The following mean parameter values of components have been established as a possible design configuration:

K_f = 2.441 v/rad,	T_s = 0.07725 oz-in,
ϕ_f = 13.46 deg,	$\dot{\theta}_m$ = 6200 rpm,
K_g = 0.03446 v/1000 rpm,	K_m = 0.002145 oz-in/v,
E_g = 2.088 mv,	B_m = 0.0002125 oz-in-sec,
ϕ_g = 18.63 deg,	E_c(start) = 1.5 v,
θ_f = 7.5 min,	J_m = 0.78 gm-cm^2,
K_a = 1980 v/v,	J_L = 939.9 gm-cm^2,
E_a = 4.0 v,	T_f = 0.55 oz-in,
ϕ_a = 9.0 deg.	N = 95.92,
	$\dot{\theta}_{in}$ = 300 deg/sec.

Calculate the following corresponding mean parameter values of the system:

a) total inertia (gm-cm^2),
b) torque constant (oz-in/rad),
c) total damping coefficient (oz-in-sec),
d) natural frequency (cps),
e) damping ratio,
f) followup rate (deg/sec),
g) bandwidth (cps).

5.4. Consider a typical servo design where the generator is supplying nearly all the damping and the load inertia is small.

a) How does the damping ratio vary with amplifier gain?
b) What change in damping ratio would result if the amplifier gain were increased by a factor of 2?
c) How does the damping ratio vary with gear ratio?

5.5. Sketch the damping ratio ζ as a function of the gear ratio for a motor-generator servo. What is the limit of ζ as N approaches infinity?

5.6. Starting from Fig. 5.4, show the derivation of Eqs. (5.2) and (5.3).

5.7. Derive the step response equation shown in Table 5.1 for $\zeta > 1$.

*5.8. Given a second-order system with ζ = 1.5 and ω_N = 15 cps. What is the time required for the system to reach 90% of a given step input?

5.9. Verify analytically that the J_d- and B_d-terms do not affect the velocity lag error of an inertially damped servo.

BIBLIOGRAPHY

BROWN, G., and D. CAMPBELL, *Principles of Servomechanisms*, Wiley, 1953.

CHESTNUT, H., and R. MAYER, *Servomechanism and Regulating System Design*, 2nd Ed., Wiley, 1959, Volume 1.

GILLE, J., M. PELEGRIN, and P. DECAULNE, *Feedback Control Systems Analysis, Synthesis, and Design*, McGraw-Hill, 1959.

IVERY, K., *AC Carrier Control Systems*, Wiley, 1964.

KOENIG, H. E., and W. A. BLACKWELL, *Electromechanical System Theory*, McGraw-Hill, 1961.

REKOFF, JR., M., "State-Variable Techniques for Control Systems," *Electro-Technology* (May 1964).

THALER, G., *Elements of Servomechanisms Theory*, McGraw-Hill, 1955.

TOU, J., *Modern Control Theory*, McGraw-Hill, 1964.

TRUXAL, J. G., *Automatic Feedback Control System Synthesis*, McGraw-Hill, 1955.

CHAPTER 6

STATISTICAL TOLERANCE THEORY
APPLIED TO SERVO DESIGN

To efficiently design and manufacture a competitive servo system, we must consider the tolerances of the components that constitute the system. The question to be answered during the design phase is, "What is the tolerance required of each individual parameter for a total system performance within a specified tolerance?" We can best answer this question in the design phase if we consider each component parameter to be a random variable. Then we can use various statistical techniques to best predict the actual performance to be encountered in production. The purpose of this chapter is to explain these techniques and show how they can be effectively applied to servomechanism design.

6.1. RANDOM VARIABLES, NORMAL AND NONNORMAL DISTRIBUTIONS

Let us first consider a single servo parameter, e.g., motor stall torque T_s. This, like other parameters in the system, is often treated as a constant. With careful consideration, the designer will see that because of manufacturing variations servo parameters are not constants but are truly variables. It is assumed, however, that each parameter is bounded by some specified manufacturing tolerance. For example, stall torque has a specified maximum and a minimum value. It is important that the stall torque lie between these limits. However, to use the statistical design process, we must also have an insight into how the actual parameter varies between the limits.

Let us consider that tests are conducted on a group of motors to measure the stall torque. Each reading is recorded as it is taken and a list of stall torques is thereby constructed. In this form the data provide relatively little useful information. About all that one can tell is how many, if any, motors fall outside the specified limits. The next step one could take would be to sum the data and divide by the number of motors tested, thereby taking the arithmetic average. One could then say, "The mean motor has a stall torque of so much." Let's go one step further and group the test data into various categories depending on the torque value measured.

A histogram is a picture of data that have been processed as outlined above. Figure 6.1 shows a typical histogram that might result from stall torque tests conducted on 25 motors. If we imagined that more and more motors were tested and corresponding histograms were constructed by grouping the measurements into intervals of smaller and smaller width, it would be possible for us to visualize a smooth curve

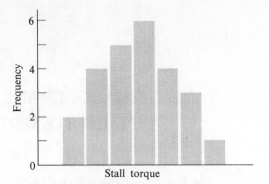

Fig. 6.1. Histogram of motor stall torque.

which would represent more truly the actual distribution of the motor stall torque. Such a curve is illustrated in Fig. 6.2, which closely resembles a theoretical curve found to be most important in statistical analysis (the *normal distribution* curve, Fig. 6.3). Figure 6.3 shows the familiar bell-shaped curve, whose ends extend infinitely far in both directions. The equation defining the normal curve is

$$Y = \frac{1}{\sigma\sqrt{2\pi}} \exp\left[-\frac{1}{2}\left(\frac{X-\mu}{\sigma}\right)^2\right], \tag{6.1}$$

where

σ = standard deviation of the distribution,

μ = mean of the distribution,

X = random variable plotted on the abscissa,

Y = height of curve corresponding to an assigned value of X.

Table 6.1 lists the ordinate values of the normal distribution curve Y as a function of the quantity $|X - \mu|$.

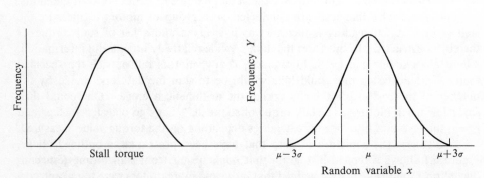

Fig. 6.2. Frequency distribution of motor stall torque data.

Fig. 6.3. The normal distribution.

Table 6.1

ORDINATE (Y) OF THE STANDARD NORMAL CURVE AS A FUNCTION OF $|X - \mu|$

$X-\mu$	0	1	2	3	4	5	6	7	8	9
0.0	.3989	.3989	.3989	.3988	.3986	.3984	.3982	.3980	.3977	.3973
0.1	.3970	.3965	.3961	.3956	.3951	.3945	.3939	.3932	.3925	.3918
0.2	.3910	.3902	.3894	.3885	.3876	.3867	.3857	.3847	.3836	.3825
0.3	.3814	.3802	.3790	.3778	.3765	.3752	.3739	.3725	.3712	.3697
0.4	.3683	.3668	.3653	.3637	.3621	.3605	.3589	.3572	.3555	.3538
0.5	.3521	.3503	.3485	.3467	.3448	.3429	.3410	.3391	.3372	.3352
0.6	.3332	.3312	.3292	.3271	.3251	.3230	.3209	.3187	.3166	.3144
0.7	.3123	.3101	.3079	.3056	.3034	.3011	.2989	.2966	.2943	.2920
0.8	.2897	.2874	.2850	.2827	.2803	.2780	.2756	.2732	.2709	.2685
0.9	.2661	.2637	.2613	.2589	.2565	.2541	.2516	.2492	.2468	.2444
1.0	.2420	.2396	.2371	.2347	.2323	.2299	.2275	.2251	.2227	.2203
1.1	.2179	.2155	.2131	.2107	.2083	.2059	.2036	.2012	.1989	.1965
1.2	.1942	.1919	.1895	.1872	.1849	.1826	.1804	.1781	.1758	.1736
1.3	.1714	.1691	.1669	.1647	.1626	.1604	.1582	.1561	.1539	.1518
1.4	.1497	.1476	.1456	.1435	.1415	.1394	.1374	.1354	.1334	.1315
1.5	.1295	.1276	.1257	.1238	.1219	.1200	.1182	.1163	.1145	.1127
1.6	.1109	.1092	.1074	.1057	.1040	.1023	.1006	.0989	.0973	.0957
1.7	.0940	.0925	.0909	.0893	.0878	.0863	.0848	.0833	.0818	.0804
1.8	.0790	.0775	.0761	.0748	.0734	.0721	.0707	.0694	.0681	.0669
1.9	.0656	.0644	.0632	.0620	.0608	.0596	.0584	.0573	.0562	.0551
2.0	.0540	.0529	.0519	.0508	.0498	.0488	.0478	.0468	.0459	.0449
2.1	.0440	.0431	.0422	.0413	.0404	.0396	.0387	.0379	.0371	.0363
2.2	.0355	.0347	.0339	.0332	.0325	.0317	.0310	.0303	.0297	.0290
2.3	.0283	.0277	.0270	.0264	.0258	.0252	.0246	.0241	.0235	.0229
1.4	.0224	.0219	.0213	.0208	.0203	.0198	.0194	.0189	.0184	.0180
2.5	.0175	.0171	.0167	.0163	.0158	.0154	.0151	.0147	.0143	.0139
2.6	.0136	.0132	.0129	.0126	.0122	.0119	.0116	.0113	.0110	.0107
2.7	.0104	.0101	.0099	.0096	.0093	.0091	.0088	.0086	.0084	.0081
2.8	.0079	.0077	.0075	.0073	.0071	.0069	.0067	.0065	.0063	.0061
2.9	.0060	.0058	.0056	.0055	.0053	.0051	.0050	.0048	.0047	.0046
3.0	.0044	.0043	.0042	.0040	.0039	.0038	.0037	.0036	.0035	.0034
3.1	.0033	.0032	.0031	.0030	.0029	.0028	.0027	.0026	.0025	.0025
3.2	.0024	.0023	.0022	.0022	.0021	.0020	.0020	.0019	.0018	.0018
3.3	.0017	.0017	.0016	.0016	.0015	.0015	.0014	.0014	.0013	.0013
3.4	.0012	.0012	.0012	.0011	.0011	.0010	.0010	.0010	.0009	.0009
3.5	.0009	.0008	.0008	.0008	.0008	.0007	.0007	.0007	.0007	.0006
3.6	.0006	.0006	.0006	.0005	.0005	.0005	.0005	.0005	.0005	.0004
3.7	.0004	.0004	.0004	.0004	.0004	.0004	.0003	.0003	.0003	.0003
3.8	.0003	.0003	.0003	.0003	.0003	.0002	.0002	.0002	.0002	.0002
3.9	.0002	.0002	.0002	.0002	.0002	.0002	.0002	.000	.0001	.0001

Integrating Eq. (6.1) from minus to plus infinity shows that the area under the curve is unity, which is the reason why the curve is called the standard normal distribution. The area under the curve between any two X-values is equal to the probability that the parameter value will lie between the two values.

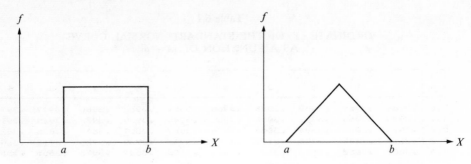

Fig. 6.4. Rectangular distribution.   **Fig. 6.5.** Triangular distribution.

Normal or approximately normal distributions occur more frequently in component manufacturing than do nonnormal distributions. However, before we go further, let's look at some nonnormal distributions that could exist.

1. Rectangular distribution. The rectangular distribution (Fig. 6.4) states the probability that all parameter values between the limits *a* and *b* are equally likely to occur. Rectangular distributions are often used to describe discrete type relationships. For example, the probability of faces 1, 2, 3, 4, 5, or 6 showing up when an unloaded die is thrown is exactly $\frac{1}{6}$ for each of these six numbers, but it is zero for all other members. This type of distribution, if used to represent a parameter in a system, does not lend itself to a tractable statistical tolerance technique. Fortunately, however, because of the nature of component manufacturing, very few, if any component parameters are described by rectangular distributions.

2. Triangular distribution. The triangular distribution results from an additive combination of two rectangular distributions. The triangular distribution rarely exists for the same reasons discussed for the rectangular distribution.

3. Near-normal distribution. Near-normal distributions could be described as distributions that have a bell-shaped appearance but do not follow the exact mathe-

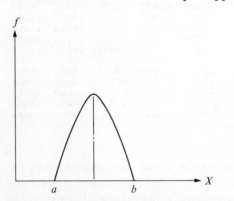

Fig. 6.6. Near-normal distribution.

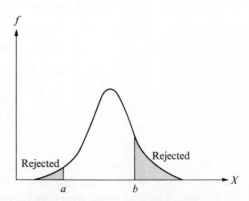

Fig. 6.7. Truncated distribution.

matical definition of the normal curve. It is of interest to note that the example of
the near-normal distribution shown in Fig. 6.6 was obtained by combining two
triangular distributions. The significance of this fact will be discussed later.

4. Truncated distribution. Truncated distributions result when a component manufacturing process does not continually meet specifications because the natural tolerance for the process is looser than the specified tolerance. Inspection of 100% of
the units is therefore required to ensure rejection of those outside the required limits.
This method of manufacturing components is costly and is avoided whenever possible. For this reason, the truncated parameter distribution is not commonly observed.

5. Binodal distribution. The binodal distribution could result when components
are purchased, to the same controlling specification, from two manufacturers. If
this distribution does occur, it usually indicates that the controlling specification
is looser than the natural manufacturing tolerance, and hence that the former could
be tightened without an increase in cost. Tightening the tolerance requirements under
these circumstances tends toward better control of the final product and also reduces
the possibility of the binodal distribution. Therefore, as with the truncated distribution, the binodal distribution is unlikely to occur when proper attention is paid
to correlation between manufacturing processes and specification procedures.

6.2. CENTRAL LIMIT PROPERTY

In Section 6.1, the normal distribution was described in considerable detail and some
of the possible nonnormal distributions were introduced. For most of the statistical
tolerance techniques introduced in the following section we will assume that every
component parameter is normally distributed. This assumption is not entirely
arbitrary, for convenience only, since there are natural factors that tend to make
plots of most component parameters resemble normal distributions. This natural
tendency, called the *central limit property*, is stated as follows:

> the distribution of the sum of K random variables of almost any form tends
> rapidly toward a normal distribution as K increases.

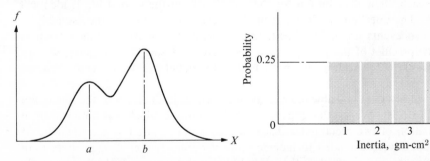

Fig. 6.8. Binodal distribution.

Fig. 6.9. Frequency distribution for selection
from first bin.

Table 6.2

PROBABILITY FOR EACH POSSIBLE ASSEMBLY

Inertia Selected from Bin 1, gm-cm^2	Inertia Selected from Bin 2, gm-cm^2	Probability of Mutual Event	Inertia of Assembly, gm-cm^2
1	1	$\frac{1}{16}$	2
1	2	$\frac{1}{16}$	3
1	3	$\frac{1}{16}$	4
1	4	$\frac{1}{16}$	5
2	1	$\frac{1}{16}$	3
2	2	$\frac{1}{16}$	4
2	3	$\frac{1}{16}$	5
2	4	$\frac{1}{16}$	6
3	1	$\frac{1}{16}$	4
3	2	$\frac{1}{16}$	5
3	3	$\frac{1}{16}$	6
3	4	$\frac{1}{16}$	7
4	1	$\frac{1}{16}$	5
4	2	$\frac{1}{16}$	6
4	3	$\frac{1}{16}$	7
4	4	$\frac{1}{16}$	8

To demonstrate this property, let us consider the following illustration. *Each of two bins is filled with an equal number of servo components with inertia values of 1, 2, 3, and 4 gm-cm^2.* The assembler selects at random one component from each bin and combines them on one shaft.

Since there are equal numbers of each size in a bin, it is equally probable that any one size will be selected. This is represented by the frequency distribution for selection from the first bin as shown in Fig. 6.9. The distribution is rectangular since all events are equally likely. Since there are four equally likely events, the probability is 0.25 for each. The distribution for the selection from the second bin is identical to the first. The question is, "What is the frequency distribution of the assembly?" Since the two events are independent, the probability of each combined event is equal to the product of the probability of each event. Using this property, we can construct Table 6.2. Adding the probabilities for equal events, we can construct Table 6.3.

The assembly data in Table 6.3 may be represented in the form of the histogram shown as Fig. 6.10. We see that the assembly distribution, which was obtained from the combination of two rectangular distributions, is not square but is triangular. If this illustration were extended to include more variables (larger K, e.g., more than two components per assembly), the assembly distribution would be more nearly

Table 6.3

ASSEMBLY PROBABILITY
TABULATION

Assembly Inertia, gm-cm^2	Probability
2	$\frac{1}{16}$
3	$\frac{2}{16}$
4	$\frac{3}{16}$
5	$\frac{4}{16}$
6	$\frac{3}{16}$
7	$\frac{2}{16}$
8	$\frac{1}{16}$

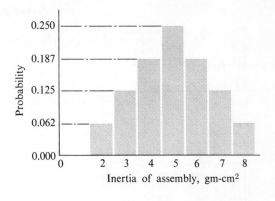

Fig. 6.10. Histogram of assembly distribution.

normal. We can make the following summary.

a) If $K > 4$, the assembly distribution can be considered normal provided that the variable ranges are comparable, even for the rare case in which all the variable distributions are rectangular.

b) If the variables have a simple hump near the middle of their ranges, the assembly distribution approaches normality much faster and K need not be so high as 4.

Usually we can regard servo component parameters as a function of a number of intrinsic random factors, each of which contributes only a small portion to the total. For example, the gain of a servo amplifier is a function of the gain of each stage and, in turn, depends on the components that make up each stage. The same thing is true for the parameters describing the servomotor, summing networks, gear train, etc. Thus, according to the central tendency principle, we should expect the random variable representing component parameters to be at least approximately normally distributed. This conjecture is largely supported by practical experience.

In view of the above, we will assume in most of the remaining discussions and design examples that each component parameter is normally distributed.

6.3. TOLERANCE AND THE STANDARD DEVIATION

The normal distribution extends from $-\infty$ to $+\infty$. At first this property might appear to limit the usefulness of this distribution since we previously defined component parameters to be bounded by a specified tolerance. However, even though the component manufacturer first states that all parts should fall within the specified limits, if pressed further, he will usually admit that he expects almost, but not all,

Table 6.4

AREA UNDER THE STANDARD NORMAL CURVE
AS A FUNCTION OF THE QUANTITY $|X - \mu|$ FOR $\sigma = 1$

$X-\mu$	0	1	2	3	4	5	6	7	8	9
0.0	.0000	.0040	.0080	.0120	.0160	.0199	.0239	.0279	.0319	.0359
0.1	.0398	.0438	.0478	.0517	.0557	.0596	.0636	.0675	.0714	.0754
0.2	.0793	.0832	.0871	.0910	.0948	.0987	.1026	.1064	.1103	.1141
0.3	.1179	.1217	.1255	.1293	.1331	.1368	.1406	.1443	.1480	.1517
0.4	.1554	.1591	.1628	.1664	.1700	.1736	.1772	.1808	.1844	.1879
0.5	.1915	.1950	.1985	.2019	.2054	.2088	.2123	.2157	.2190	.2224
0.6	.2258	.2291	.2324	.2357	.2389	.2422	.2454	.2486	.2518	.2549
0.7	.2580	.2612	.2642	.2673	.2704	.2734	.2764	.2794	.2823	.2852
0.8	.2881	.2910	.2939	.2967	.2996	.3023	.3051	.3078	.3106	.3133
0.9	.3159	.3186	.3212	.3238	.3264	.3289	.3315	.3340	.3365	.3389
1.0	.3413	.3438	.3461	.3485	.3508	.3531	.3554	.3577	.3599	.3621
1.1	.3643	.3665	.3686	.3708	.3729	.3749	.3770	.3790	.3810	.3830
1.2	.3849	.3869	.3888	.3907	.3925	.3944	.3962	.3980	.3997	.4015
1.3	.4032	.4049	.4066	.4082	.4099	.4115	.4131	.4147	.4162	.4177
1.4	.4192	.4207	.4222	.4236	.4251	.4265	.4279	.4292	.4306	.4319
1.5	.4332	.4345	.4357	.4370	.4382	.4394	.4406	.4418	.4429	.4441
1.6	.4452	.4463	.4474	.4484	.4495	.4505	.4515	.4525	.4535	.4545
1.7	.4554	.4564	.4573	.4582	.4591	.4599	.4608	.4616	.4625	.4633
1.8	.4641	.4649	.4656	.4664	.4671	.4678	.4686	.4693	.4699	.4706
1.9	.4713	.4719	.4726	.4732	.4738	.4744	.4750	.4756	.4761	.4767
2.0	.4772	.4778	.4783	.4788	.4793	.4798	.4803	.4808	.4812	.4817
2.1	.4821	.4826	.4830	.4834	.4838	.4842	.4846	.4850	.4854	.4857
2.2	.4861	.4864	.4868	.4871	.4875	.4878	.4881	.4884	.4887	.4890
2.3	.4893	.4896	.4898	.4901	.4904	.4906	.4909	.4911	.4913	.4916
2.4	.4918	.4920	.4922	.4925	.4927	.4929	.4931	.4932	.4934	.4936
2.5	.4938	.4940	.4941	.4943	.4945	.4946	.4948	.4949	.4951	.4952
2.6	.4953	.4955	.4956	.4957	.4959	.4960	.4961	.4962	.4963	.4964
2.7	.4965	.4966	.4967	.4968	.4969	.4970	.4971	.4972	.4973	.4974
2.8	.4974	.4975	.4976	.4977	.4977	.4978	.4979	.4979	.4980	.4981
2.9	.4981	.4982	.4982	.4983	.4984	.4984	.4985	.4985	.4986	.4986
3.0	.4987	.4987	.4987	.4988	.4988	.4989	.4989	.4989	.4990	.4990
3.1	.4990	.4991	.4991	.4991	.4992	.4992	.4992	.4992	.4993	.4993
3.2	.4993	.4993	.4994	.4994	.4994	.4994	.4994	.4995	.4995	.4995
3.3	.4995	.4995	.4995	.4996	.4996	.4996	.4996	.4996	.4996	.4997
3.4	.4997	.4997	.4997	.4997	.4997	.4997	.4997	.4997	.4997	.4998
3.5	.4998	.4998	.4998	.4998	.4998	.4998	.4998	.4998	.4998	.4998
3.6	.4998	.4998	.4999	.4999	.4999	.4999	.4999	.4999	.4999	.4999
3.7	.4999	.4999	.4999	.4999	.4999	.4999	.4999	.4999	.4999	.4999
3.8	.4999	.4999	.4999	.4999	.4999	.4999	.4999	.4999	.4999	.4999
3.9	.5000	.5000	.5000	.5000	.5000	.5000	.5000	.5000	.5000	.5000

the components to be "in spec." If this statement is questioned, the answer will usually be that no more than a given fraction of the manufactured components will fall outside these limits. That is, every component parameter is essentially a random variable having a frequency distribution such that only a very few components will fall outside the specified boundaries. The normal distribution approximates this state of affairs

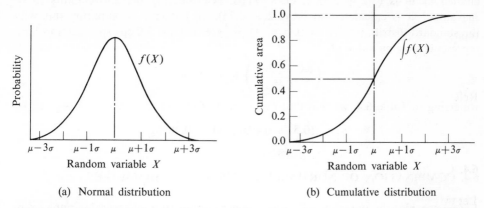

(a) Normal distribution   (b) Cumulative distribution

Fig. 6.11. The cumulative distribution and its relationship to the normal distribution.

by defining the probability of getting large deviations from the mean as insignificantly small. The question then is, "What relationship should be assumed between the specified tolerance limits and the standard deviation?"

The integral of the frequency distribution curve is called the *cumulative distribution function*. The relationship between these two functions is illustrated in Fig. 6.11. Since the normal distribution is symmetrical about its mean (μ), it is most convenient to use a cumulative distribution function defined as the integral taken from the mean value to infinity. Table 6.4 lists the values for such a cumulative distribution as a function of the quantity $|X - \mu|$ for a normal distribution with a standard deviation (σ) of unity.

Servo design practice, as well as most others, considers the specified tolerance boundaries to be equivalent to 3σ-values. This practice assumes that only 0.27% of the components lie outside the specification; therefore essentially all units are within the specification limits. A lower σ-value could be used, but this would allow a greater percentage of units to be out of specification. Choosing a higher σ-value tends toward overdesign. The 3σ-assumption provides a reasonable compromise between over- and underdesign; therefore all following tolerance limits will be assumed to represent 3σ-values.

It is often required to calculate the probability of occurrence of a particular event. This can be accomplished by using Table 6.4. Let us consider the following example.

Example 6.1 Given that the bandwidth distribution for a servo design was calculated to be

$$\text{Maximum (mean} + 3\sigma) = 5.2 \text{ cps,}$$
$$\text{Minimum (mean} - 3\sigma) = 2.3 \text{ cps.}$$

Suppose that the specification limit is 5.0 cps (maximum) with no minimum limit. Calculate the percentage of units that should fail the specification limit. The calculated mean is $(5.2 + 2.3)/2$, or 3.75 cps. Considering the above limits to be 3σ-values, 3σ is calculated to be $(5.2 - 3.75)$, or 1.45 cps. Comparing this with the standard distribution ($\mu = 0, \sigma = 1$), we see that the 5.0 cps specification limit represents a sigma value of

$$\left(\frac{5.0 - 3.75}{1.45}\right) 3\sigma = 2.59\sigma.$$

Referring to Table 6.4, we find that the percent of failure to be expected is given by

$$(0.5 - 0.4952)100 = 0.48\%.$$

6.4. COMBINATION OF NORMALLY DISTRIBUTED PARAMETERS

Let us consider the parameter Y to be a linear combination of several variables represented by the equation

$$Y = a_1 X_1 + a_2 X_2 + a_3 X_3 + \cdots + a_k X_k, \tag{6.2}$$

where $a_1, a_2, a_3, \ldots, a_k$ are constants, and $X_1, X_2, X_3, \ldots, X_k$ are independent random variables with various distribution curves. Let X_i^* and Y^* represent the mean value of X_i and Y, respectively. Then the mean value of Y is given by the equation

$$Y^* = a_1 X_1^* + a_2 X_2^* + a_3 X_3^* + \cdots + a_k X_k^*. \tag{6.3}$$

The variance of Y is given by the equation

$$\sigma_Y^2 = a_1^2 \sigma_1^2 + a_2 \sigma_2^2 + a_3 \sigma_3^2 + \cdots + a_k^2 \sigma_k^2. \tag{6.4}$$

The standard deviation of Y is defined as the square root of the variance:

$$\sigma_Y = \sqrt{a_1^2 \sigma_1^2 + a_2^2 \sigma_2^2 + a_3^2 \sigma_3^2 + \cdots + a_k^2 \sigma_k^2}. \tag{6.5}$$

For the special case where $a_1, \ldots, a_k$ are all unity, the relationship given by Eq. (6.5) is often summarized as, "The standard deviation of the total assembly is given by the square root of the sum of the squares (RSS) of the individual component deviations." If all the X variables are normally distributed, then Y is also normally distributed. Let us consider the following example.

Example 6.2 Given a gear train inertia tabulation as in Table 6.5. Calculate the mean and 3σ-values of the total effective inertia considered at the load. The equation developed in Chapter 3 for the total inertia of a system was

$$J_T = J_1 N_1^2 + J_2 N_2^2 + J_3 N_3^2 + \cdots + J_k N_k^2.$$

Applying the relationship given by Eq. (6.3), we calculate the mean value to be

$$\begin{aligned} J_T^* &= J_1^* N_1^2 + J_2^* N_2^2 + J_3^* N_3^2 \\ &= (0.12)(40)^2 + (8.0)(10)^2 + (200)(1)^2 \\ &= 192 + 800 + 200 = 1192 \text{ gm-cm}^2. \end{aligned}$$

Table 6.5

Inertia at Component, J		Gear Ratio to Load, N
Mean, gm-cm^2	Tolerance, gm-cm^2	
0.12	±.01	40
8.0	±0.6	10
200.	±12.	1

Considering the individual tolerances to represent 3σ-values and using Eq. (6.5), we see that the 3σ-value for J_T is calculated as

$$3\sigma_{J_T} = \sqrt{[(0.01)(40)^2]^2 + [(0.6)(10)^2]^2 + [(12)(1)^2]^2}$$
$$= \sqrt{256 + 3600 + 144} = 63.2 \text{ gm-cm}^2.$$

6.5. TOLERANCES AND THEIR NONLINEAR EFFECT

The previous section demonstrated the method of considering tolerance effects for parameters which were the result of direct addition or subtraction. These procedures are usually adequate for the physical dimensioning of component parts. However, the performance of a servosystem is a nonlinear function of most of the servo-component parameters. That is, most servo-design equations involve the multiplication, division, square root, etc., of these parameters. The relationships presented in Section 6.4 for equations involving addition (or subtraction) are not adequate. Therefore, a further technique must be developed. To illustrate the problems involved, let us consider the following simple example. Assume a resistive network as shown in Fig. 6.12. The transfer function for the circuit is given by the equation

$$G \equiv \frac{E_o}{E_{\text{in}}} = \frac{R_2}{R_1 + R_2}. \tag{6.6}$$

It is desired to find the effect of the tolerances of R_1 and R_2 on the gain G. Although they are usually much more complex, similar problems exist in all phases of servo design. A common approach to this problem would be to first evaluate the mean gain value (G^*),

$$G^* = \frac{R_2^*}{R_1^* + R_2^*}, \tag{6.7}$$

where the starred parameters indicate nominal values. For purposes of explanation, let us consider R_1 to have zero tolerance. Let ΔR_2 represent the tolerance on R_2.

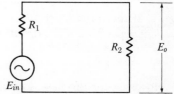

Fig. 6.12. Resistive network.

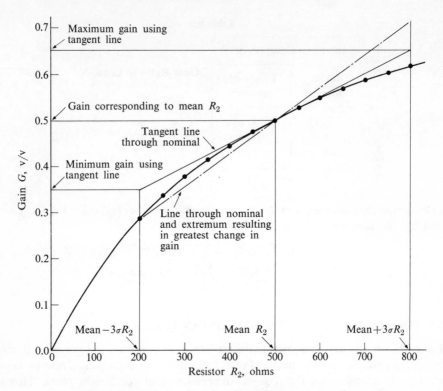

Fig. 6.13. Gain vs. R_2 for a simple resistor network.

Then the change in G due to the R_2 tolerance may be calculated by substituting $(R_2 \pm \Delta R_2)$ for R_2 and calculating the corresponding values of G. Considering R_2 to be normally distributed and setting the tolerance (ΔR_2) equal to the 3σ-limit $(3\sigma R_2)$, we see that the gain variation with the maximum value of R_2 is given by

$$G^* + (\Delta G)_1 = \frac{R_2^* + 3\sigma R_2}{R_1^* + R_2^* + 3\sigma R_2}, \tag{6.8}$$

and using the minimum value of R_2, we have

$$G^* + (\Delta G)_2 = \frac{R_2^* - 3\sigma R_2}{R_1^* + R_2^* - 3\sigma R_2}. \tag{6.9}$$

If the variables G and R_2 were linearly related, the deviation of the gain would be independent of the direction assigned to ΔR_2:

$$(\Delta G)_1 = -(\Delta G)_2. \tag{6.10}$$

However, for this case, as well as most of the cases encountered in servo design, the relationship is not linear. A previous approach, sometimes considered to be conserva-

Table 6.6
RESISTOR NETWORK TABULATION

R_2	$G(R_2)$	W	$G \times W$	$G - G^*$	$(G - G^*)^2$	$(G - G^*)^2 W$
200	0.285	0.44	0.12	-0.209	0.0437	0.0192
250	0.333	1.75	0.58	-0.161	0.0261	0.0456
300	0.375	5.40	2.02	-0.119	0.0143	0.0776
350	0.411	12.95	5.33	-0.083	0.0069	0.0895
400	0.444	24.20	10.75	-0.050	0.0025	0.0616
450	0.473	35.21	16.67	-0.021	0.0004	0.0158
500	0.500	39.89	19.94	0.005	0.0000	0.0010
550	0.523	35.21	18.44	0.028	0.0008	0.0293
600	0.545	24.20	13.19	0.050	0.0025	0.0618
650	0.565	12.95	7.31	0.070	0.0049	0.0640
700	0.583	5.40	3.14	0.088	0.0078	0.0422
750	0.600	1.75	1.05	0.105	0.0110	0.0193
800	0.615	0.44	0.27	0.120	0.0145	0.0063
	Totals	199.79	98.87	—	—	0.5338

tive, was to assign to $3\sigma_G$ that value of ΔG which had the greater magnitude. Assuming that R_1 has a value of 500 ohms and zero tolerance and that R_2 has a nominal value of 500 ohms and a 3σ-tolerance of 300 ohms and using this approach for computing G^* and $3\sigma_G$, we find that

$$G^* = 0.5, \qquad 3\sigma_G = 0.214.$$

The significance of these values and the assumptions that were made are illustrated in Fig. 6.13, which shows G as a function of R_2 with R_1 held constant at 500 ohms. The resulting tolerance using this method is certainly greater than would be calculated by using any other technique. One would normally consider this to represent a safe design condition. However, the high limit of the gain is greater than that which can physically occur. Whether or not the higher deviation obtained by this method of computation is on the safe side depends on the particular situation. If the sample given here represented a generator voltage providing damping in a servomechanism, the higher deviation would present an optimistic picture. The amount of damping would appear to be higher than it actually is. But, for velocity-lag considerations, this higher deviation would be pessimistic. The predicted amount of velocity lag would not be so great as that which would actually occur.

The major theoretical difficulty with the preceding approach is that it weighs heavily the tolerance extreme but ignores the region where R_2 is most likely to occur. If the deviation of G due to the tolerance on R_2 could be based on the effect of R_2 on G in the area where R_2 is most likely to be, the results would be more reliable.

Let us now consider a realistic solution to the preceding network example that accounts for both the probabilities associated with the various values of R_2 and the nonlinearity. Divide Fig. 6.13 into equal 0.5σ-increments of R_2 as shown. Referring to Table 6.1, we can establish the probability of each value of R_2. This probability can be used as a weighting factor W associated with each corresponding value of the gain $G(R_2)$. The mean of the gain is calculated by the equation

$$G^* = \Sigma G(R_2)W/\Sigma W. \tag{6.11}$$

The standard deviation is calculated by the equation

$$\sigma G_2 = \sqrt{[\Sigma G(R_2) - G^*]W/\Sigma W}. \tag{6.12}$$

Table 6.6 summarizes the above calculations for the network problem. The resulting values for the mean and 3σ-deviation of the gain are respectively

$$G^* = \frac{\Sigma G(R_2)xW}{\Sigma W} = \frac{98.87}{199.79} = 0.4949,$$

$$3\sigma_G = 3\sqrt{\frac{\Sigma(X_i - X^*)W}{\Sigma W}} = 3\sqrt{\frac{0.5338}{199.79}} = 0.15507.$$

Observe that the difference in $3\sigma_G$ from that using the previous "worst case" tolerance extreme amounted to

Difference $(\%) = [(0.214 - 0.1551)/0.1551]100 = 6.4/0.15 = 42.6\%.$

This confirms that using the method of taking the largest end-point value as the 3σ-limit is unrealistic and should therefore be avoided.

6.6. TAYLOR SERIES EXPANSION FOR CALCULATING TOLERANCE EFFECTS

The technique for calculating tolerance effects for nonlinear parameters as presented in Section 6.5 is undoubtedly accurate. But the number of calculations required in multivariable problems results in a very time-consuming process.

A more practical solution is to expand the function into a Taylor series around the mean parameters. The higher-order terms of the series are neglected. This requires taking the partial derivative of the equation with respect to each variable. For the network example, the mean is given by

$$G^* = \frac{R_2^*}{R_1^* + R_2^*} = \frac{500}{500 + 500} = 0.5, \tag{6.13}$$

and the 3σ-deviation is given by

$$3\sigma_G = \sqrt{\left((3\sigma R_2)\frac{\partial G}{\partial R_2}\bigg|_*\right)^2 + \left((3\sigma R_1)\frac{\partial G}{\partial R_1}\bigg|_*\right)^2}, \tag{6.14}$$

where the $|_*$ notation signifies that the partial derivative is evaluated at the point of all nominal values. Since in the example R_1 was assumed constant, $\sigma G/\sigma R_1$ is zero and Eq. (6.14) can be written as

$$3\sigma_G = (3\sigma_{R_2}) \left[\frac{R_1 + R_2 + R_2}{(R_1 + R_2)^2} \right]_*$$

$$= (500 - 200) \left(\frac{500 + 500 - 500}{1000^2} \right) \tag{6.15}$$

$$= (300)(0.5 \times 10^{-3})$$

$$= 0.150.$$

Note that using the Taylor series expansion method results in mean and $3\sigma_G$ values that differ only a slight amount (about 1.0%) from the value obtained by using the weighting procedure.

We can generalize this method to a multivariable function, using the following notation. Let Y be some function of $X_1, X_2, X_3, \ldots, X_k$ represented as

$$Y = F(X_1, X_2, X_3, \ldots, X_k). \tag{6.16}$$

Then the mean value of Y is given by

$$Y^* = F(X_1^*, X_2^*, X_3^*, \ldots, X_k^*), \tag{6.17}$$

and the 3σ-deviation of Y is given by

$$3\sigma_Y^* = \sqrt{ \left((3\sigma_1) \frac{\partial Y}{\partial X_1}\bigg|_* \right)^2 + \left((3\sigma_2) \frac{\partial Y}{\partial X_2}\bigg|_* \right)^2 + \left((3\sigma_3) \frac{\partial Y}{\partial X_3}\bigg|_* \right)^2 + \cdots + \left((3\sigma_k) \frac{\partial Y}{\partial X_k}\bigg|_* \right)^2 }.$$

$$\tag{6.18}$$

Let us consider the following example applied to a two-variable function.

Example 6.3 Given mean and tolerance values for the torque constant and inertia as

$$K_T = 2000 \pm 400 \text{ oz-in/rad},$$

$$J_T = 0.2 \pm 0.04 \text{ oz-in/rad/sec}^2,$$

calculate the resulting mean and 3σ-tolerance for the natural frequency,

$$\omega_N = \sqrt{K_T/J_T}.$$

The mean value ω_N^* is given by

$$\omega_N^* = \sqrt{K_T^*/J_T^*} = 100 \text{ rad/sec}.$$

Calculating the two required partial derivatives, we obtain

$$\frac{\partial \omega_N}{\partial K_T}\bigg|_* = \frac{1}{2\sqrt{K_T^* J_T^*}} = 0.025, \qquad \frac{\partial \omega_N}{\partial J_T}\bigg|_* = -\frac{1}{2J_T^*}\sqrt{\frac{K_T}{J_T^*}} = -250.$$

The $3\sigma\omega_N$ value is given directly by application of Eq. (6.18) as

$$3\sigma\omega_N = \sqrt{[(3\sigma K_T)(\partial\omega_N/\partial K_T)]^2 + [(3\sigma J_T)(\partial\omega_N/\partial J_T)]^2}$$

$$= \sqrt{[(400)(0.025)]^2 + [(0.04)(-250)]^2}$$

$$= 14.14 \text{ rad/sec}.$$

6.7. APPROXIMATE SLOPE METHOD OF CALCULATING TOLERANCE EFFECTS

The Taylor series technique sometimes involves difficult computation. Since the partial derivative of the desired performance parameter with respect to each component parameter must be determined manually in general terms before the problem can be programmed on a digital computer, it is a tedious task to solve mathematical expressions of any complexity.

The approximate-slope technique developed in this section uses an incremented approach to approximate the required partial derivatives; therefore the actual expressions need not be generated. One need work with only the basic equation defining the desired performance parameter. This technique is most effective for complex equations and lends itself directly to automated digital computer programming.

The partial derivatives in Eq. (6.18) are replaced by the corresponding $\Delta Y_i / \Delta X_i$ approximations. Choosing ΔX_i to be $3a\sigma_i$ and ΔY_i to be $(Y_i - Y^*)$ and substituting these expressions into Eq. (6.18) yields

$$3\sigma_Y = \frac{1}{a}\sqrt{(Y_1 - Y^*)^2 + (Y_2 - Y^*)^2 + (Y_3 - Y^*)^2 + \cdots + (Y_k - Y^*)^2},$$

$$(6.19)$$

where

$a =$ a constant representing the percentage of the tolerance to be used to approximate the derivative,

$Y_i =$ the values of Y obtained by replacing the corresponding value of X_i by $(X_i^* + 3a\sigma_i)$.

Selecting smaller values for the constant a results in better accuracy except for the possible effect of truncation error. Choosing a value of a equal to 1% has been found satisfactory for digital computer calculations, whereas 10% appears to be more ideal for hand calculations.

To calculate the mean $\pm 3\sigma$ limits of a function by the approximate-slope method, we outline the following procedure:

1) All the X_i's are set equal to their mean value X_i^* and the corresponding value of Y is calculated to be the mean value Y^*.

2) X_1 is replaced by $(X_1^* + 3a\sigma_1)$ and the corresponding value of Y_1 is calculated with all other X's at their mean value.

3) Step (2) is repeated for each X_i resulting in values for $Y_1, Y_2, Y_3, \ldots, Y_k$.

4) Equation (6.19) is used to calculate the resulting 3σ-value of Y.

Let us consider the following example.

Table 6.7

	PARAMETER DATA			DAMPING RATIO CALCULATIONS		
Par.	Mean	3σ	Mean $+ \Delta_i$	ζ_i	$\zeta_i - \zeta^*$	$(\zeta_i - \zeta^*)^2$
K_f	2.441E − 00	4.882E − 01	2.489E − 00	0.6850	−6.816E − 03	4.646E − 05
K_g	3.290E − 04	3.290E − 05	3.323E − 04	0.6978	6.005E − 03	3.606E − 05
K_a	1.980E + 03	3.960E + 02	2.019E + 03	0.6969	5.076E − 03	2.576E − 05
K_m	2.145E − 03	4.290E − 04	2.187E − 03	0.6969	5.076E − 03	2.576E − 05
B_m	2.125E − 04	6.375E − 05	2.188E − 04	0.6946	2.739E − 03	7.504E − 06
J_m	1.107E − 05	1.107E − 06	1.118E − 05	0.6888	−3.038E − 03	9.233E − 06
J_L	1.334E − 02	2.669E − 03	1.361E − 02	0.6910	−7.998E − 04	6.398E − 07
				$\sum(\zeta_1 - \zeta^*)^2$		1.514E − 04

Example 6.4 Given the following component data:

$$K_f = 2.441 \text{ oz-in/rad} \pm 20\%, \quad K_g = 0.03446 \text{ v/1000 rpm} \pm 10\%,$$
$$K_a = 1980 \text{ v/v} \pm 20\%, \quad K_m = 0.002145 \text{ oz-in/v} \pm 20\%,$$
$$B_m = 0.0002125 \text{ oz-in/rad/sec} \pm 30\%,$$
$$J_m = 0.78 \text{ gm-cm}^2 \pm 10\%, \quad J_L = 939.9 \text{ gm-cm}^2 \pm 20\%,$$
$$\phi_f = 0 \text{ deg}, \quad \phi_a = 0 \text{ deg}, \quad \phi_g = 0 \text{ deg}, \quad N = 95.92.$$

Calculate the mean and 3σ-value for the damping ratio ζ.

Following the outlined procedure and using the damping ratio equation developed in Chapter 5, we first calculate the mean damping ratio. To convert units on the required parameters, we use

$$K_g = 0.000329 \text{ v/rad/sec},$$
$$J_m = 1.107 \times 10^{-5} \text{ oz-in/rad/sec}^2,$$
$$J_L = 1.334 \times 10^{-2} \text{ oz-in/rad/sec}^2.$$

1. Using Eq. (5.25) with ϕ_f, ϕ_a, ϕ_g equal to zero, we calculate the mean damping ratio

$$\zeta^* = \frac{N^2(B_m^* + K_g^* K_a^* K_m^*)}{2\sqrt{K_f^* K_a^* K_m^* N(N^2 J_m^* + J_L^*)}}.$$

Substituting the required values, we find that

$$\zeta^* = 0.6918.$$

2. Let us now consider varying K_f:

$$3\sigma_{K_f} = (0.20)(2.44) = 0.4882.$$

Letting $a = 10\%$, we see that

$$K_f^* + \Delta K_f = 2.441 + (0.10)(0.4882) = 2.489 \text{ v/rad.}$$

Using this value for K_f and all other parameters at their mean values, we again calculate ζ and find it to be

$$\zeta_{K_f} = 0.685.$$

3. Step (2) is repeated for each of the parameters. The results are tabulated in Table 6.7.

4. The values of $(\zeta_i - \zeta^*)$ and $(\zeta_i - \zeta^*)^2$ are also calculated, as shown in the preceding tabulation. Using Eq. (6.19), we determine the $3\sigma_\zeta$-value as

$$3\sigma_\zeta = \frac{1}{0.1}\sqrt{1.514 \times 10^{-4}} = 0.1235.$$

The mean $\pm 3\sigma$-values for ζ are therefore given by

$$\zeta(\text{mean} + 3\sigma) = 0.8153, \qquad \zeta(\text{mean} - 3\sigma) = 0.5683.$$

6.8. MONTE CARLO METHOD OF DETERMINING COMPONENT TOLERANCE EFFECTS

The preceding portions of this chapter present a method of tolerance consideration that has proved to be most realistic and yet is easily applied to conventional design procedure. However, there is an additional method of considering component tolerance effects. This method is commonly called the *Monte Carlo method*. It provides a unique method for selecting component parameter values for a simulation. It is also most helpful in selecting the controllable parameter settings used in hardware tests.

The Monte Carlo approach does not necessarily assume that each component parameter under investigation has a normal distribution. In fact, the technique is adaptable to any form of component distribution. For example, one parameter could be represented by a truncated distribution, another by a rectangular distribution, and the remaining one by any other form desired. Using the Monte Carlo technique and given some distribution for each parameter, one can "construct" a system by randomly selecting a value for each parameter according to its distribution. After parameter values for each component in the system, simulation, or equation are chosen, a solution is obtained. Then each parameter value is again chosen as above and the new solution is obtained. The above sequence is repeated many times (usually between 25 and several hundred). This procedure results in a tabulation of data representing the desired output variable distribution. From these data, either a histogram can be plotted or one can calculate the resulting mean and the 3σ-value using the two equations

$$Y^* = \frac{\sum_1^n Y_j}{n}, \tag{6.20}$$

$$3\sigma_Y = 3\sqrt{\sum_1^n (Y_j - Y^*)^2/n}, \tag{6.21}$$

Table 6.8

RANDOM NORMAL NUMBERS BASED ON A NORMAL DISTRIBUTION WITH MEAN OF ZERO AND SIGMA OF UNITY*

0.464	0.137	2.455	-0.323	-0.068	0.296	-0.288	1.298	0.241	-0.957
0.060	-2.526	-0.531	-0.194	0.543	-1.558	0.187	-1.190	0.022	0.525
1.486	-0.354	-0.634	0.697	0.926	1.375	0.785	-0.963	-0.853	-1.865
1.022	-0.472	1.279	3.521	0.571	-1.851	0.194	1.192	-0.501	-0.273
1.394	-0.555	0.046	0.321	2.945	1.974	-0.258	0.412	0.439	-0.035
0.906	-0.513	-0.525	0.595	0.881	-0.934	1.579	0.161	-1.885	0.371
1.179	-1.055	0.007	0.769	0.971	0.712	1.090	-0.631	-0.255	-0.702
-1.501	-0.488	-0.162	-0.136	1.033	0.203	0.448	0.748	-0.423	-0.432
-0.690	0.756	-1.618	-0.345	-0.511	-2.051	-0.457	-0.218	0.857	-0.465
1.372	0.225	0.378	0.761	0.181	-0.736	0.960	-1.530	-0.260	0.120
-0.482	1.678	-0.057	-1.229	-0.486	0.856	-0.491	-1.983	-2.830	-0.238
-1.376	-0.150	1.356	-0.561	-0.256	-0.212	0.219	0.779	0.953	-0.869
-1.010	0.598	-0.918	1.598	0.065	0.415	-0.169	0.313	-0.973	-1.016
-0.005	-0.889	0.012	-0.725	1.147	-0.121	1.096	0.481	-1.691	0.417
1.393	-1.163	-0.911	1.231	-0.199	-0.246	1.239	-2.574	-0.558	0.056
-1.787	-0.261	1.237	1.046	-0.508	-1.630	-0.146	-0.392	-0.627	0.561
-0.105	-0.357	-1.384	0.360	-0.992	-0.116	-1.698	-2.832	-1.108	-2.357
-1.339	1.827	-0.959	0.424	0.969	-1.141	-1.041	0.362	-1.726	1.956
1.041	0.535	0.731	1.377	0.983	-1.330	1.620	-1.040	-0.524	-0.281
0.279	-2.056	0.717	-0.873	-1.096	-1.396	1.047	0.089	-0.573	0.932
-1.805	-2.008	-1.633	0.542	0.250	-0.166	0.032	0.079	0.471	-1.029
-1.186	1.180	1.114	0.882	1.265	-0.202	0.151	-0.376	-0.310	0.479
0.658	-1.141	1.151	-1.210	-0.927	0.425	0.290	-0.902	0.610	2.709
-0.439	0.358	-1.939	0.891	-0.227	0.602	0.873	-0.437	-0.220	-0.057
-1.399	-0.230	0.385	-0.649	-0.577	0.237	-0.289	0.513	0.738	-0.300
0.199	0.208	-1.083	-0.219	-0.291	1.221	1.119	0.004	-2.015	-0.594
0.159	0.272	-0.313	0.084	-2.828	-0.439	-0.792	-1.275	-0.623	-1.047
2.273	0.606	0.606	-0.747	0.247	1.291	0.063	-1.793	-0.699	-1.347
0.041	-0.307	0.121	0.790	-0.584	0.541	0.484	-0.986	0.481	0.996
-1.132	-2.098	0.921	0.145	0.446	-1.661	1.045	-1.363	-0.586	-1.023
0.768	0.079	-1.473	0.034	-2.127	0.665	0.084	-0.880	-0.579	0.551
0.375	-1.658	-0.851	0.234	-0.656	0.340	-0.086	-0.158	-0.120	0.418
-0.513	-0.344	0.210	-0.736	1.041	0.008	0.427	-0.831	0.191	0.074
0.292	-0.521	1.266	-1.206	-0.899	0.110	-0.528	-0.813	0.071	0.524
1.026	2.990	-0.574	-0.491	-1.114	1.297	-1.433	-1.345	-3.001	0.479
-1.334	1.278	-0.568	-0.109	-0.515	-0.566	2.923	0.500	0.359	0.326
-0.287	-0.144	-0.254	0.574	-0.451	-1.181	-1.190	-0.318	-0.094	1.114
0.161	-0.886	-0.921	-0.509	1.410	-0.518	0.192	-0.432	1.501	1.068
-1.346	0.193	-1.202	0.394	-1.045	0.843	0.942	1.045	0.031	0.772
1.250	-0.199	-0.288	1.810	1.378	0.584	1.216	0.733	0.402	0.226

* This table is reproduced from a larger table in *Introduction to Statistical Analysis*, by Dixon and Massey. Copyright © 1957, McGraw-Hill Book Company. Used by permission of McGraw-Hill Book Company.

where n = the number of runs conducted,

           Y_j = output parameter value obtained for run j.

The Monte Carlo technique is equivalent to selecting hardware components at random and building up a system. It thereby provides very good correlation with manufactured hardware and requires no assumptions regarding the nonlinearity effects of the tolerances. When a digital computer is used, an ample number of solutions can be obtained.

Let us consider as an example that each of the component parameters is to be represented by a normal distribution with some mean and 3σ-value. The required calculations may then be accomplished with the aid of a random normal number subroutine or a standard table, as illustrated in Table 6.8. This table presents a random collection of numbers which are based on a normal distribution with a mean equal to zero and standard deviation of unity. The parameter value X_i corresponding to random normal number N_i is given by either of the equations

$$X_i = X^* \pm N_i \left[\frac{X(\text{max}) - X^*}{3} \right]. \tag{6.22}$$

Let us consider the following example.

Example 6.5 Determine, by hardware testing, realistic values for the limits on amplifier gain and phase angle resulting from tolerances of the amplifier load. The load is specified as

$$Z_L = 460 \pm 92 + j\,320 \pm 48 \text{ ohms.}$$

Assume 30 test runs to be conducted. If R_L and X_L are considered to be independent quantities, two separate random numbers are necessary for each setting of R_L, X_L. Using Eq. (6.22) and the first two numbers in Table 6.8 gives values of R and X for the first run as follows:

$$R_1 = R^* - N_1 \left(\frac{R(\text{max}) - R^*}{3} \right)$$

$$= 460 - (0.464)(92/3) = 445.7.$$

In a similar manner,

$$X_1 = 320 - (0.137)(48/3) = 317.8.$$

The remaining 29 settings are calculated in the same manner by using additional random normal numbers from Table 6.8. The results are presented in Table 6.9. A hardware test is then made with each load setting as calculated above. The gain and the phase angle are measured for each load setting. Assume that the results are as shown in Table 6.10. Using Eq. (6.20), we calculate the mean values for the amplifier gain and the phase shift,

$$K^* = \frac{10091}{30} = 336.37 \text{ v/v,} \quad \phi^* = \frac{848}{30} = 28.27 \text{ deg.}$$

These values are then subtracted from each measured value of gain and phase, respectively, and the difference is squared. These results are also shown in the same table. Using Eq. (6.21), we calculate the 3σ-values as

$$3\sigma_K = 3\sqrt{1744.96/30} = 22.87 \text{ v/v,}$$
$$3\sigma_\phi = 3\sqrt{69.86/30} = 4.578 \text{ deg.}$$

Table 6.9

Run no.	RANDOM NORMAL NUMBERS		IMPEDANCE VALUES, ohms	
	N_1	N_2	R_L	X_L
1	0.464	0.137	445.7	317.8
2	2.455	−0.323	384.7	325.1
3	−0.068	−0.296	462.0	315.2
4	−0.288	1.298	468.8	299.2
5	0.060	−2.526	458.1	360.4
6	−0.531	−0.194	476.2	323.1
7	0.543	−1.558	443.3	323.1
8	0.187	−1.190	454.2	339.0
9	1.486	−0.354	414.4	325.6
10	−0.634	0.697	479.4	308.8
11	0.926	1.375	431.6	298.0
12	0.785	−0.963	435.9	335.4
13	1.022	−0.472	428.6	327.5
14	1.279	3.521	420.7	263.6
15	0.571	−1.851	442.4	349.6
16	0.194	1.192	454.0	300.9
17	1.394	−0.555	417.2	328.8
18	0.046	0.321	458.5	314.8
19	2.945	1.974	369.6	288.4
20	−0.258	0.412	467.9	313.4
21	0.906	−0.513	432.2	328.2
22	−0.525	0.595	476.0	310.4
23	0.881	−0.934	432.9	334.9
24	1.579	0.161	411.5	317.4
25	1.179	−1.055	423.8	336.8
26	0.007	0.769	459.7	307.6
27	0.971	0.712	430.2	308.6
28	1.090	−0.631	426.5	330.0
29	−1.501	−0.488	506.0	327.8
30	−0.162	−0.136	464.9	322.1

6.9. SUMMARY

In this chapter, it was demonstrated how statistical tolerance theory can be applied to servomechanism design problems. We started by describing the fundamental concepts of a histogram, frequency distribution, and the normal curve. The central limit property was then introduced as a basis for considering most system parameters to have at least an approximately normal distribution. Based on this property, a working relationship was established by assuming component parameters to be normally distributed with their limits considered as 3σ-values.

Table 6.10

Run no.	HARDWARE TEST DATA		CALCULATED DATA	
	Gain K	Phase ϕ	$(K - K^*)^2$	$(\phi - \phi^*)^2$
1	336	30	0.13	3.00
2	336	30	0.13	3.00
3	350	28	185.86	0.07
4	342	30	31.73	3.00
5	340	27	13.20	1.60
6	340	28	13.20	0.07
7	332	27	19.06	1.60
8	340	30	13.20	3.00
9	328	29	70.00	0.53
10	340	27	13.20	1.60
11	336	27	0.13	1.60
12	316	30	414.80	3.00
13	342	27	31.73	1.60
14	332	20	19.06	3.00
15	336	27	0.13	1.60
16	340	29	13.20	0.53
17	316	26	414.80	5.13
18	340	30	13.20	3.00
19	338	27	2.66	1.60
20	340	30	13.20	3.00
21	340	27	13.20	1.60
22	330	27	40.53	1.60
23	338	27	2.66	1.60
24	340	30	13.20	3.00
25	332	28	19.06	0.07
26	338	27	2.66	1.60
27	350	31	185.86	7.47
28	342	29	31.73	0.53
29	337	28	0.40	0.07
30	324	25	152.93	10.67
Totals	10091	848	1744.96	69.86

Equations were obtained for calculating the mean and standard deviation of an assembly which is a linear combination of several parameters. Nearly all system design problems, however, are complex in nature and cannot be represented by this simple linear case. For this reason, several methods were generated to handle the nonlinear situation. We started by using a weighting-factor technique that accounted for the probabilities associated with the various parameters as well as the nonlinear effect. Application of this technique to multivariable design problems is impractical, however, because of the excessive number of calculations required.

The Taylor series or moment method was shown to provide a more practical solution to the general tolerance problem. Employment of this method required derivation of the partial derivative of each performance parameter with respect to each component parameter. To circumvent this limitation, an approximate-slope technique was developed that used a parameter-perturbation approach to approximate the required partial derivatives. Thus one need work only with the basic equation defining each performance parameter. Finally, these equations must be solved once for nominal conditions and once for each parameter in the system.

The Monte Carlo technique was presented as an alternative method of considering the effects of component tolerances. Its main advantages are its close similarity to actual hardware performance and its capability to use any desired distribution to represent the various components.

The approximate-slope and Monte Carlo techniques both lend themselves directly to digital computer programming. In either case one need program only the nominal equation, and standard subroutines can be used to automatically vary the component parameters and arrive at the tolerance values for the total system. The Monte Carlo technique is more accurate but usually requires more runs than the approximate-slope technique. On the other hand, the latter provides information showing the sensitivity of each of the system performance parameters with respect to each component parameter. With this information the designer can easily determine how the component tolerances should be altered to arrive at the optimum system.

PROBLEMS

*6.1. Assume that the damping ratio for a servo design was calculated to be

$$\text{maximum} = 0.865, \qquad \text{minimum} = 0.486.$$

Consider the above to be 3σ-limits. Assuming that the allowable specification limits were set between 0.8 and 0.6, calculate the percentage of units that will probably fail the specification requirements.

*6.2. Consider the distributions in Table 6.11 to exist for the motor and generator damping coefficients:

Table 6.11

Parameter	Units	Maximum	Minimum
f_m	oz-in-sec/rad	5.2	2.6
f_g	oz-in-sec/rad	15.3	7.4

Calculate the resulting distribution for the total damping coefficient f_T, where $f_T = f_g + f_m$.

6.3. Given the mean and tolerance values for the torque constant and total inertia as

$$K_T = 2000 \pm 400 \text{ oz-in/rad}, \qquad J_T = 0.2 \pm 0.04 \text{ oz-in-sec}^2/\text{rad},$$

calculate, using the Monte Carlo technique, the resulting mean and 3σ-tolerance expected for the natural frequency. Use the sets of random normal numbers in Table 6.12 to make four calculations.

Table 6.12

Run	1	2	3	4
K_T	−0.482	1.678	−0.057	−1.229
J_T	−1.229	−0.057	1.678	−0.482

6.4. Solve Problem 6.3 by the approximate-slope technique to obtain the resulting natural frequency distribution.

*6.5. Solve the problem in Example 6.4 by the Taylor series expansion technique to determine the resulting damping ratio.

6.6. If a parameter is described by a normal distribution, what percentage of units will fall outside the 1σ-, 2σ-, and 3σ-limits?

6.7. Given that Y is a ratio of two products,

$$Y = \frac{X_1 X_2 \ldots}{Z_1 Z_2 \ldots},$$

show that in place of using the Taylor series technique you could calculate the sigma of Y by using the simplified equation

$$\sigma_Y = Y^* \sqrt{\left(\frac{\sigma_{X1}}{X_1}\right)^2 + \left(\frac{\sigma_{X2}}{X_2}\right)^2 + \cdots + \left(\frac{\sigma_{Z1}}{Z_1}\right)^2 + \left(\frac{\sigma_{Z2}}{Z_2}\right)^2 + \cdots}$$

*6.8. The following values for servo torque constant were obtained by testing 15 production units:

479	445	414
435	462	439
442	468	464
467	458	459
423	443	458

Calculate the corresponding mean and 3σ-limits.

BIBLIOGRAPHY

BOWKER, A., and G. LIEBERMAN, *Engineering Statistics*, Prentice-Hall, 1959.

DIXON, W., and F. MASSEY, *Introduction to Statistical Analysis*, McGraw-Hill, 1957.

KIRKPATRICK, E. G., "Statistical Tolerancing," Lear Siegler, Inc., Instrument Division, Engineering Report No. GR-1408 (August 1962).

MARK, D., "Choosing the Best Method for a Variability Analysis," *Electronic Design* (November 8, 1963).

MARK, D., and L. STEMBER, JR., "Variability Analysis," *Electro-Technology* 37–48 (July 1965).

PETERSON, E. L., *Statistical Analysis and Optimization of Systems*, Wiley, 1961.

CHAPTER 7

THE CONSIDERATION AND EFFECTS
OF NONLINEARITIES

The behavior of an actual servo differs to some degree from the linear theory presented in the previous chapters. The amount of deviation depends on both the nonlinearities and the input command. There are at least three important nonlinearities which must be considered in any judicious servo design: (1) saturation, (2) load friction, and (3) backlash. Normally only these three need be considered in the design or analysis of instrument servos to predict the final servo performance with satisfactory accuracy.

7.1. AMPLIFIER SATURATION AND THE DESCRIBING FUNCTION

Saturation is a major cause of a servo response being other than linear. We can best understand the effect of saturation by developing a nonlinear transfer function or describing function for the amplifier with saturation. The approach to be used is based on the assumption that the amplifier is linear up to a definite output level and then abruptly goes into saturation (Fig. 7.1).

The amplifier output voltage E_c can be expressed in terms of the input E_i and the saturation levels shown in Fig. 7.1 by the following set of equations:

$$E_c = K_a E_i, \qquad \text{for} \quad |E_i| \leq E_{i\,\text{sat}}, \tag{7.1}$$

$$E_c = E_{c\,\text{sat}}, \qquad \text{for} \quad E_i \geq E_{i\,\text{sat}},$$

$$E_c = -E_{c\,\text{sat}}, \qquad \text{for} \quad E_i \leq -E_{i\,\text{sat}}. \tag{7.2}$$

If a sine input signal with peak amplitude greater than $E_{i\,\text{sat}}$ is applied to the amplifier, the output will be an amplified but "clipped" reproduction of the original input (Fig. 7.2). The output waveform can be analyzed by means

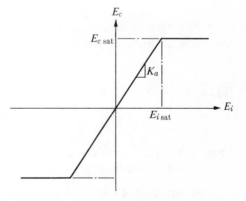

Fig. 7.1. Idealized amplifier gain curve.

145

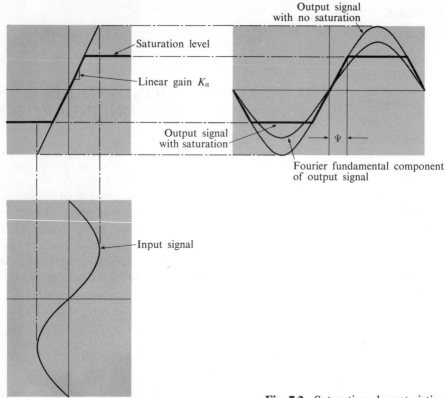

Fig. 7.2. Saturation characteristics.

of a Fourier series. If E_i is taken as the peak amplitude of the input signal, then the peak amplitude of the fundamental of the clipped output is given by

$$E_c(\text{first}) = \frac{2K_a}{\pi}\left(\psi + \frac{\sin 2\psi}{2}\right) E_i, \tag{7.3}$$

where ψ is the angle shown in Fig. 7.2, defined by

$$\psi = \arcsin (E_{c\,\text{sat}}/K_a E_i). \tag{7.4}$$

Higher odd-harmonics are also generated, the third being

$$E_c(\text{third}) = \frac{2K_a}{3\pi}\left(\frac{\sin 2\psi}{2} + \frac{\sin 4\psi}{4}\right) E_i. \tag{7.5}$$

These higher harmonics are usually neglected in the describing function approach. There are two basic reasons why this approximation is valid. These are:

1. The harmonics are usually considerably reduced in amplitude compared with the fundamental and therefore are of lesser importance in defining the output waveform.

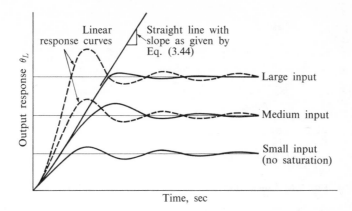

Fig. 7.3. Transient response to step input showing effects of saturation.

2. The harmonics are at higher frequencies than the fundamental and consequently are filtered out or attenuated as they pass through the rest of the servo. This happens because most servo components act like low-pass filters.

For this application, the approximation is in general very good. As an example, let us consider an amplifier which drives a 400-cps servomotor. The lowest harmonic is the third, which is at 1200 cps. This can be ignored since its main effect is the production of heat in the servomotor.

If we neglect the higher harmonics, we can obtain the effective gain of the amplifier from the describing function. Since the describing function is defined as the ratio of the Fourier fundamental to the input, the effective gain is given by

$$K_a(\text{effective}) = \frac{2}{\pi}\left(\psi + \frac{\sin 2\psi}{2}\right) K_a(\text{linear}). \tag{7.6}$$

Using the describing function analogy to describe the amplifier, we see that for small amplitudes for which saturation does not occur, $\psi = 0$ and the gain is the linear value. As the amplitude is increased, saturation occurs and the output waveform peaks are clipped. Saturation has more effect on the servo response for larger amplitudes since more clipping takes place. Using this approach, we can often analyze the effect of amplifier saturation almost as easily as if it were linear. The only difference is that when we include saturation, whose characteristics are a function of amplitude, we must use families of curves or data instead of single values.

From the above equation, as well as from Fig. 7.2, we see that the describing function for amplifier saturation can have only attenuation and does not exhibit any phase angle. The larger the input amplitude beyond saturation, the lower the gain. Figure 7.3 shows the effect of amplifier saturation on the servo transient response to various levels of step inputs. The response of the servo with and without saturation is shown to allow direct observation of the saturation effect.

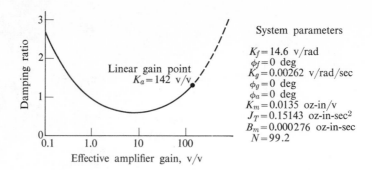

Fig. 7.4. Linear damping ratio vs. effective amplifier gain.

Each of the transient response curves with saturation approaches the same straight line, as shown in Fig. 7.3. The slope of this line is the servo followup rate, which is given by Eq. (3.44). The response also appears more sluggish for inputs large enough to cause saturation due to the effective reduction in amplifier gain. The period of any oscillation is also greater since the reduction in gain lowers the natural frequency. The effect of saturation on the damping is not in general quite so straight-forward. The linear damping ratio for a motor-generator servo was shown in Chapter 5 to be given by

$$\zeta = \frac{N^2[K_g K_a K_m \cos{(\phi_g + \phi_a)} + B_m]}{2\sqrt{K_f K_a K_m N \cos{(\phi_f + \phi_a)}} J_T}. \tag{7.7}$$

Normally when a generator is used,

$$K_g K_a K_m \cos{(\phi_g + \phi_a)} \gg B_m, \tag{7.8}$$

and thus the damping ratio is approximately directly proportional to the square root of the amplifier gain. During periods of heavy saturation, however, the effective value of K_a becomes small, the inequality sign in Eq. (7.8) changes direction, and ζ becomes approximately inversely proportional to the square root of the amplifier gain. Figure 7.4 shows a plot of Eq. (7.7) for typical design values of the parameters. The linear damping ratio is seen to be 1.29. As saturation takes place, K_a effectively decreases, thereby causing first a reduction in ζ and then an increase. The value of K_a that yields the minimum value of ζ can be obtained directly by differentiating Eq. (7.7) with respect to K_a, setting the derivative equal to zero, and solving for K_a. This procedure yields

$$K_a(\min \zeta) = \frac{B_m}{K_g K_m \cos{(\phi_g + \phi_a)}}. \tag{7.9}$$

Substituting this relationship into Eq. (7.7) shows the minimum effective value of ζ to be

$$\zeta(\min) = \sqrt{B_m K_g / J_T K_f}. \tag{7.10}$$

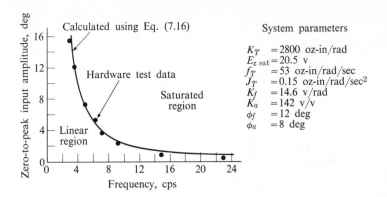

Fig. 7.5. Saturation zone curve for a typical instrument servomechanism excited with a sinusoidal input signal.

7.2. AMPLIFIER SATURATION AND THE SYSTEM FREQUENCY RESPONSE

In general, the servo operates in a saturated state and an unsaturated state. For example, let us consider a servo being excited by a sinusoidal driving function. The output voltage for operation in the linear region can be seen from Fig. 5.7 to be given by

$$E_c(s) = -K_a N K_g \cos(\phi_g + \phi_a) s \theta_o(s) + K_a K_f \cos(\phi_f + \phi_a)\theta_i(s)$$
$$- K_a K_f \cos(\phi_f + \phi_a)\,\theta_o(s). \tag{7.11}$$

Using Eq. (5.15), we can express the output displacement $\theta_o(s)$ in terms of the input $\theta_i(s)$ as

$$\theta_o(s) = \frac{K_T \theta_i(s)}{J_T s^2 + f_T s + K_T}. \tag{7.12}$$

Substituting this into Eq. (7.11), we find

$$E_c(s) = -K_f K_a \cos(\phi_f + \phi_a)\left(\frac{f_T s + K_T}{J_T s^2 + f_T s + K_T} - 1\right)\theta_i(s). \tag{7.13}$$

Placing the bracketed quantity over a common denominator and letting $s = j\omega$ to obtain the steady-state frequency characteristics, we have

$$E_c(j\omega) = -K_f K_a \cos(\phi_f + \phi_a)\frac{J_T \omega^2}{(K_T - J_T \omega^2) + j(f_T \omega)}\,\theta_i(j\omega). \tag{7.14}$$

The magnitude of the voltage is thus

$$|E_c(\omega)| = K_f K_a \cos(\phi_f + \phi_a)\frac{J_T \omega^2}{\sqrt{(K_T - J_T \omega^2)^2 + (f_T \omega)^2}}\,\theta_i(\omega). \tag{7.15}$$

Setting $|E_c(\omega)|$ equal to the amplifier saturation level ($E_{c\,\text{sat}}$), and solving for $\theta_i(\omega)$, one obtains the zero-to-peak magnitude of the input sinusoid required to cause the

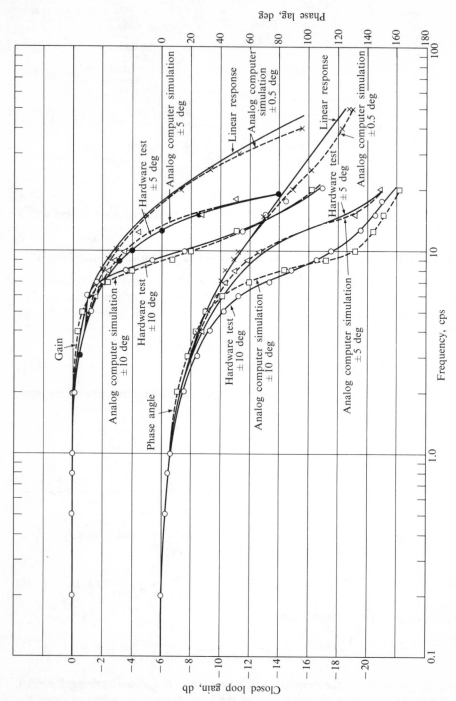

Fig. 7.6. Closed-loop frequency response of a typical instrument servomechanism (comparison of calculated and hardware test data).

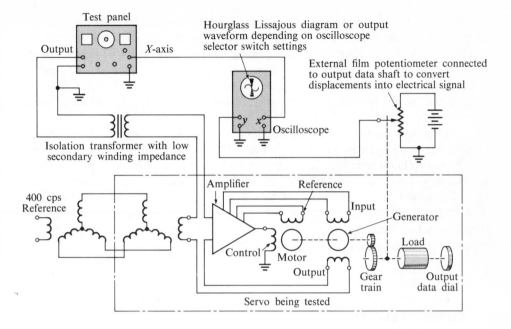

Fig. 7.7. Test setup diagram for measuring servo frequency response.

amplifier to just saturate. This value is

$$\theta_{i\,\text{sat}}(\omega) = \frac{E_{c\,\text{sat}}}{K_f K_a \cos\,(\phi_f + \phi_a)}\frac{\sqrt{(K_T - J_T\omega^2)^2 + (f_T\omega)^2}}{J_T\omega^2}. \qquad (7.16)$$

Figure 7.5 shows a plot of the measured $\theta_{i\,\text{sat}}$ for various values of frequency as obtained from a typical instrument servomechanism with the parameter values shown. The corresponding curve obtained from Eq. (7.16) is also shown. For combinations of θ_i and ω that lie above the curve, the amplifier saturates, and those that lie below the curve provide linear operation.

Figure 7.6 shows the frequency response of the same servomechanism to ± 5- and ± 10-deg input amplitudes. For comparison the analog computer-simulated response is also shown for ± 5- and ± 10-deg inputs. The linear closed-loop response was determined on a digital computer and is also shown, along with the analog computer response, with ± 0.5-deg inputs.

We can determine the frequency response of the hardware using the test setup shown in Fig. 7.7. The test panel generates a suppressed-carrier modulated 400-cps signal. This signal is summed in series along with the generator and synchro inputs. The isolation transformer connects the test panel output into the servo circuitry. To avoid altering the follow-up and generator gains, the transformer should have a low secondary impedance. The test used to measure the servo torque constant may be repeated with the transformer and test panel connected to verify that the setup has not altered the servo performance. The output of the film potentiometer is recorded on the y-axis of the oscilloscope. The reference output from the test panel is recorded on the x-axis of the oscilloscope. The test frequencies and amplitude are set, and the resulting phase lag is determined by adjusting the reference phase of the test panel until the pattern on the oscilloscope displays a zero phase lag. The reading on the phase dial is then recorded as the amount of phase lag. The gain is determined by reading the output amplitude on the oscilloscope and dividing by the fixed input amplitude.

The schematic diagram used for obtaining the frequency response on the analog computer is very similar to that shown in Fig. 5.17. The only changes required, besides rescaling, are (1) the amplifier between potentiometers 3 and 4 is modified to include saturation, (2) potentiometer 10 is replaced by an appropriate signal generator, and (3) the recorder x-axis is connected to the generator so that standard Lissajous diagrams are obtained. From this, one can calculate the gain and phase for each frequency set on the signal generator and obtain a corresponding plot. One must, of course, be careful to wait for steady-state conditions before making the recording.

7.3. EFFECTS OF QUADRATURE SIGNAL ON THE AMPLIFIER GAIN CHARACTERISTICS

With quadrature present at the input of a high-gain amplifier, system performance can be degraded because of saturation even for operation near null. This is because the amplifier operates on the total signal presented at its input terminals. In general, this input consists of an in-phase (torque-producing at the motor) signal and quadrature. The servo nulls only the torque-producing component, and thus the quadrature component may remain and, when amplified, cause the amplifier to saturate. This in turn reduces the gain to the in-phase signal, thereby degrading the servo performance.

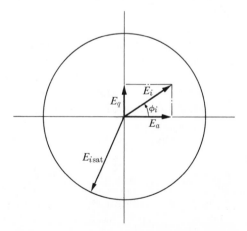

The amount of gain reduction due to quadrature saturation of the amplifier can be determined in the following way. Let the total amplifier input voltage E_i be represented by the components, as shown in Fig. 7.8, where E_a is the torque-producing component and E_q is the quadrature. When $E_i > E_{i\,\text{sat}}$, which occurs when

$$\sqrt{E_a^2 + E_q^2} > E_{i\,\text{sat}}, \qquad (7.17)$$

the amplifier is saturated, and for $E_i \leq E_{i\,\text{sat}}$ or

$$\sqrt{E_a^2 + E_q^2} \leq E_{i\,\text{sat}}, \qquad (7.18)$$

Fig. 7.8. Vectorial relationships of amplifier input voltages with quadrature and saturation.

the amplifier is in the linear range. The latter case is represented by all E_i-vectors inside the circle shown. Using the describing function established in Eq. (7.3) to represent the amplifier characteristics, we obtain the effective or torque-producing output:

$$E_c(\text{eff}) = \frac{2K_a}{\pi}\left(\psi - \frac{\sin 2\psi}{2}\right) E_i \cos \phi_i, \qquad (7.19)$$

where for $K_a E_i \geq E_{c\,\text{sat}}$,

$$\psi = \text{arcsine}\,(E_{c\,\text{sat}}/K_a E_i), \qquad (7.20)$$

and for $K_a E_i \leq E_{c\,\text{sat}}$,

$$\psi = \pi/2. \qquad (7.21)$$

The total rms input voltage and phase shift are in turn given by

$$E_i = \sqrt{E_a^2 + E_q^2}, \qquad (7.22)$$

$$\phi_i = \arctan\,(E_q/E_a). \qquad (7.23)$$

The quantity $E_i \cos \phi_i$ is the torque-producing component of the input. Thus, the effective gain of the amplifier, including the presence of quadrature, is given by

$$K_a(\text{eff}) = \frac{2K_a}{\pi}\left(\psi + \frac{\sin 2\psi}{2}\right), \qquad (7.24)$$

where for $K_a\sqrt{E_a^2 + E_q^2} \geq E_{c\,\text{sat}}$,

$$\psi = \text{arcsine}\left(\frac{E_{c\,\text{sat}}}{K_a\sqrt{E_a^2 + E_q^2}}\right), \qquad (7.25)$$

and for $K_a\sqrt{E_a^2 + E_q^2} \leq E_{c\,\text{sat}}$,

$$\psi = \pi/2. \qquad (7.26)$$

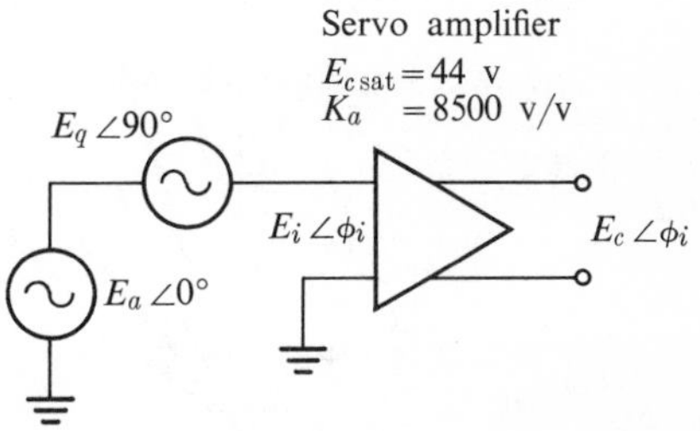

Fig. 7.9. Servo amplifier circuit with quadrature input.

Since ψ is a function of the quadrature voltage E_q, Eq. (7.24) shows that the effective gain of the amplifier to the in-phase signal is a function of quadrature. If the total amplifier input signal, in-phase plus quadrature, is not sufficient to cause saturation, then the output is the input multiplied by the amplifier linear gain. However, as soon as quadrature is allowed to saturate the amplifier, the effective gain to the in-phase signal is reduced. To illustrate this, let us consider the circuit shown in Fig. 7.9.

The effective gain characteristics of the amplifier can be observed by plotting $E_c(\text{eff})$ vs. E_a for various levels of quadrature. Figure 7.10 shows such a plot obtained from Eqs. (7.19), (7.25), and (7.26). The effect of the quadrature is readily apparent.

Of particular interest to the servo designer is the gain near null. This can be obtained directly from Eqs. (7.24) through (7.26) by letting E_a go to zero. This yields

$$K_a(\text{eff}) = \frac{2K_a}{\pi}\left(\psi + \frac{\sin 2\psi}{2}\right), \qquad (7.27)$$

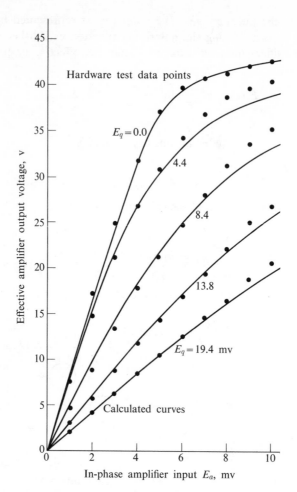

Fig. 7.10. Servo amplifier output vs. input characteristics for various levels of quadrature.

where for $K_a E_q \geq E_{c\,\text{sat}}$,

$$\psi = \text{arcsine}\,(E_{c\,\text{sat}}/K_a E_q), \qquad (7.28)$$

and for $K_a E_q \leq E_{c\,\text{sat}}$,

$$\psi = \pi/2. \qquad (7.29)$$

Figure 7.11 shows a plot of the gain near null vs. quadrature as obtained using the above equations for the system shown in Fig. 7.10. So long as the quadrature does not saturate the amplifier, the gain is simply the linear value K_a. Once quadrature saturation does occur, the gain near null is lowered, eventually approaching zero for large amounts of quadrature.

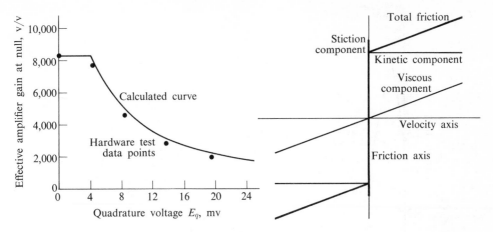

Fig. 7.11. Effective amplifier gain at null vs. quadrature voltage.

Fig. 7.12. Friction characteristics.

7.4. COULOMB FRICTION AND ITS EFFECTS ON PERFORMANCE

In an instrument servomechanism, the presence of friction may be desirable for some conditions and undesirable for others. It produces a steady-state or *static* error, and therefore is undesirable. On the other hand, under special conditions friction provides appreciable damping. But of utmost importance is the fact that all simple motor-generator positional servomechanisms with backlash would display continuous oscillations about null except for the friction existing at the load. This latter characteristic will be considered in detail in Section 7.4. For now, let us examine the friction effects on a system without gear train backlash and with infinite stiffness.

Friction may be divided into three components: (1) viscous, (2) kinetic coulomb (running friction), and (3) static coulomb (starting friction). The static coulomb is often called *stiction*. These three components as well as the total are shown graphically in Fig. 7.12. The static friction level is normally between 1 and 1.5 times the kinetic friction level. For most instrument servo applications it is customary to not distinguish between the static and running values, but to consider a single friction tolerance distribution large enough that it includes both. The maximum levels are of interest when we consider the static accuracy. The minimum levels of friction at the load (output side of any backlash) are of interest since they represent the worst case of friction contributing to stability. The viscous component is only appreciable when either a fluid or a magnetic field is involved, such as with lubricated bearings or rotation in a magnetic field. The effect of the viscous component, which was treated in Chapter 5, can usually be neglected in describing the load friction of an instrument system.

The friction levels, both static and kinetic, associated with typical instrument servo gear trains and load components vary considerably with life for "identical"

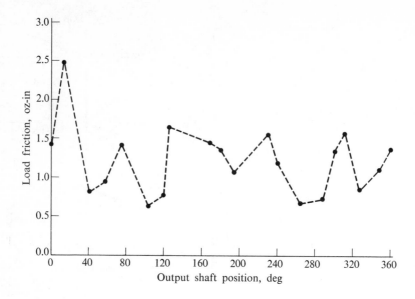

Fig. 7.13. Load friction characteristics as a function of shaft position (hardware test data).

production line units. The variance is a function of temperature and even a function of angular position of the output. Figure 7.13 shows a plot of the friction level of a typical instrument servomechanism as a function of the output shaft position.

With friction present in a servo, the output response to a low-frequency sinusoidal input appears as shown in Fig. 7.14. It is apparent that the output follows the input except for a phase lag and flat spots at the peaks. The output lags the input by the maximum steady-state error caused by the friction until the input reverses. Since the load stops at the point of reversal, the output remains at the same position while the error reverses through zero and then builds up enough torque to move the load again.

The amount of phase lag γ can be calculated, since from Fig. 7.14 the steady-state error is given by

$$\epsilon_{ss} = \theta_o \sin \gamma, \tag{7.30}$$

and the steady-state error resulting from friction is given by

$$\epsilon_{ss} = T_f/K_T. \tag{7.31}$$

Setting the two equations equal and solving for the constant phase lag angle γ, we obtain

$$\gamma = \sin^{-1} (T_f/K_T\theta_o). \tag{7.32}$$

We see that the phase lag is a constant, that is, independent of frequency, and that it is inversely proportional to the magnitude of the input. The phase lag, for a given friction level and input, can be decreased only by increasing the servo torque constant K_T.

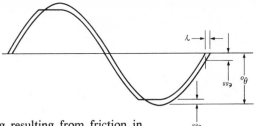

Fig. 7.14. Phase lag resulting from friction in servomechanism.

Because of the high requirements for accuracy, friction effects are often forced to play a minor role in determining system response. However, there are situations where friction is significant and provides appreciable damping. The linear damping ratio alone is not sufficient to describe the servo stability when friction effects are large. For example, if ζ were 0.2, one would consider the design unsatisfactory. However, if the designer could adequately include the stabilization effect of coulomb friction in his estimate of system performance, he might find the design to be completely satisfactory.

Figure 7.15 illustrates the damping provided by the typical friction levels associated with instrument servos and also the static or steady-state error resulting from the friction. The damping provided by the friction is usually small but it is more influential for operation in the saturation region than it is in the linear region.

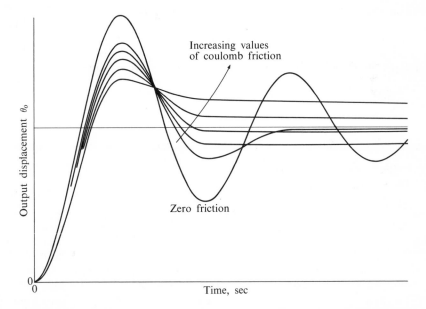

Fig. 7.15. Transient response for various values of load coulomb friction.

7.5. PHASE-PLANE TECHNIQUES FOR ANALYZING THE EFFECTS OF SATURATION AND COULOMB FRICTION

The exact alteration in system performance resulting from the presence of saturation and coulomb friction can be easily determined by means of the phase plane. The phase-plane technique consists in plotting the response of a servo as velocity vs. displacement instead of the more conventional displacement vs. time. This velocity vs. displacement plane is called the *phase plane*. Trajectories are plotted for a variety of initial conditions and from these the stability of the servo can be determined and design improvement planned. The main advantage of using the phase plane is that it makes it relatively easy to consider nonlinearities such as coulomb friction and saturation. To familiarize ourselves with the phase-plane technique, let us first consider the linear case. The differential equation that describes the behavior of the linear second-order system was shown previously to be

$$K_T \theta_\epsilon = J_T \ddot{\theta}_o + f_T \dot{\theta}_o. \tag{7.33}$$

The step function input can be considered by holding the input at zero displacement while the output is offset by the amount of the step. At time $t = 0$, the output is released so that it can return to zero. Since the input is considered zero, the error displacement ($\theta_\epsilon = \theta_i - \theta_o$) is equal to the output displacement θ_o. Making this substitution, we can rewrite Eq. (7.33),

$$K_T \theta_o = J_T \ddot{\theta}_o + f_T \dot{\theta}_o. \tag{7.34}$$

The acceleration is related to the velocity by the differential equation

$$\ddot{\theta}_o = d\dot{\theta}_o/dt. \tag{7.35}$$

Substituting this into Eq. (7.34) and solving for $d\dot{\theta}_o/dt$, we obtain

$$\frac{d\dot{\theta}_o}{dt} = \frac{K_T \theta_o - f_T \dot{\theta}_o}{J_T}. \tag{7.36}$$

Since

$$\dot{\theta}_o = d\theta_o/dt, \tag{7.37}$$

one can divide the left-hand side of Eq. (7.36) by $d\theta_o/dt$ and the right-hand side by $\dot{\theta}_o$. The resulting equation is

$$\frac{d\dot{\theta}_o}{d\theta_o} = \frac{K_T \theta_o - f_T \dot{\theta}_o}{J_T \dot{\theta}_o}, \tag{7.38}$$

where the term $d\dot{\theta}_o/d\theta_o$ is the slope of the trajectory on the phase portrait which represents the instantaneous change in velocity per change in displacement. For every point (θ_o, $\dot{\theta}_o$) in the plane there is a trajectory which passes through that point with the slope given by Eq. (7.38). As with the transient response curves presented in Section 5.6, the response in the phase plane can be characterized by the single parameter ζ by substitution of variables. Using the relationships for ω_N and ζ defined

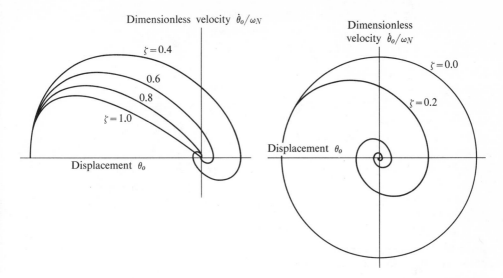

Fig. 7.16. Phase portrait of a linear second-order system for various values of damping ratio.

Fig. 7.17. Phase portrait of a linear second-order system for damping ratio values of 0 and 0.2.

by Eqs. (5.22) and (5.23), respectively, we can rewrite Eq. (7.38),

$$\frac{d\dot{\theta}_o}{d\theta_o} = \frac{\omega_N^2 \theta_o - 2\zeta\omega_N\dot{\theta}_o}{\dot{\theta}_o}. \tag{7.39}$$

If we divide through by ω_N and let

$$\dot{\theta}_o^* = \dot{\theta}_o/\omega_N \tag{7.40}$$

be a normalized or dimensionless velocity, Eq. (7.39) becomes

$$\frac{d\dot{\theta}_o^*}{d\theta_o} = \frac{\theta_o - 2\zeta\dot{\theta}_o^*}{\dot{\theta}_o^*}. \tag{7.41}$$

The resulting phase portrait is thus only a function of the damping ratio ζ. Figure 7.16 illustrates such trajectories.

We shall find it most convenient, before including the effects of coulomb friction, to first consider the zero damping case. If we let $\zeta = 0$, Eq. (7.41) becomes simply

$$d\dot{\theta}_o^*/d\theta_o = \theta_o/\dot{\theta}_o^*, \tag{7.42}$$

and the resulting phase trajectory is a circle about the origin. This is illustrated in Fig. 7.17. As we expected, the phase portrait shows the system to be neutrally stable. That is, the oscillation does not converge or diverge but remains constant and equal to the step amplitude. It is interesting to note that the phase trajectory crosses the horizontal axis at right angles. This is essential to any phase trajectory, as further illustrated by the curve $\zeta = 0.2$, since at the peak amplitude of any oscillation the velocity must be zero.

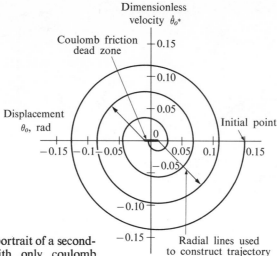

Fig. 7.18. Phase portrait of a second-order system with only coulomb damping.

Load coulomb friction can be added easily to the case $\zeta = 0$, since the torque available to accelerate the system inertia is equal to that developed by the θ_o-displacement minus the friction T_{fo}. Thus the system equation can be written as

$$K_T\theta_o - T_{fo}\,\text{sgn}\,\dot{\theta}_o = J_T\ddot{\theta}_o, \tag{7.43}$$

where the sgn $\dot{\theta}_o$-term refers to the algebraic sign of $\dot{\theta}_o$ and accounts for the fact that coulomb friction has the same magnitude but always opposes motion. By definition,

$$\text{sgn}\,\dot{\theta}_o = \dot{\theta}_o/|\dot{\theta}_o|. \tag{7.44}$$

By dividing through by $K_T\dot{\theta}_o$ in Eq. (7.43) and canceling terms, one can write

$$\left(\theta_o - \frac{T_{fo}}{K_T}\,\text{sgn}\,\dot{\theta}_o\right)\frac{1}{\dot{\theta}_o} = \frac{J_T}{K_T}\frac{d\dot{\theta}_o}{d\theta_o}. \tag{7.45}$$

Again making the substitution $\dot{\theta}_o = \omega_N\theta^*$, we find that

$$\frac{d\dot{\theta}_o^*}{d\theta_o} = \left(\theta_o - \frac{T_{fo}}{K_T}\,\text{sgn}\,\dot{\theta}_o^*\right)\frac{1}{\dot{\theta}_o^*}. \tag{7.46}$$

From the above equation we see that the addition of the coulomb friction has merely shifted the phase portrait in the horizontal axis by the amount $\pm T_{fo}/K_T$. The upper half ($\dot{\theta}_o > 0$) is displacement to the left (minus sign) and the lower half ($\dot{\theta}_o < 0$) is displaced to the right (plus sign). Figure 7.18 shows the trajectory of a system with the parameters

$$T_{fo} = 16 \text{ oz-in}, \qquad K_T = 1536 \text{ oz-in/rad},$$

to an initial displacement of 0.15 rad. The system response has six overshoots and eventually terminates as soon as it intersects the dead zone resulting from the coulomb friction. The width of this dead zone is given by

$$T_{fo}/K_T = \pm 16/1536 \text{ rad} = \pm 0.0104 \text{ rad}.$$

The system remains stationary once this intersection occurs since the velocity is zero and the torque generated by the displacement is not enough to overcome the coulomb friction. As shown, the response obtained from only coulomb damping is unsatisfactory since the number and size of the overshoots is excessive. This is especially true since for larger displacements the situation is even worse. The situation, however, can be significantly improved if the nonlinear effect of amplifier saturation is included along with that of coulomb friction.

The effect of amplifier saturation can be included as follows. For convenience, let T_{sat} represent the equivalent level of torque saturation given by NK_mE_{sat}. If one considers first the situation without a damping generator, then the system operates in the unsaturated mode only when

$$|K_T\theta_o| \leq T_{sat}, \tag{7.47}$$

and the corresponding phase equation is that shown as Eq. (7.46), which can be written in the form

$$\frac{d\dot\theta_o^*}{d\theta_o} = \frac{K_T\theta_o - T_{fo}\,\text{sgn}\,\dot\theta_o^*}{K_T}\frac{1}{\dot\theta_o^*}. \tag{7.48}$$

For values of θ_o such that

$$K_T\theta_o \geq T_{sat}, \tag{7.49}$$

the amplifier is saturated and the phase equation becomes

$$\frac{d\dot\theta_o^*}{d\theta_o} = \frac{T_{sat} - T_{fo}\,\text{sgn}\,\dot\theta_o^*}{K_T}\frac{1}{\dot\theta_o^*}. \tag{7.50}$$

To visualize the trajectory resulting from Eqs. (7.48) and (7.50) on the phase plane, we will use the isocline concept. The phase equation for the second-order system is in general a function of three variables, namely $\dot\theta_o^*$, θ_o, and $d\dot\theta_o^*/d\theta_o$, where the latter is the slope m of the phase trajectory. If a specific numerical value is chosen for m, say $m = m_1$, then the equation is a function of $\dot\theta_o^*$ and θ_o only, thus defining a curve on the phase plane. This curve, called an *isocline*, has the special property of being the locus of all points for which the slope of the phase trajectory is m_1. If a number of values of m are chosen and the isoclines plotted, one can visualize the behavior of the phase portrait. In fact, we can sketch the trajectory from any initial condition, using only straight-line segments whose directions are determined by the slopes associated with the isoclines.

Returning to the problem at hand, we see that the isoclines associated with Eq. (7.48) are radial lines emanating from the two points given by $\pm T_{fo}/K_T$ and for Eq. (7.50) the isoclines are simply straight lines parallel to the θ_o-axis. Equation (7.47) shows that the transition between the two sets of isoclines occurs at the intersection of two lines parallel to $\dot\theta_o^*$, which in turn intersect the θ_o-axis at $\pm T_{sat}/K_T$. Figure 7.19

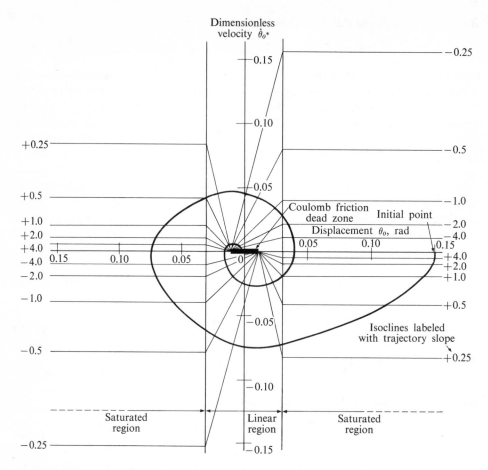

Fig. 7.19. Phase portrait of second-order system with saturation and only coulomb damping.

shows a plot of the isoclines associated with the previous problem, where

$$T_{fo} = 16 \text{ oz-in}, \qquad K_T = 1536 \text{ oz-in/rad},$$

and where we assumed an amplifier saturation level corresponding to

$$T_{\text{sat}} = 48 \text{ oz-in}.$$

The trajectory resulting from an initial displacement of 0.15 rad is also shown. Comparing this trajectory to that obtained in Fig. 7.18, we readily see the stabilizing effect of the amplifier saturation. To illustrate this further, Fig. 7.20 shows the corresponding transient response for the two conditions.

The effect of motor damping can be added in the following manner. Let the reflected motor damping coefficient be denoted by f_m. That is,

$$f_m = N^2 B_m. \tag{7.51}$$

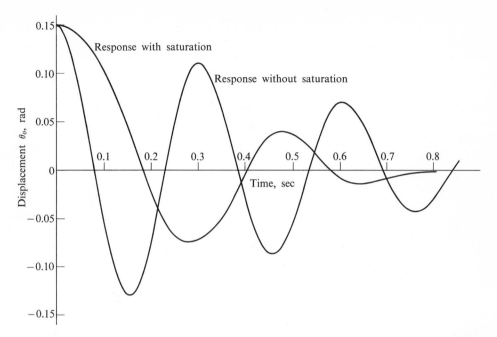

Fig. 7.20. Comparison of transient response with only coulomb damping with and without saturation.

The corresponding damping torque is thus given by $f_m\dot\theta_o$. Using the relationship $\dot\theta_o = \omega_N\dot\theta_o^*$, we see that the motor damping torque is given by $\omega_N f_m\dot\theta_o^*$, which can be added along with the coulomb friction torque in Eqs. (7.48) and (7.50). The corresponding new equations are then, for $|K_T\theta_o| \le T_{sat}$,

$$\frac{d\dot\theta_o^*}{d\theta_o} = \frac{K_T\theta_o - \omega_N f_m\dot\theta_o^* - T_{fo}\,\mathrm{sgn}\,\dot\theta_o^*}{K_T}\,\frac{1}{\dot\theta_o^*}\,, \qquad (7.52)$$

and for $K_T\theta_o \ge T_{sat}$,

$$\frac{d\dot\theta_o^*}{d\theta_o} = \frac{T_{sat} - \omega_N f_m\dot\theta_o^* - T_{fo}\,\mathrm{sgn}\,\dot\theta_o^*}{K_T}\,\frac{1}{\dot\theta_o^*}\,. \qquad (7.53)$$

Using the relationship $\omega_N = \sqrt{K_T/J_T}$, we can convert Eqs. (7.52) and (7.53) to

$$\frac{d\dot\theta_o^*}{d\theta_o} = \frac{K_T\theta_o - T_{fo}\,\mathrm{sgn}\,\dot\theta_o^*}{K_T}\,\frac{1}{\dot\theta_o^*} - 2\zeta_m, \qquad (7.54)$$

for $|K_T\theta_o| \le T_{sat}$, and for $|K_T\theta_o| \ge T_{sat}$, we obtain

$$\frac{d\dot\theta_o^*}{d\theta_o} = \frac{T_{sat} - T_{fo}\,\mathrm{sgn}\,\dot\theta_o^*}{K_T}\,\frac{1}{\dot\theta_o^*} - 2\zeta_m, \qquad (7.55)$$

where ζ_m is defined as the damping ratio component due to the motor. Thus

$$\zeta_m = f_m/2\sqrt{K_T J_T}\,. \qquad (7.56)$$

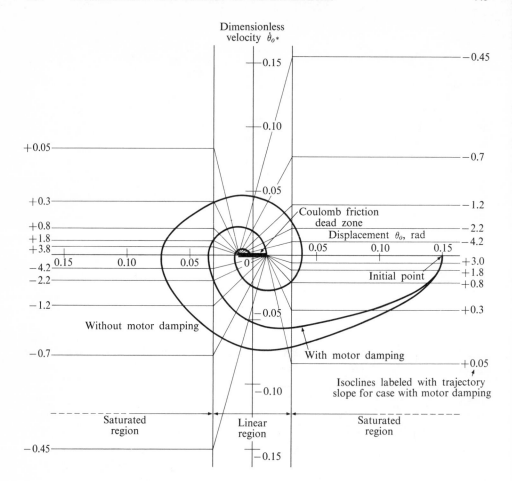

Fig. 7.21. Phase portrait of system showing the effect of motor damping.

From Eqs. (7.54) and (7.55), we see that the general effect of including the motor damping is to reduce the slope m associated with each point in the phase plane. For example, let us consider a typical case where $\zeta_m = 0.1$. Figure 7.21 shows the phase-plane trajectory including this value as compared to that obtained previously without it. The number of overshoots has now been reduced to two of reasonable size. The design might therefore be considered satisfactory even though the linear damping ratio is only 0.1. The corresponding transient response curves are shown in Fig. 7.22.

The phase portrait becomes more involved when a damping generator is added to the system. This is because the inclusion of the generator makes the saturation region become a function of $\dot{\theta}_o^*$ as well as of θ_o. Specifically, amplifier saturation occurs any time that

$$|K_T\theta_o + f_g\dot{\theta}_o| \geq T_{\text{sat}},\tag{7.57}$$

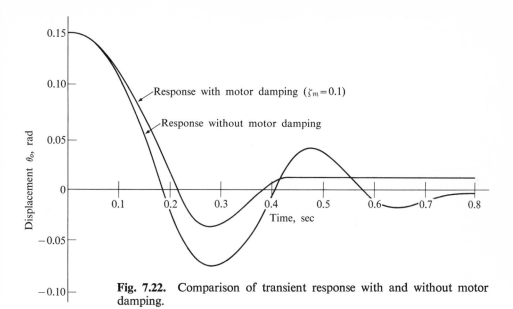

Fig. 7.22. Comparison of transient response with and without motor damping.

where f_g is defined as the damping coefficient due to the generator,

$$f_g = N^2 K_g K_a K_m \cos (\phi_g + \phi_a). \tag{7.58}$$

We can find the saturation boundary on the phase plane by determining the case where Eq. (7.57) is an equality. Dividing through by K_T and using the relationship $\dot{\theta}_o = \omega_N \dot{\theta}_o^*$, we can establish the following relationship:

$$\left| \theta_o + \frac{f_g}{\sqrt{K_T J_T}} \dot{\theta}_o^* \right| \geq \frac{T_{\text{sat}}}{K_T}. \tag{7.59}$$

Let ζ_g be defined as the damping ratio component due to the generator. Thus

$$\zeta_g = f_g / 2\sqrt{K_T J_T} \cdot \tag{7.60}$$

Using this relationship, we can write Eq. (7.59) as

$$|\theta_o + 2\zeta_g \dot{\theta}_o^*| \geq T_{\text{sat}}/K_T. \tag{7.61}$$

The boundary thus becomes two straight lines, each with negative slope given by $-1/(2\zeta_g)$, and intercepts on the θ_o-axis of $\pm T_{\text{sat}}/K_T$. The corresponding slope equations for the phase trajectories which include the ζ_g-term are for the linear region,

$$\frac{d\dot{\theta}_o^*}{d\theta_o} = \frac{K_T \theta_o - T_f \operatorname{sgn} \dot{\theta}_o^*}{K_T} \frac{1}{\dot{\theta}_o^*} - 2(\zeta_m + \zeta_g), \tag{7.62}$$

and for the saturated region,

$$\frac{d\dot{\theta}_o^*}{d\theta_o} = \frac{T_{\text{sat}} - T_f \operatorname{sgn} \dot{\theta}_o^*}{K_T} \frac{1}{\dot{\theta}_o^*} - 2\zeta_m. \tag{7.63}$$

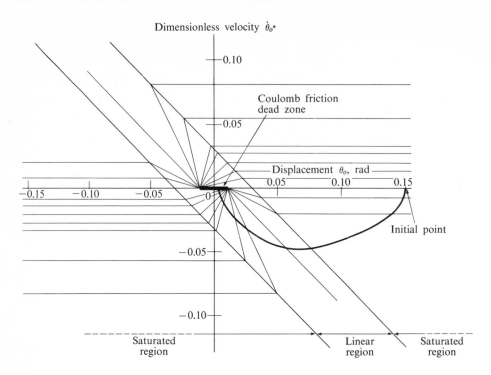

Fig. 7.23. Phase portrait of system with damping generator.

The ζ_g-term does not appear in Eq. (7.63) since the effect of the generator signal is included in T_{sat} for operation in the saturated region. Figure 7.23 illustrates the phase-plane change when a generator is added (with $\zeta_g = 0.5$) to the previous system.

7.6. STABILITY EFFECT OF FRICTION FOR INSUFFICIENT GEAR STIFFNESS

The stiffness of a gear train was introduced as a component parameter in Chapter 3. Chapter 5 demonstrated that in the linear system, with zero load damping, the stability requirement was that $K_s > K_T$. It was shown that if load viscous damping were included, K_s could be smaller than K_T by an amount determinable directly from the component parameters by using Eq. (5.5). The discussion in these chapters provided a qualitative insight for parameter relationships that yield greatest stability but did not produce quantitative data since typical load friction is more coulomb than viscous in nature.

The purpose of this section is to develop the stability relationships for the case of load coulomb friction. An equation is derived for the amount of coulomb friction required to stabilize a system when K_s is less than K_T.

Figure 7.24 shows a mathematical block diagram representing the servo including gear train stiffness and the nonlinearity of load friction. The amount of load

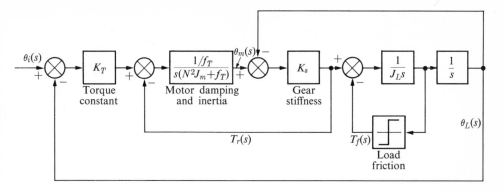

Fig. 7.24. Block diagram of motor-generator servo with gear train stiffness and load friction.

coulomb friction required to avoid an unstable system when $K_s < K_T$ can be derived from describing function theory. To investigate stability by this approach, we must divide the system into two blocks, one linear and one nonlinear. Figure 7.24 is rearranged as shown in Fig. 7.25 by setting the input equal to zero and repositioning the blocks to isolate the nonlinearity. The linear blocks can be reduced to one with the transfer function given by

$$G(s) = \frac{(N^2 J_m)s^3 + (f_T)s^2 + (K_s)s}{(J_L N^2 J_m)s^4 + (J_L f_T)s^3 + (J_L K_s + N^2 J_m K_s)s^2 + (K_s f_T)s + (K_s K_T)}.$$

$$(7.64)$$

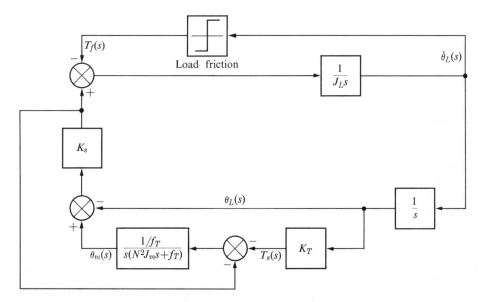

Fig. 7.25. Autonomous block diagram of servo system rearranged to isolate load friction.

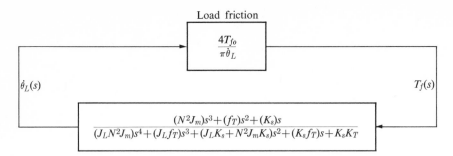

Fig. 7.26. Reduced block diagram.

The gain of the coulomb friction block is given by the following describing function:

$$N(T_f, \dot\theta_L) = 4T_{fo}/\pi\dot\theta_L, \tag{7.65}$$

and the reduced block diagram is therefore as shown in Fig. 7.26.

The servo is neutrally stable (any oscillations present neither increase nor decrease) when the product of the transfer and describing functions equals -1:

$$G(s)N(T_f, \dot\theta_L) = -1. \tag{7.66}$$

Since the nonlinear portion varies with amplitude only and the linear with frequency, the two are independent and can be separated as

$$G(s) = -1/N(T_f, \dot\theta_L). \tag{7.67}$$

Substituting for the describing function, we find that

$$G(s) = \pi\dot\theta_L/4T_{fo}. \tag{7.68}$$

The servo is neutrally stable at any point where the $G(s)$ function intersects the negative real axis since the describing function displays no phase shift. Figure 7.27 shows the loci of the stability point for the following typical system parameters:

$$K_T = 2800 \text{ oz-in/rad}, \qquad f_T = 49.1 \text{ (oz-in)/(rad/sec)},$$
$$N = 99.2, \qquad J_m = 1.0 \text{ gm-cm}^2, \qquad J_L = 665 \text{ gm-cm}^2.$$

The loci of the linear portion for $K_s < K_T$ form near-circles which intersect the negative real or stability locus at one point for each K_s. This intersection represents a neutral stability point. For $K_s = K_T = 2800$, the linear locus is the $j\omega$-axis and for $K_s > K_T$, the locus lies in the right half-plane. Therefore no limit cycle can exist.

Let us consider, for an example, the servo to have a gear stiffness of 2000 oz-in/rad. Figure 7.27 shows that the critical value of $\dot\theta_L/T_f$ is 16 and the oscillation frequency is 72.67 cps. Consider a load friction value of 0.1 oz-in. The critical value of velocity is then 1.6 rad/sec or 91 deg/sec. That is, if the velocity of the oscillation is greater than 91 deg/sec the oscillation will diverge and if the velocity is less, the oscillation will dampen out.

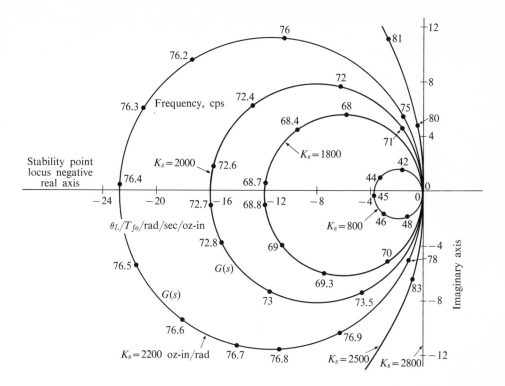

Fig. 7.27. Stability point and frequency response loci for various values of gear train stiffness.

To reverse the situation and look at Fig. 7.27 from the design viewpoint of selecting the gear train stiffness requirement, let us consider the following. Suppose that the minimum friction level is to be 0.1 oz-in and the maximum load velocity is 90 deg/sec. The maximum possible limit cycle velocity is also 90 deg/sec (1.6 rad/sec). Therefore from Fig. 7.28 we see that the critical gear train stiffness is 2000 oz-in/rad. Values lower than this can lead to oscillation.

An analytical expression of the friction required to circumvent oscillations caused by low stiffness may be obtained in the following manner. The frequency at which

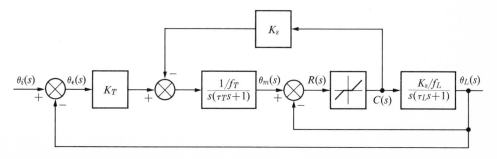

Fig. 7.28. Combined servo block diagram including backlash and load viscous damping.

this intersection occurs is the frequency of the resulting limit cycle. This frequency may be found by substituting $j\omega$ for s in Eq. (7.64) and combining the real and imaginary coefficients:

$$G(j\omega) = \frac{-(f_T)\omega^2 - j[(N^2 J_m)\omega^3 - (K_s)\omega]}{(J_L N^2 J_m)\omega^4 - (J_L K_s + N^2 J_m K_s)\omega^2 + (K_s K_T) - j[(J_L f_T)\omega^3 - (K_s f_T)\omega]}. \tag{7.69}$$

The frequency ω_o of the limit cycle is the frequency of $G(j\omega)$ at which the function crosses the abscissa. Therefore, equating the ratio of the two real parts to the ratio of the two imaginary parts, we have

$$\frac{-(f_T)\omega_o^2}{(J_L N^2 J_m)\omega_o - (J_L K_s + N^2 J_m K_s)\omega_o + K_s K_T} = \frac{(N^2 J_m)\omega_o^3 - (K_s)\omega_o}{(J_L f_T)\omega_o - (K_s f_T)\omega_o}. \tag{7.70}$$

This results in the polynomial in ω_o of

$$A_3 \omega_o^6 + A_2 \omega_o^4 + A_1 \omega_o^2 + A_o = 0, \tag{7.71}$$

where

$$\begin{aligned}
A_3 &= N^4 J_m^2 J_L, \\
A_2 &= f_T^2 J_L - 2J_L N^2 J_m K_s - K_s N^4 J_m^2, \\
A_1 &= N^2 J_m K_s K_T - f_T^2 K_s + J_L K_s^2 + N^2 J_m K_s^2, \\
A_o &= -K_s^2 K_T.
\end{aligned} \tag{7.72}$$

The frequency ω_o is therefore

$$\omega_o = \sqrt{\sqrt[3]{-Q + P} + \sqrt[3]{-Q - P} - A_2/3A_3}, \tag{7.73}$$

where

$$Q = A_o/2A_3 - A_2 A_1/6A_3^2 + A_2^3/27A_3^3, \tag{7.74}$$

$$P = \sqrt{Q^2 + (A_1/3A_3 - A_2^2/9A_3^2)^3}.$$

Since the imaginary part of $G(j\omega_o)$ is zero, multiplying by the complex conjugate of the denominator results in

$$G(\omega_o) = \frac{B_5 \omega_o^2}{B_4 \omega_o^8 + B_3 \omega_o^6 + B_2 \omega_o^4 + B_1 \omega_o^2 + B_o}. \tag{7.75}$$

where

$$\begin{aligned}
B_5 &= f_T K_s^2 - f_T K_s K_T, \\
B_4 &= N^4 J_m^2 J_L^2, \\
B_3 &= J_L^2 f_T^2 - 2N^2 J_m J_L^2 K_s - 2N^4 J_m^2 J_L K_s, \\
B_2 &= 2N^2 J_m J_L K_s K_T + 2N^2 J_m J_L K_s^2 + J_L^2 K_s^2 + N^4 J_m^2 K_s^2 - 2J_L f_T^2 K_s, \\
B_1 &= f_T^2 K_s^2 - 2J_L K_s^2 K_T - 2N^2 J_m K_s^2 K_T, \\
B_o &= K_s^2 K_T^2.
\end{aligned} \tag{7.76}$$

Therefore the amount of load friction required to avoid an oscillation with zero backlash must always be greater than that given by

$$T_f = -\pi \dot{\theta}_L(\max)/4G(\omega_o). \tag{7.77}$$

7.7. DEVELOPMENT OF EQUATIONS SHOWING THAT LOAD FRICTION IS A NECESSARY CONDITION FOR STABILITY WITH BACKLASH

With respect to zero backlash and zero load damping, Section 5.3 demonstrated that for stable operation the gear train stiffness must be greater than the servo torque constant. It is usually desirable to have the gear train designed such that its stiffness is at least several times greater than the servo torque constant. Once this is accomplished, the effect of K_s becomes minor and the resilience can be neglected as a design consideration. However, for $K_s > K_T$, instability will result if backlash is introduced without any load damping. This section will demonstrate that all motor-generator positional servos with backlash will have a null oscillation or limit cycle if some form of damping at the load side of the backlash is not present.

Gear train backlash, stiffness, inertia, and friction are actually distributed parameters. An exact analysis would require that each of the above parameters for each gear pass be reflected to the load and considered as a separated item. However, for simplicity it is usually considered adequate to lump the various reflected gear train inertias together and consider the total as a single parameter at the output. The total effective backlash and stiffness of the gear train are then considered to exist between this total load and the equivalent motor. This assumption represents a safe approximation of the actual system since concentration of the total inertia at the output shaft is a worst-case situation. Also, it is customary to consider the total gear train friction to exist at the load side of the backlash even though this does not represent the worst case.

The above simplifying procedure represents an approximation that in general provides a safe design. The approximation simulates the actual system very closely for simple gear trains driving relatively high inertia loads. On the other hand, the approximation becomes poor when the gear train is complicated by many individual trains to different loads and components. The latter is especially true when the load represents a relatively low inertia. However, for this case, friction levels are often high and therefore the backlash effects are less critical.

Let us consider for simplicity the case which exhibits backlash and load viscous damping as illustrated by Fig. 7.28 with all external inputs zero. Since θ_i equals zero, the linear portion of the system may be regarded as having an input $C(s)$ and output $R(s)$. The resulting open-loop linear transfer function may be derived from Fig. 7.28 as

$$G(s) = -\frac{R(s)}{C(s)} = \frac{K_s/f_L}{s(\tau_{LS} + 1)} + \left[K_s + \frac{K_T K_s/f_L}{s(\tau_{LS} + 1)}\right]\frac{1/N^2 f_M}{s(\tau_{MS} + 1)}. \tag{7.78}$$

Substituting in for τ_T and τ_L and simplifying, we obtain

$$G(s) = \frac{K_s}{s^2}\left[\frac{(N^2 J_M + J_L)s^2 + (f_L + f_T)s + K_T}{(J_L N^2 J_M)s^2 + (J_L f_T + N^2 J_M f_L)s + f_L f_T}\right]. \tag{7.79}$$

The describing function of the backlash deadband is given by

$$G(\psi) = \frac{C(s)}{R(s)} = 1 - \frac{2\psi}{\pi} + \frac{\sin 2\psi}{\pi} + \cdots, \tag{7.80}$$

where
$$\psi = \sin^{-1}(B/2A_m). \tag{7.81}$$

These can be combined to give

$$G(\psi) = 1 - \frac{2}{\pi}\left(\sin^{-1}\frac{B}{2A_M} + \frac{B}{2A_M}\sqrt{1 - (B/2A_M)^2} + \cdots\right). \tag{7.82}$$

Equation (7.82) shows the describing function for the backlash deadband to be a positive real number dependent only on the backlash width B and peak input amplitude A_M. It is also seen that $G(\psi)$ can only have values between zero and unity,

$$0 \leq G(\psi) \leq 1. \tag{7.83}$$

When the initial input amplitude is less than half the dead zone $G(\psi) = 0$, $G(\psi)$ will approach unity as the input amplitude increases to infinity.

The total open-loop "transfer function" is

$$G(\psi, s) = G(s)G(\psi). \tag{7.84}$$

System instability results when the over-all loop "transfer function" passes through or encircles the $-1 + j0$ point on the Nyquist diagram. In equation form,

$$G(s)G(\psi) > -1 + j0. \tag{7.85}$$

The locus of the over-all "transfer function" is a function of both frequency and amplitude. By separating the two functions, we can study the effect of frequency and amplitude independently:

$$G(s) = -1/G(\psi). \tag{7.86}$$

Substituting this $G(s)$ into Eq. (7.79) and dividing through by K_s, we obtain

$$\frac{1}{s^2}\left[\frac{(N^2J_M + J_L)s^2 + (f_L + f_T)s + K_T}{J_LN^2J_Ms^2 + (J_Lf_T + N^2J_Mf_L)s + f_Lf_T}\right] \geq \frac{-1}{K_sG(\psi)}. \tag{7.87}$$

If we factor out K_T and f_Lf_T, Eq. (7.87) becomes

$$\frac{K_T/f_Lf_T}{s^2}\frac{(1/\omega_N^2)s^2 + (2\zeta/\omega_N)s + 1}{\tau_L\tau_Ts^2 + (\tau_L + \tau_T)s + 1} \geq \frac{-1}{K_sG(\psi)}. \tag{7.88}$$

Figure 7.29 illustrates a stability locus and two typical frequency response loci of Eq. (7.88). The frequency response, curve A, represents a conditionally stable system, since the $G(j\omega)$ locus encloses part of the stability locus. For small oscillations, $\theta_L < \theta_o$, the system is unstable and the oscillations increase in amplitude. For large oscillations, $\theta_L > \theta_o$, the system is stable and the oscillations decrease in amplitude. Therefore, the steady-state condition is one of continuous oscillations at a frequency and amplitude determined by the intersection of the stability and transfer function loci. On the other hand, curve B shows a stable system, since there is not an intersection between the stability and transfer function locus; therefore a limit cycle will not exist. From Eq. (7.87), it may be seen that one can solve for the frequency of oscillation (ω_o) by solving for the required value of ω to make the phase angle of the bracketed quantity equal to zero.

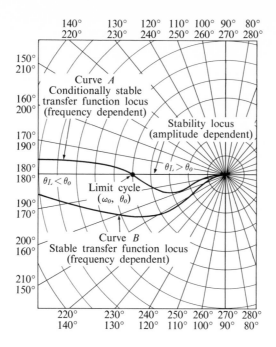

Fig. 7.29. Backlash stability locus.

Substituting $j\omega$ for s in Eq. (7.87) and combining terms, we obtain

$$-\frac{1}{\omega^2}\left(\frac{[K_T - (N^2 J_M + J_L)\omega^2] + j(f_L + f_T)\omega}{(f_L f_T - J_L N^2 J_M \omega^2) + j(J_T f_T + N^2 J_M f_L)\omega}\right) \geq \frac{-1}{K_s G(\psi)}. \qquad (7.89)$$

At $\omega = \omega_o$, the phase angle of the two quadratics must be equal; therefore the ratio of the real parts of the numerator and denominator of Eq. (7.89) must be equal to the ratios of their imaginary parts:

$$\frac{K_T - (N^2 J_M + J_L)\omega_o^2}{f_L f_T - J_L N^2 J_M \omega_o^2} = \frac{(f_L + f_T)\omega_o}{(J_L f_T + N^2 J_M f_L)\omega_o}. \qquad (7.90)$$

Solving for ω_o, we have

$$\omega_o = \sqrt{\frac{(J_L f_T + N^2 J_M f_L)K_T - (f_L + f_T)f_T f_L}{(N^2 J_M)^2 f_L + J_L^2 f_T}}. \qquad (7.91)$$

It is seen that the system will *not* oscillate if

$$(J_L^2 f_T + N^2 J_M f_L)K_T < (f_L + f_T)f_T f_L, \qquad (7.92)$$

since the frequency ω_o becomes imaginary. Multiplying out the above inequality, we find that

$$f_L^2 - \left(\frac{K_T N^2 J_M}{f_T} - f_T\right)f_L - K_T J_L > 0. \qquad (7.93)$$

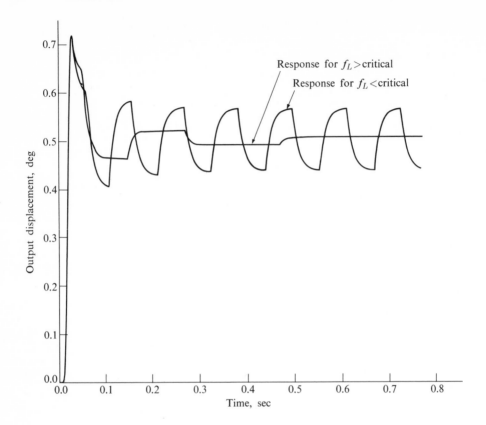

Fig. 7.30. Transient response for various values of load viscous damping.

Equation (7.93) demonstrates that for zero damping at the load side of the backlash ($f_L = 0$) it is impossible to avoid a limit cycle about null.

Solving for the positive value of f_L for which Eq. (7.93) becomes an equality, we obtain

$$f_L = \frac{[K_T N^2 J_m / f_T - f_T] + \sqrt{[K_T N^2 J_m / f_T - f_T]^2 + 4 K_T J_L}}{2}. \qquad (7.94)$$

Equation (7.94) defines the minimum amount of load viscous friction that is required to avoid a limit cycle caused by backlash in the system. For example, let us consider the amount of load viscous damping required to stabilize a servo with component parameters as established in Section 5.6 if backlash were present. These parameter values were

$$K_f = 18 \text{ v/rad}, \qquad K_a = 240 \text{ v/rad},$$
$$K_g = 0.14 \text{ v/1000 rpm}, \qquad K_m = 0.0026 \text{ oz-in/v},$$
$$B_m = 0.0002 \text{ (oz-in)/(rad/sec)}, \qquad J_m = 1.0 \text{ gm-cm}^2,$$
$$J_L = 3000 \text{ gm-cm}^2, \qquad N = 100.$$

Converting units on the required parameters,

$$K_g = 1.336 \times 10^{-3} \text{ v/rad/sec,}$$
$$J_m = 1.42 \times 10^{-5} \text{ (oz-in)/(rad/sec}^2\text{),}$$
$$J_L = 4.26 \times 10^{-2} \text{ (oz-in)/(rad/sec}^2\text{),}$$

and substituting into Eq. (7.94) results in a value for f_L of

$$f_L = 9.46 \text{ (oz-in)/(rad/sec).}$$

Figure 7.30 illustrates the transient response of the system for values of f_L both greater than and less than the critical value. The lower value results in a system that displays a continuous limit cycle about null, and the other provides the damping required to stabilize the system.

Table 7.1

LOAD VISCOUS DAMPING VALUES REQUIRED
TO STABILIZE A TYPICAL INSTRUMENT SERVOMECHANISM
WITH BACKLASH FOR VARIOUS VALUES OF LOAD INERTIA

Load inertia J_L, gm-cm^2	Required load damping f_L, oz-in/rad/sec
30000	24.41
3000	9.46
300	4.73
30	3.23
3	2.76

We see from Eq. (7.94) that for large values of load inertia J_L, correspondingly larger minimum values of load damping are required. For small values of J_L the minimum load damping required approaches zero. Table 7.1 illustrates this numerically by listing the value of f_L calculated from Eq. (7.94) for various values of J_L, while the other component parameters are held fixed at their previously defined values.

7.8. DEVELOPMENT OF THE SYSTEM NONLINEAR STATE MODEL AND COMPUTER SIMULATION

Equations were developed in Section 5.6 that described the transient behavior of the linear system. Both the digital and analog computers were used to perform the computations required to obtain the response. In this section, the linear model will be extended to include the nonlinearities of saturation, load coulomb friction, and backlash, which may be represented as summarized in Table 7.2.

Table 7.2

SYSTEM NONLINEARITIES

Block diagram	Equations*
Backlash	$T_r = K_s[|\theta_m - \theta_L| - B]\,\text{sgn}\,(\theta_m - \theta_L)$ for $|\theta_m - \theta_L| \geq B$ $T_r = 0$ for $|\theta_m - \theta_L| \leq B$
Saturation	$T_s = K_T(\theta_i - \theta_o) - f_g\dot{\theta}_m$ for $|K_T(\theta_i - \theta_o) - f_g\dot{\theta}_m| \leq K_m E_{c\ \text{sat}}$ $T_s = K_m E_{c\ \text{sat}}$ for $|K_T(\theta_i - \theta_o) - f_g\dot{\theta}_m| \geq K_m E_{c\ \text{sat}}$
Coulomb friction	$T_f = |T_{fo}|\,\text{sgn}\,\dot{\theta}_L$ for $\dot{\theta}_L \neq 0$ $T_f = -T_r$ for $\dot{\theta}_L = 0$

* where sgn $\theta = \theta/|\theta|$.

The linear system state model shown as Eq. (5.49) can be extended to include the nonlinearities as follows. Factoring out the terms that contain $K_T, f_g,$ and f_L, we can write the state model in two parts as

$$\frac{d}{dt}\begin{bmatrix} \dot{\theta}_m \\ \theta_m \\ \dot{\theta}_o \\ \theta_o \end{bmatrix} = \begin{bmatrix} \dfrac{-f_m}{N^2 J_m} & 0 & 0 & 0 \\ 1 & 0 & 0 & 0 \\ 0 & 0 & 0 & 0 \\ 0 & 0 & 1 & 0 \end{bmatrix}\begin{bmatrix} \dot{\theta}_m \\ \theta_m \\ \dot{\theta}_o \\ \theta_o \end{bmatrix} + \begin{bmatrix} \dfrac{K_s(\theta_m - \theta_L)}{N^2 J_m} + \dfrac{(K_T\theta_i - K_T\theta_o - f_g\dot{\theta}_m)}{N^2 J_m} \\ 0 \\ \dfrac{K_s(\theta_m - \theta_L)}{J_L} - \dfrac{f_L\dot{\theta}_L}{J_L} \\ 0 \end{bmatrix}$$

$$(7.95)$$

The nonlinearities can now be included by replacing $K_s(\theta_m - \theta_L)$ by T_r, $(K_T\theta_i - K_T\theta_o - f_g\dot{\theta}_m)$ by T_s, and $f_L\dot{\theta}_L$ by T_f, which yields the following nonlinear

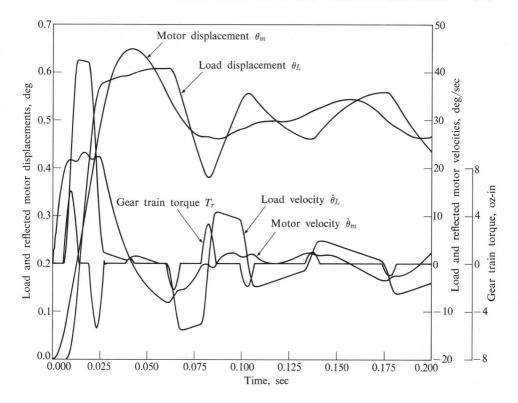

Fig. 7.31. Transient response of four state variables and gear train torque.

state model:

$$\frac{d}{dt}\begin{bmatrix} \dot{\theta}_m \\ \theta_m \\ \dot{\theta}_o \\ \theta_o \end{bmatrix} = \begin{bmatrix} \dfrac{-f_m}{N^2 J_m} & 0 & 0 & 0 \\ 1 & 0 & 0 & 0 \\ 0 & 0 & 0 & 0 \\ 0 & 0 & 1 & 0 \end{bmatrix}\begin{bmatrix} \dot{\theta}_m \\ \theta_m \\ \dot{\theta}_o \\ \theta_o \end{bmatrix} + \begin{bmatrix} \dfrac{T_r - T_s}{N^2 J_m} \\ 0 \\ \dfrac{T_r - T_f}{J_L} \\ 0 \end{bmatrix}, \qquad (7.96)$$

where T_r, T_s, and T_f are defined in Table 7.2. The derivative of the state vector is thus given as the sum of a linear and a nonlinear part. Any standard numerical method of solving nonlinear differential equations can be applied to obtain a solution to Eq. (7.96). Figure 7.31 shows such a solution where each of the state variables is plotted, for a step input to the system, as a function of time. To illustrate how one can calculate every point in the system in terms of the state variables using algebraic equations, let us consider the torque transmitted by the gear train (T_r). From Fig. 5.1 and the equations given for the backlash dead band in Table 7.2, we can define T_r

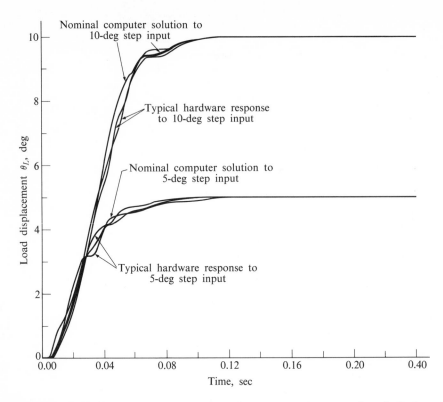

Fig. 7.32. Comparison of transient response of hardware with that of analytical model.

in terms of the state variables as follows. For $|\theta_m - \theta_L| \geq B$,

$$T_r = K_s(|\theta_m - \theta_L| - B) \, \text{sgn} \, (\theta_m - \theta_L), \tag{7.97}$$

and for $|\theta_m - \theta_L| \leq B$,

$$T_r = 0. \tag{7.98}$$

Thus at any instant in time the gear train torque can be determined directly from the corresponding state variables θ_m and θ_L along with the system constants K_s and B. This was accomplished during the previous calculations of the four state variables, and the resulting values of T_r are also plotted in Fig. 7.31. It is interesting to note that due to the presence of backlash, the gear teeth are in contact for only short periods of time while the system is in the transient state. This period of contact occurs only when the distance between the θ_m- and θ_L-curves exceeds the value of the backlash width B. Torque is transmitted only during these periods of contact and thus occurs as the series of pulses shown.

The plotting of all the state variables and possibly some of the other parameters permits the engineer to obtain a good insight into the servo behavior. Analytically, this can be accomplished, but output position is normally the only state variable that

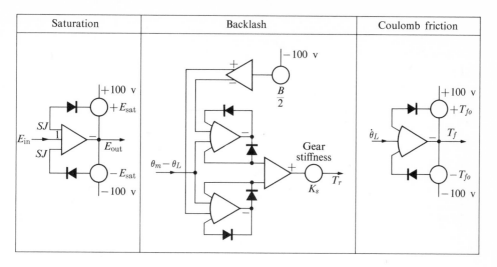

Fig. 7.33. Standard analog circuits for simulating nonlinearities.

can be observed or measured. Because of this, θ_L is ordinarily the only parameter used when the final instrument hardware is correlated with the analytical design model. Since the actual load friction and backlash vary with position, the transient response of the hardware depends somewhat on the exact initial starting point. Two hardware response curves are shown in Fig. 7.32 for each of the 5- and 10-deg step inputs to illustrate this variation. For comparison, the calculated response with the nominal system parameters is also shown for each step size. This figure demonstrates the close degree of correlation that can be obtained by using the approach presented.

The linear analog simulation diagram developed as Fig. 5.16 can also be extended to include the effects of nonlinearities. Figure 7.33 depicts standard diode circuits that may be used to simulate the three nonlinearities. Substituting these circuits into Fig. 5.16, we obtain the schematic diagram shown in Fig. 7.34. In Chapter 5, only time scaling had to be considered since the linear system is independent of amplitude. This is not the case when the nonlinearities are added. A definite scale factor must be used to relate the actual servo parameters to the voltages in the analog circuit. This scale factor was set at unity or 1 v/unit in Fig. 7.34 and the circuit is scaled for a 1.0-deg input step. The parameters shown are identical to those used in Fig. 5.16 except that the following values are included for amplifier saturation, load coulomb friction, and backlash:

$$E_{c\,sat} = 26.0\,\text{v}, \qquad T_f = 0.1\,\text{oz-in}, \qquad B = 6.0\,\text{min}.$$

The resulting transient response is shown in Fig. 7.35 with no trace of any steady-state oscillation or limit cycle around null. However, for comparison, the same response is repeated with a backlash value of 12.0 min. This time a steady-state limit cycle does exist.

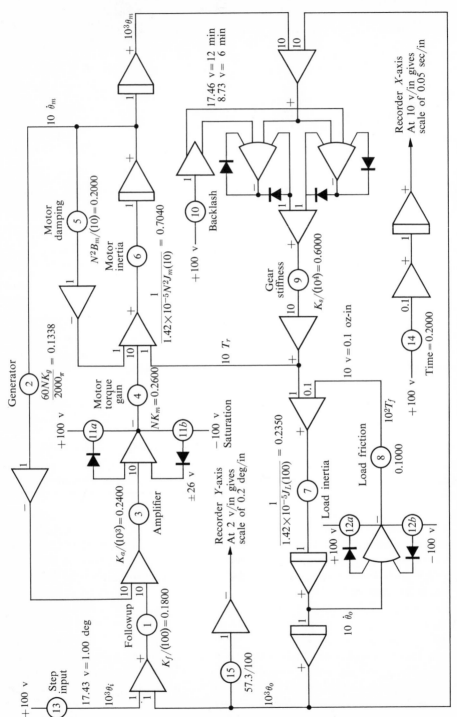

Fig. 7.34. Nonlinear analog computer diagram for motor generator servomechanism.

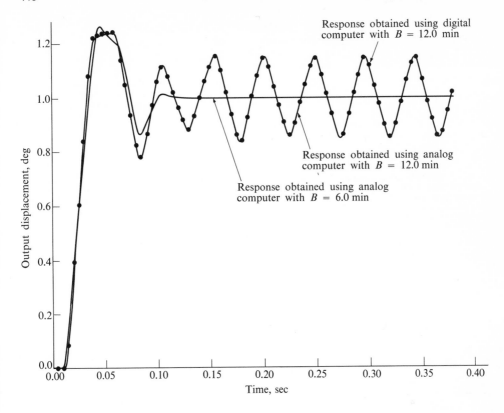

Fig. 7.35. Transient response of servomechanism for two levels of backlash.

Figure 7.35 demonstrated that the system was stable with a backlash value of 6 min. From this demonstrated stability, it might be assumed that the design is satisfactory with that value. However, such an assumption would be premature, since it would include no allowance for the effects of component tolerances. These effects will now be investigated.

The manner in which component tolerances affect the transient behavior is most easily determined by using the Monte-Carlo approach presented in Section 6.8. A digital computer program can be written using a random number generator and Eq. (6.22) to determine the system component parameters to be used for each run. In fact, if the transient response curves are to be computed on an analog computer, the digital program can calculate the actual potentiometer voltage settings to be used for each run. Table 7.3 illustrates a typical output sheet from such a program. The engineer provides, as inputs, the maximum and minimum values to be expected for each of the component parameters along with the number of Monte-Carlo runs desired. The inputs are printed out (as the first two blocks of data) along with the calculated mean values. The first step in scaling an analog simulation is to determine the factor to be associated with each potentiometer so that the coefficient settings range between zero and unity. These coefficients are calculated in the program and

Table 7.3*

EXAMPLE OF COMPUTER OUTPUT SHEET
USED TO CALCULATE MONTE CARLO POTENTIOMETER SETTINGS

```
                                                    LEAR SIEGLER INC
                                                    INSTRUMENT DIVISION
                                                    PROGRAM SD015A

                  MOTOR GENERATOR SERVO ANALOG SIMULATION
                     MONTE CARLO POTENTIOMETER SETTINGS

              K-F         K-G         K-A         K-M         B-M         J-M
            (V/RAD)    (V/1000RPM)    (V/V)    (OZ IN/V)  (OZ IN SEC) (GM CMSQ)
    MAX   2.016E+01   1.610E-01   2.760E+02   3.120E-03   3.000E-04  1.050E+00
    MEAN  1.800E+01   1.400E-01   2.400E+02   2.600E-03   2.000E-04  1.000E+00
    MIN   1.584E+01   1.190E-01   2.040E+02   2.080E-03   1.000E-04  9.500E-01

              J-L         T-F         K-S          B        E-C (SAT)      N
           (GM-CMSQ)    (OZ-IN)  (OZ-IN/RAD)  (MINUTES)    (VOLTS)
    MAX   3.300E+03   1.250E-01   7.200E+03   7.200E+00   2.800E+01
    MEAN  3.000E+03   1.000E-01   6.000E+03   6.000E+00   2.600E+01   1.000E+02
    MIN   2.700E+03   7.500E-02   4.800E+03   4.800E+00   2.400E+01
```

```
POT NO.  A-1   A-2   A-3   A-4   A-5   A-6   A-7   A-8   A-9   A-10  A-11
POT SF   -2     0    -3     0    -1    -1    -2     0    -4     0    -2
```

```
                             POT SET LIMITS
           A-1   A-2   A-3   A-4   A-5   A-6   A-7   A-8   A-9   A-10  A-11
   MAX  20.16 15.37 27.60 31.20 30.00 67.06 21.34 12.50 72.00 10.49 28.00
  MEAN  18.00 13.36 24.00 26.00 20.00 70.42 23.47 10.00 60.00  8.74 26.00
   MIN  15.84 11.36 20.40 20.80 10.00 74.12 26.08  7.50 48.00  6.99 24.00
```

```
                        MONTE CARLO POT SETTINGS
 RUN   A-1   A-2   A-3   A-4   A-5   A-6   A-7   A-8   A-9   A-10  A-11
  1   18.44 12.91 21.93 28.76 19.39 70.75 23.55 10.60 66.87  9.12 26.46
  2   17.50 12.22 25.91 25.68 19.04 70.54 22.92 11.43 62.62  9.15 25.81
  3   16.76 14.43 23.78 25.50 19.66 69.58 22.20 10.54 62.78  8.58 25.10
  4   19.14 13.24 23.65 25.82 22.40 68.46 22.97 10.57 58.90  7.96 26.82
  5   17.86 13.17 23.88 27.25 25.72 69.66 22.94  9.77 54.64  9.47 25.59
  6   17.79 13.30 24.86 28.97 22.18 69.61 23.69  8.88 64.98  8.38 24.99
  7   17.92 13.85 26.06 27.13 22.31 70.74 24.57 11.03 57.54  7.86 26.71
  8   18.51 14.51 24.78 27.20 19.08 72.03 22.53  9.48 53.98  9.37 26.04
  9   19.23 13.80 24.83 25.52 15.53 68.99 23.96  8.74 64.28  8.78 25.74
 10   18.47 13.83 23.67 23.67 24.14 71.15 24.71 10.89 60.26  8.52 25.14
 11   18.50 13.18 22.39 28.15 17.95 72.23 22.66 10.05 58.45  8.00 26.41
 12   17.80 12.47 25.49 24.93 14.98 69.18 23.42  9.67 54.88  9.10 25.54
 13   17.03 14.20 23.26 23.39 23.56 70.34 23.78  8.93 62.46  8.34 24.85
 14   18.89 12.95 22.19 27.85 20.21 70.87 24.52 10.51 57.25  7.74 27.06
 15   17.55 12.36 25.28 26.11 18.71 71.95 23.00  9.42 53.12  9.67 25.87
 16   16.91 14.08 24.07 25.33 15.73 69.70 24.02  8.56 66.38  8.63 25.80
 17   18.77 13.41 23.53 23.78 22.05 71.23 24.90 11.32 59.26  8.57 25.93
 18   18.04 13.11 22.46 27.06 17.71 72.49 22.28  9.84 58.85  8.68 26.48
 19   17.72 12.51 24.74 24.81 14.27 68.59 23.61  9.76 59.60  9.16 27.14
 20   17.07 13.78 23.17 23.02 25.31 70.63 23.70  9.91 62.88  9.74 26.43
```

```
        E SIGNIFIES CONVENTIONAL POWER-OF-TEN NOTATION
```

* Reprinted by courtesy of Lear Siegler, Inc., Instrument Division, Grand Rapids, Michigan.

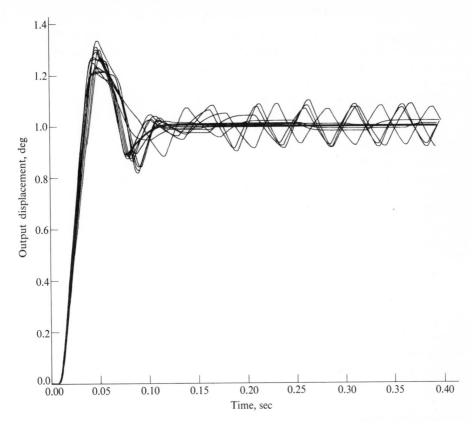

Fig. 7.36. Monte Carlo transient response curves for the first 14 runs taken from Table 7.3.

printed out with the label POT SF. The scale factors, as shown, represent the power-of-ten exponent required for each potentiometer. For example, potentiometer $A1$ must be multiplied by a factor of 10^{-2}, and looking at Fig. 7.34, we see that this was accomplished by letting potentiometer 1 be representative of $K_f/100$. Following the scale factors in Table 7.3 are the calculated potentiometer settings corresponding to the maximum, mean, and minimum values of the parameters. These settings are given in terms of potentiometer output with 100 v applied. The remainder of the output sheet lists the potentiometer readings required for the number of Monte Carlo runs selected, in this case 20.

The mean parameter of the components listed in Table 7.3 are identical to those used for the response in Fig. 7.35 with the backlash at 6.0 min. A typical manufacturing tolerance is, however, assumed for each component so that their effects can be realized. Figure 7.36 shows the transient response curves obtained for the first 14 of the Monte-Carlo runs. As we can see, the design is unsatisfactory, since 4 of the 14 samples caused definite limit cycles. Specifically, these were runs 5, 6, 8, and 9. These results show that component tolerances can be devastating if they are not thoroughly considered in the design phase and controlled in production.

7.9. BACKLASH-FRICTION CURVE THEORY

The last example in the previous section demonstrated that too much backlash in an instrument servomechanism can result in a continuous oscillation about null. However, holding the backlash to too small a value results in excessive cost. Thus the servo designer is continually faced with the question, "How much backlash can a given design tolerate without experiencing sustained oscillations?" Although one can quite easily answer this question by using the nonlinear simulations developed in the previous sections, the graphical technique discussed in this section provides a clearer insight into the null stability problem and its solution.

One characteristic that simplifies the analysis of the null stability problem is that the magnitude of the oscillation is small. The amplifier thus normally operates within its linear range and only the nonlinearities of backlash and coulomb friction need be considered. Even if this were not the case, considering the amplifier gain to be the linear value represents a worst-case situation and thus a safe design.

The limit cycle condition is independent of the size of the input step. Thus if only the two nonlinearities are considered, the amount of backlash that a servo can withstand without experiencing sustained oscillation is directly proportional to the amount of friction on the load side of the backlash. We can verify this by considering the scaling problem associated with the analog simulation. Given any system with an associated friction level, we can vary the backlash until the critical value is established. This critical value of backlash is defined as that required to cause the system to just sustain oscillations. Any decrease from this value causes the limit cycle to dampen out. Once this critical value is established, we can change the backlash value being simulated by simply assigning a new value for the magnitude-to-voltage scale factor. But this changes the coulomb friction being simulated by the same amount. The response continues to oscillate under critical conditions, thereby requiring a proportional relationship to exist between the two nonlinearities. Thus there is a ratio of backlash to friction that cannot be exceeded without a null oscillation. It is this ratio that is called the *slope m* of the backlash-friction curve.

The allowable backlash vs. load friction curve can be determined, for each servo design, by computer simulation. One simply increases backlash or decreases friction until the critical condition is obtained. The best way of presenting these data is to use a backlash friction diagram. To construct this diagram or graph, we assign the ordinate to backlash and the abscissa to load friction. A straight line can be plotted on this graph to represent the backlash vs. friction curve with slope m (Fig. 7.37). So long as the actual backlash and friction values lie below this line, the servo will not exhibit a null oscillation. However, for every combination of backlash and load friction that lies above this line, a null oscillation will occur. This line must intersect the origin for $K_s > K_T$, since for zero load friction, a limit cycle will always exist for any finite amount of backlash. This was proved in Section 7.7. It is only the presence of load friction that makes it possible for any backlash to be tolerated.

The amount of backlash B that a servo can withstand without a null oscillation is given at least empirically by the equation

$$B(\text{allowable}) = (f_T/K_T^2)[F(J, K_s)]T_{fo}, \tag{7.99}$$

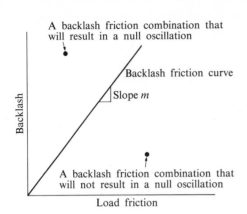

Fig. 7.37. General backlash friction diagram.

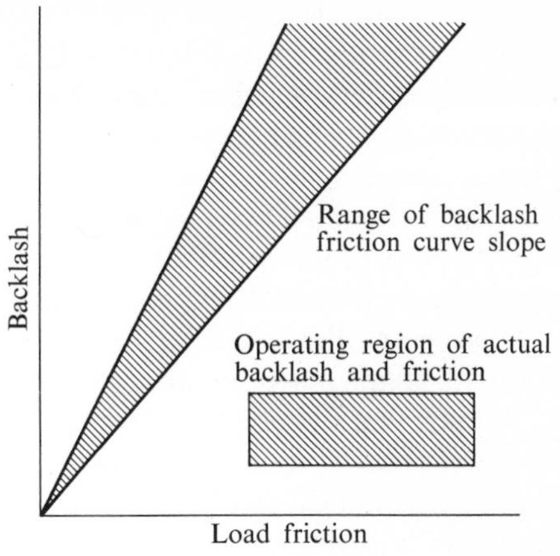

Fig. 7.38. General backlash friction diagram with tolerances.

where

f_T = the total servo damping coefficient given by Eq. (5.9),

K_T = the servo torque constant given by Eq. (5.10),

$F(J, K_s)$ = a function of J_L, $N^2 J_m$, and K_s,

T_{fo} = the value of coulomb friction at the load side of the backlash.

The slope m of the backlash vs. friction curve is thus given by

$$m = (f_T/K_T^2)[F(J, K_s)]. \tag{7.100}$$

In actual applications, the tolerances on f_T, K_T, J_L, J_m, and K_s cause variations in the slope of the backlash vs. friction curve and the single line transforms into a triangular zone emanating from the origin. Also, because of manufacturing tolerances, the backlash and load friction values have some bounded operating range. The latter is normally represented by a rectangular region on the backlash friction diagram. The complete picture for a design can be presented as shown in Fig. 7.38. A satisfactory design (one that has no null oscillations) requires that there be no intersection between the two shaded areas. The optimum design therefore requires that the slope m be maximized.

7.10. SUMMARY

In this chapter the nonlinearities of saturation, load coulomb friction, and backlash were described in detail. We started each discussion by first describing the characteristics of the nonlinearity itself and then developing analytical expressions to determine its effect.

The saturation nonlinearity normally has the greatest effect on system performance and therefore was treated first. The amplifier characteristic including saturation was analyzed by using a describing function. This approach demonstrated that the "effective gain" of the amplifier varies as a function of the degree of saturation. By combining the concept of the followup rate as a saturated velocity and the lower gain effect upon ζ and ω_N, we obtained a qualitative measure of the servo transient response. Equations were then developed to establish the frequency at which saturation would be encountered by a system excited with a sinusoidal input. Using this relationship and the describing function, we determined the effect of saturation upon the system frequency response.

We saw that the presence of sufficient quadrature at the amplifier input to cause saturation of a servo amplifier lowered the apparent gain as seen by the in-phase signal. An analytical expression was obtained for the in-phase signal gain at null as a function of amplifier quadrature. Since this gain determines the static and dynamic accuracy of the servo, it should be considered in every design.

Load friction and its general effect on system behavior were discussed. An equation was derived to calculate, for sinusoidal inputs, the steady-state phase lag caused by coulomb friction.

The phase plane was then introduced as an ideal method of determining the transient behavior of the instrument servo with both saturation and coulomb friction. The axes of the phase plane corresponded to the two-system state variable, namely velocity and displacement. The state of the system is therefore defined for every point on this plane, and one can plot the transient response of the system. This can be accomplished easily with or without a computer even when amplifier saturation and coulomb friction are present. Using this approach, the designer can completely account for the stabilizing effects of both nonlinearities. The phase-plane technique sometimes permits one to avoid the requirement of additional system damping such as furnished by a generator.

Load friction was shown to aid in stabilizing a system where the gear train stiffness is smaller than the torque constant. By using a describing function to represent the coulomb friction, we developed analytical expressions for calculating the amount of friction required for stability. It was further shown that even with $K_s \gg K_T$, instability will result if backlash is present without any load friction or damping. An equation, therefore, was derived to establish the amount of load viscous damping required to stabilize a system with backlash.

The state model developed for the linear system in Chapter 5 was extended in this chapter to account for the nonlinearities of saturation, friction, and backlash. The exact response of the total system can then be obtained. This was accomplished by using both analog and digital computers, and correlation of the design with the actual hardware was shown.

The chapter was concluded by the introduction of the concept of a backlash vs. friction diagram. The amount of backlash that a servo can withstand without sustained oscillation is proportional to the amount of load friction; therefore a straight line can be plotted on this diagram for each design. So long as the actual backlash and friction values are such that their intersections lie below this line, a stable system results.

PROBLEMS

7.1. For a second-order system with saturation and only coulomb damping, the following parameters are given:

$$K_T = 1536 \text{ oz-in/rad}, \qquad T_{sat} = 96 \text{ oz-in}, \qquad T_{fo} = 16 \text{ oz-in}.$$

Construct a phase portrait similar to that shown in Fig. 7.19 for a 0.15 rad/step displacement. Compare the size of the first overshoot with that of Fig. 7.19.

7.2. Given the phase portrait shown in Fig. 7.21 and the following associated parameters:

$$K_T = 1536 \text{ oz-in/rad}, \qquad T_{sat} = 48 \text{ oz-in}, \qquad T_{fo} = 16 \text{ oz-in}.$$

Can the system inertia be uniquely determined? If so, what is the value? If not, what additional data are required? Does Fig. 7.22 help?

*7.3. Given a simple viscous damped servomechanism that has a gear train with zero backlash, unknown friction, and a stiffness of 4000 oz-in/rad. What can be said about the stability, if the torque constant of the loop is 2500 oz-in/rad? What can be said if the torque constant is doubled?

7.4. A return spring is added to the output of a servo to drive the servo to a zero position in case of a power failure. The following parameters are given:

$$J_T = \text{total system inertia},$$
$$T_{fo} = \text{total system coulomb friction},$$
$$T_p = \text{spring preload at zero position},$$
$$K = \text{spring constant}.$$

Show that the time required for the servo to return from position θ_o at time of power failure to zero position is given by the equation

$$T = \sqrt{J_T/K} \cos^{-1}\left[\frac{1}{1 + \theta_o K/(T_p - T_{fo})}\right]$$

(neglecting any viscous friction).

*7.5. Consider a motor-generator servo whose effective motor damping can be considered negligible. The generator gain is increased 20%, the followup gain is increased 50%, and the amplifier gain is increased 40%. What is the corresponding change in the allowable backlash that the servo can withstand without experiencing a null oscillation?

7.6. Given the amplifier characteristics shown in Fig. 7.2 for a sinusoidal input signal $[E_i(t) = E_i \sin \omega t]$ and the following Fourier series expression for the saturated output:

$$E_c(t) = Y_1 \sin (\omega_t + \phi_1) + Y_2 \sin (\omega_t + \phi_2) + \cdots,$$

where

$$Y_k = \sqrt{a_k^2 + b_k^2}, \qquad \phi_k = \arctan a_k/b_k,$$

$$a_k = (2/\pi) \int_o^\pi E_c(t) \cos k\omega t \, d(\omega t), \qquad b_k = (2/\pi) \int_o^\pi E_c(t) \sin k\omega t \, d(\omega t).$$

Show the derivation of Eqs. (7.3), (7.5), and the saturation describing function given as Eq. (7.6) in the text.

7.7. Set up an analog computer simulation to match the curves presented in Figs. 5.27 and 5.28 and then show the effects of adding amplifier saturation.

BIBLIOGRAPHY

CHESTNUT, H., "Approximate Frequency-Response Methods for Representing Saturation and Dead Band," *Transactions of the ASME* (November 1954).

COSGRIFF, R., *Nonlinear Control Systems*, McGraw-Hill, 1958.

COSGRIFF, R., "Open-Loop Frequency Response Method for Nonlinear Servomechanisms," *AIEE Transactions* **72**, II (September 1953), pp. 222–225.

GRAHAM, D., and D. McRUER, *Analysis of Nonlinear Control Systems*, Wiley, 1961.

GREIF, H. D., "Describing Function Method of Servomechanisms Analysis Applied to Most Commonly Encountered Nonlinearities," *AIEE Transactions* **72**, II (September 1953), pp. 243–248.

HAAS, V. B., JR., "Coulomb Friction in Feedback Control Systems," *AIEE Transactions* **72**, II (May 1953), pp. 119–126.

HARMER, J., "The Jerking Motion Caused by Static Friction in Position Control Systems," *Automatic and Manual Control*, Academic Press, 1952, pp. 329–341.

JOHNSON, E. C., "Sinusoidal Analysis of Feedback-Control Systems Containing Nonlinear Elements," *AIEE Transactions* **71**, II (July 1952), pp. 169–181.

LIVERSIDGE, J., "Backlash and Resilience within Closed Loop of Automatic Control Systems," *Cranfield Conference (1951)*, *Automatic and Manual Control*, Academic Press, pp. 343–372.

McCANN, G., F. LINDVAL, and C. WILTS, "The Effect of Coulomb Friction on the Performance of Servomechanisms," *AIEE Transactions* **67** (1948).

McDONALD, D. C., "Backlash Compensation Improves Servo System Operation," *Instruments and Automation* (28 October 1955), pp. 1728–1731.

NICHOLS, N. B., "Backlash in a Velocity Lag Servomechanism," *AIEE Transactions* **72**, II (1953), pp. 462–476.

OGATA, K., and C. P. ATKINSON, "An Analysis of a Servomechanism with Backlash by the Ritz-Galerkin Method," *AIEE Transactions* **77**, II (May 1958), pp. 82–85.

PASTEL, M., and G. THALER, "Instrument Servomechanisms with Backlash Coulomb Friction and Stiction," *AIEE Transactions* **79**, II (July 1960), pp. 215–219.

RITOW, IRA, "The Impact-Momentum Equation in Servo Design," *Electrical Manufacturing* **57** (May 1956), pp. 107–111, 286–288.

RITOW, IRA, "Designing Servos by the Phase-Plane Method," *Electrical Manufacturing* (June 1956), pp. 98–106 and 326.

SATYENDRA, K. N., "Describing Function Representing the Effects of Inertia, Backlash, and Coulomb Friction on the Stability of an Automatic Control System-1," *AIEE Transactions* **75**, II (September 1956), pp. 243–249.

SZEGO, G. P., "A New Procedure for Plotting Phase Plane Trajectories," *AIEE Transactions* II (July 1962), pp. 120–125.

THALER, G., and M. PASTEL, *Analysis and Design of Nonlinear Feedback Control Systems*, McGraw-Hill, 1962.

THOMAS, C. H., "Stability Characteristics of Closed-Loop Systems with Dead Band," *Transactions of the ASME* (November 1954).

TUSTIN, A., "A Method of Analyzing the Effect of Certain Kinds of Non-Linearity in Closed-Cycle Control Systems," *Journal IEE* **94**, IIA, pp. 152–160 (1947).

TUSTIN, A., "The Effects of Backlash and of Speed-Dependent Friction on the Stability of Closed-Cycle Control Systems," *Journal IEE* **94**, IIA, pp. 143–151 (1947).

VALLESE, L. M., "Comparison of Backlash and Hysteresis Effects in Second-Order Feedback Systems," *AIEE Transactions* **75**, II (September 1956), pp. 240–243.

VALLESE, L. M., "Analysis of Backlash in Feedback Control Systems with One Degree of Freedom," *AIEE Transactions* **74**, II (March 1955), pp. 1–4.

WEST, J., *Analytical Techniques for Non-Linear Control Systems*, D. Van Nostrand, 1960.

CHAPTER 8

SERVO ANALYSIS AND DESIGN TECHNIQUES

There are three major questions that have not been answered in the previous chapters. These are:

1) What are the magnitudes of the errors that can exist between input and output for a given servo design?
2) With what resolution or repeatability will a given design perform?
3) How can I be sure that the design is optimum?

The purpose of this chapter is to introduce techniques that the servomechanism designer can use to answer these questions.

8.1. STATIC ACCURACY CALCULATIONS

The positional accuracy of the servo is of utmost concern. It is a measure of the servo capability of duplicating accurately the input command. In this section we will be concerned only with calculating the accuracy under static conditions. Dynamic conditions will be introduced in the next section.

To begin our error analysis study, we present the following two definitions.

Static error: Static error θ_ϵ is defined as the difference between the input command θ_i and the actual output θ_o under static conditions at any time t.

Static accuracy: Static accuracy ϵ_s is defined as the magnitude of the static error that *can* exist.

It should be understood that for any given fixed selection of parameter values, the static accuracy represents the magnitude of the maximum static error which is possible. However, if we consider that all the component parameters have tolerances, the resulting static accuracy also has a maximum and a minimum value. Chapter 6 presented statistical design techniques and outlined how they can be applied to servo design. The statistical methods lend themselves directly to error analysis calculations and provide the only realistic picture of the static behavior of a servo.

A static error in an instrument servomechanism at any time t may result from three basic causes.

1. Load friction and starting voltage. Load friction and motor starting voltage prevent a servo from reducing an existing error to zero. This is due to the fact that servos, unless driven by sufficiently strong signals, cannot overcome starting voltage and friction, and thus they do not respond at all to errors which create only weak signals.

2. Null voltages. Null voltages cause a motor torque which in turn displaces the output until an equal opposing torque is generated.

3. Followup errors. The most basic error in an instrument system is a result of the error detectors or followup. For example, if a nonperfect synchro pair is used for position comparison, any inherent errors will show up in the system. Unlike the above two error sources, which can be reduced by high loop gain, the followup error is a direct function only of the followup components. A servo cannot be made more accurate than this followup error.

Let us now consider in detail the effects of each individual error described above. Once this is accomplished, we will present an effective method of combining the errors to give the total static accuracy.

1. Load Friction T_{fo}. The quantity of load friction which exists for a given servo design may be described by a mean value along with a standard deviation about this mean. This deviation covers changes in load friction which are due to load position and inherent variations between units. The resulting frequency distribution is assumed to be normal and is illustrated in Fig. 8.1.

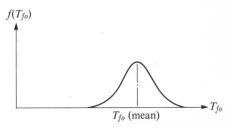

Fig. 8.1. Assumed distribution of friction.

Load friction creates a dead space about any static null. That is, there exists some zone in which the servo will not respond and reduce existing errors. For any fixed value of load friction T_{fo} and servo torque constant K_T, this dead zone, caused by friction, is given by the ratio $\pm T_{fo}/K_T$. Because of variations in the command input and the response of the instrument, the output is likely to lie anywhere within this zone. One could say that the output is equally likely to be at any point within this dead zone and thus define a square distribution for the error due to friction. However, this need not concern the designer since it is the accuracy that is of interest, not the error existing at any particular instant in time. The designer as well as the user is concerned only with the magnitude of the error that can exist. Since for the case of load friction this is the limit of the dead zone, the contribution of load friction to the static accuracy of a servo is given by the equation

$$\epsilon_s(T_f) = \frac{T_{fo}}{K_f K_a K_m N \cos{(\phi_f + \phi_a)}} . \tag{8.1}$$

However, all the parameters in the above equation have tolerances which must be considered if a meaningful value for accuracy is to be obtained. Considering them will result in a mean value $\epsilon_s^*(T_{fo})$ and a standard deviation $\sigma_{\epsilon s}(T_{fo})$, which may be calculated by using the techniques presented in Chapter 6.

2. Motor starting voltage E_s. The voltage necessary to start the motor under no-load conditions in a given servo design may be specified as a mean and a standard deviation about this mean. This standard deviation allows for variations due to motor position and the inherent variations from unit to unit. The resulting frequency distribution is similar to that shown in Fig. 8.1 for load friction.

The motor starting voltage creates a dead zone like that caused by load friction. Therefore the same arguments apply and the contribution of motor starting voltage to the static accuracy of a servo is given by the equation

$$\epsilon_s(E_s) = \frac{E_s}{K_f K_a \cos{(\phi_f + \phi_a)}} . \tag{8.2}$$

As for load friction, $\epsilon_s(E_s)$ has a mean $\epsilon_s^*(E_s)$ and a standard deviation $\sigma_{\epsilon s}(E_s)$.

3. Generator null voltage E_g(null). The effective generator null voltage which produces an error is the in-phase voltage applied to the servomotor control winding. Unlike load friction and starting voltage, which cause dead zones, the generator null voltage causes a hangoff error without any loss of system sensitivity. The actual in-phase null voltage is defined by a maximum specified value (e.g., ± 15 mv). For any set value of null voltage and followup characteristics, the resulting hangoff error would be equal to $E_g/K_f \cos{\phi_f}$. Sometimes this expression is written as $E_g \cos{(\phi_g + \phi_a)}/K_f \cos{(\phi_f + \phi_a)}$ in an attempt to obtain higher accuracy. This would be possible if the total null were in phase. Since this is not the case, the actual error can increase as well as decrease with ϕ_g. Therefore it is customary to consider only the in-phase null and neglect the ϕ_g and ϕ_a phase shift effects. We should remember that E_g refers to the effective null voltage as seen at the amplifier input terminals or summing point and should not be confused with E_{go}.

The preceding paragraph defines the kind of error that might occur at any particular time t. However, it is the accuracy or the magnitude of the possible error that is of primary interest. This may be obtained by using the magnitude of the null voltage distribution. The maximum null voltage corresponds to the actual maximum and the minimum is considered to be zero. The resulting distribution is therefore assumed to be normally distributed about a mean value equal to half its maximum specified magnitude. The 3σ-deviation is then considered equal to the difference between this mean and the maximum specified. This represents an approximation, but it is considered to be safe although not excessively pessimistic. The resulting distribution describes the variation of the null voltage at the output of the generator and variation in the attenuation of the summing network connecting the generator output to the amplifier input or summing point. These variations can be attributed to such things as shaft position and component tolerances. The contribution of generator null voltage to the static accuracy of a servo is given by

$$\epsilon_s[E_g(\text{null})] = \frac{E_g(\text{null}) \cos (\phi_g + \phi_a)}{K_f \cos (\phi_f + \phi_a)}.$$

(8.3)

By considering the component tolerances, values for the mean $\epsilon_s^*[E_g(\text{null})]$, and standard deviation, we can establish $\sigma_{\epsilon s}[E_g(\text{null})]$.

4. Amplifier null voltage $E_a(\text{null})$. The amplifier null voltage is the voltage at the amplifier output when the input has a zero net voltage applied. We assume that the amplifier null, like the generator null, is normally distributed about a mean equal to half the magnitude of the specified maximum value. The magnitude of the total deviation about this mean is equal to the difference between the mean and the specified maximum value. This deviation describes variations in the amplifier null voltage level and amplifier component tolerances. The contribution of amplifier null voltage to the static accuracy of a servo is given by

$$\epsilon_s[E_a(\text{null})] = \frac{E_a(\text{null})}{K_f K_a \cos (\phi_f + \phi_a)}.$$

(8.4)

By considering the component tolerances, values for the mean, $\epsilon_s^* E_a(\text{null})$, and standard deviation, we can establish $\sigma \epsilon_s[E_a(\text{null})]$.

5. Followup error θ_f. Followup error may be described as the difference existing between mechanical and electrical zero. It is normally made up of several components resulting from such items as

synchro error,	potentiometer linearity,
scale marking,	excitation tolerance,
calibration tolerance,	followup backlash.

These are essentially all mechanical errors and can be combined to yield a total followup error θ_f. To arrive at the total value, we first refer to an equivalent output displacement each of the above items which apply. We assume each error to be normally distributed about its mean. The deviation of each component about its mean has a magnitude equal to the difference between the mean and the specified maximum value. The total followup error is therefore defined by the mean $\epsilon_s^*(\theta_f)$ given by the sum of the component means, and the standard deviation, $\sigma\epsilon_s(\theta_f)$, given by the square root of the sum of the squares (rss) of the individual component deviations. The contribution of the followup error to the static accuracy of the servo is given by

$$\epsilon_s(\theta_f) = \theta_f.$$

(8.5)

The simplicity of this relationship establishes the mean, $\epsilon_s^*(\theta_f)$, and standard deviation, $\sigma\epsilon_s(\theta_f)$, to be exactly equal to the mean and standard deviation of θ_f itself. Therefore the approximate expansion approach is not necessary for this computation.

The mean, ϵ_s^*, and standard deviation, $\sigma\epsilon_s$, of the static accuracy of a servo are computed in terms of the values discussed above by combining them statistically. Since all these errors are assumed to be normally distributed about a mean and are independent,

$$\epsilon_s^* = \epsilon_s^*(T_f) + \epsilon_s^*(E_s) + \epsilon_s^*[E_g(\text{null})] + \epsilon_s^*[E_a(\text{null})] + \epsilon_s^*(\theta f), \qquad (8.6)$$

$$\sigma^2\epsilon_s = \sigma^2\epsilon_s(T_f) + \sigma^2\epsilon_s(E_s) + \sigma^2\epsilon_s[E_g(\text{null})] + \sigma^2\epsilon_s[E_a(\text{null})] + \sigma^2\epsilon_s(\theta_f). \qquad (8.7)$$

It should be noted that all the components in Eq. (8.6) and (8.7) are functions of the various gains in the servo except for the followup error $\epsilon_s(\theta_f)$. A typical design problem is to select the amplifier gain required to meet a specified value of static accuracy. Figure 8.2 illustrates a plot of static accuracy vs. amplifier gain K_a for a typical design. The figure illustrates that for very high gain the accuracy approaches that of the followup and generator null but for low gain values the errors increase rapidly. If the gain was selected to be below 100 v/v, the specified static accuracy requirement would not be met. However, if the gain was selected to be 300 v/v or higher, the design would satisfy the specification requirement of 0.25 deg. A gain of 200 would result in a 0.5 probability of specification failure. Unless other restrictions, such as resolution or bandwidth, demand a higher gain, the 300 v/v value would probably be used since it is the minimum gain that will ensure fulfilling the accuracy requirement.

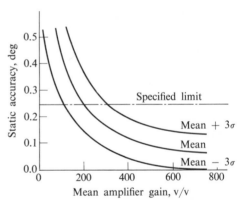

Fig. 8.2. Static accuracy vs. amplifier gain.

8.2. DYNAMIC ACCURACY CALCULATIONS

The equations developed in the previous two sections help the engineer to predict the static performance of the instrument servo. For many applications, a measure of the accuracy under static conditions is all that is required. However, under more stringent circumstances, it is often required that the accuracy under some sort of dynamic situation also be specified.

The dynamic requirement most often stipulated is the velocity lag error. The velocity lag of a servomechanism is defined as the difference between the output and input when a ramp function is applied to the input. This lag is directly related to the slope of the input ramp and therefore must be expressed as a certain value at a particular input velocity (e.g., 1.0-deg velocity lag at 20 deg/sec input).

Velocity lag may be resolved into that due to generator damping, motor damping, and static accuracy.

1. *Generator damping.* The amount of velocity lag existing in a servo due to generator damping may be expressed as

$$\epsilon_{VL}(K_g) = \dot{\theta}_i \left(\frac{NK_g \cos (\phi_a + \phi_g)}{K_f \cos (\phi_a + \phi_f)} \right). \tag{8.8}$$

The mean, $\epsilon_{VL}^*(K_g)$, and standard deviation, $\sigma\epsilon_{VL}(K_g)$, are computed using the techniques described in Chapter 6. All the system parameters in Eq. (8.8) are assumed to have a mean and standard deviation (with the exception of N, which is inherently exact).

2. *Motor damping.* The amount of velocity lag existing in a servo due to motor damping may be expressed as

$$\epsilon_{VL}(B_m) = \dot{\theta}_i \left(\frac{NB_m}{K_f K_a K_m \cos (\phi_a + \phi_f)} \right). \tag{8.9}$$

3. *Static accuracy.* In addition to the velocity lag due to generator damping and motor damping, there is also the static accuracy as computed in Eqs. (8.6) and (8.7).

The total velocity lag existing in a servo may be computed by combining these three contributions as follows:

$$\epsilon_{VL}^* = \epsilon_{VL}^*(K_g) + \epsilon_{VL}^*(B_m) + \epsilon_s^*, \tag{8.10}$$

$$\sigma\epsilon_{VL}^2 = \sigma\epsilon_{VL}^2(K_g) + \sigma\epsilon_{VL}^2(B_m) + \sigma\epsilon_s^2. \tag{8.11}$$

It was shown in Chapter 5 that a convenient method of specifying the performance of a servo was to define its response to a step input. The transient error obtained when an instrument servomechanism responds to the unit step input is sometimes used to qualify its dynamic accuracy. The most common measure of this error is called the *integral squared error.* Mathematically this is defined as

$$E = \int_o^\infty \theta_\epsilon^2(t)\, dt, \tag{8.12}$$

in which $\theta_\epsilon(t)$ is

$$\theta_\epsilon(t) = \theta_i(t) - \theta_o(t), \tag{8.13}$$

where $\theta_i(t)$ and $\theta_o(t)$ are respectively the step input or desired response and the actual output. In general, if the integral exists and is finite, the constant E provides a good over-all measure of the system performance. When E is small, the designer can be assured that the servo exhibits a fast transient response with no excessive overshooting and has zero steady-state error. Since the latter is a requirement for Eq. (8.12) to be finite, it is obvious that the factors which contributed to the static accuracy (e.g., coulomb friction) cannot be included in calculation of the integral squared error. Because of this, E will be calculated only for the linear second-order case.

Let $\theta_\epsilon(t)$ have the Fourier transform

$$\theta_\epsilon(s) = \int_{-\infty}^{\infty} e(t)e^{-st}\,dt, \tag{8.14}$$

where $s = j\omega$ and the inverse transform

$$e(t) = \frac{1}{2\pi j} \int_{-j\infty}^{j\infty} \theta_\epsilon(s)e^{st}\,ds. \tag{8.15}$$

Then

$$E = \int_{-\infty}^{\infty} \theta_\epsilon^2(t)\,dt = \frac{1}{2\pi j} \int_{-j\infty}^{j\infty} \theta_\epsilon(s)\theta_\epsilon(-s)\,ds. \tag{8.16}$$

Equation (8.16) is called *Parseval's theorem* and allows the integral squared of a transient function $\theta_\epsilon(t)$ to be expressed in the frequency domain in terms of the Fourier transform. For the linear second-order system, $\theta_\epsilon(s)$ can be found by writing Eq. (8.13) in the form

$$\theta_\epsilon(s) = \left(1 - \frac{\theta_o(s)}{\theta_i(s)}\right)\theta_i(s) \tag{8.17}$$

and substituting for the ratio $\theta_o(s)/\theta_i(s)$ using Eq. (5.26):

$$\theta_\epsilon(s) = \left(1 - \frac{1}{(1/\omega_N)^2 s^2 + (2\zeta/\omega_N)s + 1}\right)\theta_i(s). \tag{8.18}$$

Letting $\theta_i(s)$ take the form $1/s$ characteristic for a unit step and simplifying, we have

$$\theta_\epsilon(s) = \frac{(1/\omega_N)^2 s + (2\zeta/\omega_N)}{(1/\omega_N)^2 s^2 + (2\zeta/\omega_N)s + 1}. \tag{8.19}$$

Since this is a rational form for which the contour integral on the right-hand side of Eq. (8.16) has been tabulated in terms of the coefficients of $\theta_\epsilon(s)$, then

$$\theta_\epsilon(s) = \frac{a_{n-1}s^{n-1} + a_{n-2}s^{n-2} + \cdots + a_o}{b_n s^n + b_{n-1}s^{n-1} + \cdots + b_o}. \tag{8.20}$$

An evaluation of Eq. (8.16) gives

$$E = \frac{a_o^2}{2b_o b_1} \qquad\qquad \text{for}\quad n = 1,$$

$$E = \frac{a_1^2 b_o + a_o^2 b_2}{2b_o b_1 b_2} \qquad\qquad \text{for}\quad n = 2, \tag{8.21}$$

$$E = \frac{a_2^2 b_o b_1 + (a_1^2 - 2a_o a_2)b_o b_3 + a_o^2 b_2 b_3}{2b_o b_3 (b_1 b_2 - b_o b_3)} \quad \text{for}\quad n = 3.$$

Equating coefficients in Eq. (8.19) and (8.20) for the case $n = 2$,

$$a_1 = 1/\omega_N^2, \qquad a_o = 2\zeta/\omega_N,$$
$$b_2 = 1/\omega_N^2, \qquad b_1 = 2\zeta/\omega_N, \qquad b_o = 1,$$

and substituting into Eqs. (8.21) and simplifying, we obtain

$$E = \frac{1 + 4\zeta^2}{4\zeta\omega_N}. \tag{8.22}$$

From this as well as from the physical significance of E we see that the integral squared error is inversely proportional to the natural frequency of the system. Figure 8.3 shows a plot of $\omega_N E$ as a function of the damping ratio. As we expected, E increases as ζ is made very small or very large. The value of ζ for which $\omega_N E$ is a minimum can be obtained directly from Eq. (8.22) by differentiating with respect to ζ and setting the derivative equal to zero as

$$\frac{dE}{d\zeta} = \frac{(1 + 4\zeta^2)4\omega_N - (4\zeta\omega_N)(8\zeta)}{16\zeta^2\omega_N^2} = 0,$$

from which (8.23)

$$4(1 + 4\zeta^2) - 32\zeta^2 = 0$$

or

$$\zeta = 0.5.$$

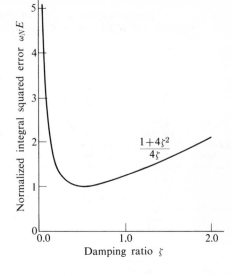

Fig. 8.3. Normalized integral squared error vs. damping ratio for a second-order system.

8.3. RESOLUTION AND SENSITIVITY CALCULATIONS

The resolution of a servomechanism is defined as the maximum change which can be made in the input without causing a change in the output. We can develop a method of finding this maximum change as follows.

Referring to the definition of static accuracy given in Section 8.1, we observe that it is possible for the load to have an initial positional error equal to this static accuracy. Then if the input is displaced in an attempt to move the load in the direction of the original displacement, the amount of input change necessary will be a maximum. This is the quantity desired. We can divide it into the following two segments.

1. The amount of input change necessary for the input to "catch up to" the output mechanically:

$$\delta_1 = \epsilon_s(T_{fo}) + \epsilon_s(E_s) + \epsilon_s[E_g(\text{null})] + \epsilon_s[E_a(\text{null})] + \epsilon_s(\theta_f). \quad (8.24)$$

2. The amount of input change which can be made beyond the final position of step 1 without causing a change in the output:

$$\delta_2 = \epsilon_s(T_{fo}) + \epsilon_s(E_s) - \epsilon_s[E_g(\text{null})] - \epsilon_s[E_a(\text{null})] - \epsilon_s(\theta_f). \quad (8.25)$$

The values of the servo resolution then is the sum of δ_1 and δ_2 given in Eqs. (8.24) and (8.25),

$$\epsilon_{\text{res}} = \delta_1 + \delta_2 = 2[\epsilon_s(T_{fo}) + \epsilon_s(E_s)]. \quad (8.26)$$

Table 8.1*

EXAMPLE OF A COMPUTER OUTPUT SHEET USED FOR
MOTOR GENERATOR SERVO SYSTEM PERFORMANCE CALCULATIONS

LEAR SIEGLER INC
INSTRUMENT DIVISION
PROGRAM SD010B

MOTOR GENERATOR SERVO SYSTEM PERFORMANCE

	K-F (V/RAD)	PHI-F (DEG)	K-G (V/1000RPM)	E-G (MV)	PHI-G (DEG)	THETA-F (MIN)
MAXIMUM	2.911E+00	1.728E+01	3.920E-02	4.180E+00	2.864E+01	1.500E+01
MEAN	2.578E+00	1.346E+01	3.446E-02	2.090E+00	1.863E+01	7.500E+00
MINIMUM	2.245E+00	9.640E+00	2.972E-02	0.000E-99	8.634E+00	0.000E-99

	K-A (V/V)	E-A (VOLTS)	PHI-A (DEG)	T-S (OZ IN)	THETA DOT-M (RPM)	K-M (OZ IN/V)
MAXIMUM	2.095E+03	2.000E+00	1.500E+01	1.000E-01	7.000E+03	2.780E-03
MEAN	1.740E+03	1.000E+00	0.000E-99	7.600E-02	6.200E+03	2.115E-03
MINIMUM	1.385E+03	0.000E-99	-1.500E+01	5.200E-02	5.400E+03	1.450E-03

	B-M (OZ IN SEC)	E-C START (VOLTS)	J-M (GM CM CM)	J-L (GM CM CM)	T-F (OZ IN)
MAXIMUM	1.770E-04	2.000E+00	7.900E-01	8.509E+02	7.000E-01
MEAN	1.240E-04	1.500E+00	7.800E-01	4.254E+02	5.500E-01
MINIMUM	7.100E-05	1.000E+00	7.700E-01	0.000E-99	4.000E-01

	N	THETA DOT-IN (DEG/SEC)
	9.592E+01	3.000E+02

MAXIMUM	MEAN	MINIMUM	SYSTEM PARAMETERS
1.240E+03	8.850E+02	5.294E+02	TORQUE CONSTANT(OZ IN/RAD)
1.490E+01	1.054E+01	6.189E+00	GENERATOR DAMPING COEF.(OZ IN SEC)
1.628E+00	1.140E+00	6.532E-01	MOTOR DAMPING COEF.(OZ IN SEC)
1.607E+01	1.168E+01	7.302E+00	TOTAL DAMPING COEF.(OZ IN SEC)
9.057E+01	7.571E+01	6.085E+01	VELOCITY CONSTANT(RAD/SEC)
1.733E+01	1.441E+01	1.148E+01	NATURAL FREQUENCY(CPS)
7.317E-01	5.979E-01	4.640E-01	DAMPING RATIO
1.938E+01	1.658E+01	1.378E+01	BANDWIDTH (CPS)
4.064E+02	3.585E+02	3.107E+02	FOLLOW-UP RATE(DEG/SEC)
			STATIC ACCURACY DUE TO
5.286E-02	3.560E-02	1.834E-02	LOAD FRICTION(DEG)
2.790E-02	1.970E-02	1.149E-02	MOTOR STARTING VOLTAGE(DEG)
9.098E-02	4.525E-02	-4.736E-04	GENERATOR NULL(DEG)
2.667E-02	1.313E-02	-4.030E-04	AMPLIFIER NULL(DEG)
2.500E-01	1.250E-01	0.000E-99	FOLLOWUP ERROR(DEG)
3.748E-01	2.386E-01	1.025E-01	TOTAL STATIC ACCURACY(DEG)
1.531E-01	1.106E-01	6.806E-02	RESOLUTION(DEG)
7.658E-02	5.530E-02	3.403E-02	SENSITIVITY(DEG)
			VELOCITY LAG DUE TO
3.748E-01	2.386E-01	1.025E-01	STATIC ACCURACY(DEG)
4.290E+00	3.575E+00	2.860E+00	GENERATOR DAMPING(DEG)
6.133E-01	3.867E-01	1.601E-01	MOTOR DAMPING(DEG)
5.003E+00	4.200E+00	3.398E+00	TOTAL VELOCITY LAG(DEG)

E SIGNIFIES CONVENTIONAL POWER-OF-TEN NOTATION

* Reprinted by courtesy of Lear Siegler, Inc., Instrument Division, Grand Rapids, Michigan.

The mean value ϵ_{res} and the standard deviation $\sigma\epsilon_{res}$ of the servo resolution may then be computed in terms of the mean and standard deviation of $\epsilon_s(T_f)$ and $\epsilon_s(E_s)$ computed in Section 8.1:

$$\epsilon_{res}^* = 2[\epsilon_s^*(T_{fo}) + \epsilon_s^*(E_s)], \tag{8.27}$$

$$\sigma\epsilon_{res}^2 = 4[\sigma_{\epsilon s}^2(T_{fo}) + \sigma_{\epsilon s}^2(E_s)]. \tag{8.28}$$

The above equations show that the resolution of the servo is equivalent to twice the error that can exist due to combined effects of motor starting voltage and friction.

If the servo is at null when the change in input is applied, then only half this value is required before movement of the output occurs. This latter value is normally defined as the sensitivity ϵ_{sen} of the servo. The mean value ϵ_{sen}^* and the standard deviation $\sigma_{\epsilon\,sen}$ of the servo sensitivity is thus computed in terms of the mean and standard deviation of $\epsilon_s(T_f)$ and $\epsilon_s(E_s)$ as

$$\epsilon_{sen}^* = \epsilon_s^*(T_{fo}) + \epsilon_s^*(E_s), \tag{8.29}$$

$$\sigma_{\epsilon\,sen}^2 = \sigma_{\epsilon s}^2(T_{fo}) + \sigma_{es}^2(E_s). \tag{8.30}$$

8.4. COMPUTER AIDED DESIGN

The design engineer is continuously faced with the problem of selecting the best components or component parameters to meet some desired or specified performance. Although the actual specification requirements vary with each application, the previous sections of this book should provide adequate background for handling any design situation that may exist. The appropriate equations, corresponding to the system parameters with specifications, can be used to calculate the actual performance for any selected hardware components.

It is most advantageous if the performance calculations can be programmed on a digital computer. This enables one to include the effects of all component tolerances and perform an analysis of many more component combinations than otherwise would be possible. Table 8.1 illustrates a typical output sheet from such a program. The upper half of the sheet summarizes the input data representing the component parameters of the system being analyzed. The bottom half lists the program outputs which are the calculated system performance parameters. This program covers all performance parameters most often specified for a motor generator instrument servomechanism, such as natural frequency, velocity constant, damping ratio, bandwidth, static accuracy, resolution, velocity lag, etc. A similar output sheet is shown as Table 8.2, except that it is for an inertial damped servo, the main difference being that the natural frequency and damping ratio outputs are replaced by the first, second, and third break frequencies, the crossover frequency, and the phase margin. By using programs such as these, the engineer can obtain a thorough and accurate analysis of a given design in a matter of a few seconds. The components or input parameters can be varied, as specified by the designer, until the desired performance is obtained. To use such a program, the engineer simply fills out a cor-

Table 8.2*

EXAMPLE OF A COMPUTER OUTPUT SHEET USED FOR
INERTIAL DAMPED SERVO SYSTEM PERFORMANCE CALCULATIONS

```
                                                      LEAR SIEGLER INC.
                                                      INSTRUMENT DIVISION
                                                      PROGRAM SD027A

              INERTIAL DAMPED SERVO SYSTEM PERFORMANCE

              K-F         PHI-F       K-A         E-A         PHI-A       THETA-F
            (V/RAD)       (DEG)       (V/V)      (VOLTS)      (DEG)        (MIN)
MAXIMUM  3.250E+01    6.000E+00   2.520E+02  1.000E+00    1.500E+01   1.000E+00
   MEAN  2.600E+01    0.000E-99   2.400E+02  7.500E-01    0.000E-99   5.000E-01
MINIMUM  1.950E+01   -6.000E+00   2.280E+02  5.000E-01   -1.500E+01   0.000E-99


              T-S       THETA DOT-M     K-M        B-M       E-C START       J-M
            (OZ IN)       (RPM)     (OZ IN/V)  (OZ IN SEC)   (VOLTS)    (GM CM CM)
MAXIMUM  2.256E-01    6.861E+03   7.682E-03  3.677E-04    1.717E+00   5.000E-01
   MEAN  1.866E-01    5.995E+03   6.665E-03  2.972E-04    1.281E+00   4.500E-01
MINIMUM  1.476E-01    5.129E+03   5.648E-03  2.268E-04    8.453E-01   4.000E-01


              B-D         J-D          J-L        T-F
          (OZ IN SEC) (GM CM CM)  (GM CM CM)   (OZ IN)
MAXIMUM  1.150E-03    4.800E+00   3.300E+02  2.500E+00
   MEAN  1.000E-03    4.300E+00   3.000E+02  1.875E+00
MINIMUM  8.500E-04    3.800E+00   2.700E+02  1.250E+00


         N       THETA DOT-IN
                   (DEG/SEC)
     5.000E+02    1.000E+01

     MAXIMUM        MEAN        MINIMUM     SYSTEM PARAMETERS
     1.253E+05    1.128E+05   1.003E+05      TOTAL INERTIA (GM CM CM)
     2.697E+04    2.079E+04   1.462E+04      TORQUE CONSTANT (OZ IN/RAD)
     9.193E+01    7.431E+01   5.669E+01      MOTOR DAMPING COEF.(OZ IN SEC)
     3.861E+02    2.798E+02   1.736E+02      VELOCITY CONSTANT (RAD/SEC)
     7.281E-01    5.973E-01   4.664E-01      FIRST BREAK FREQUENCY (CPS)
     3.101E+00    2.604E+00   2.112E+00      SECOND BREAK FREQUENCY (CPS)
     3.767E+01    3.222E+01   2.678E+01      THIRD BREAK FREQUENCY (CPS)
     1.223E+01    9.563E+00   6.897E+00      CROSSOVER FREQUENCY (CPS)
     6.515E+01    6.252E+01   5.989E+01      PHASE MARGIN (DEG)
     8.069E+01    7.050E+01   6.030E+01    FOLLOW-UP RATE (DEG/SEC)
                                           STATIC ACCURACY DUE TO
     7.470E-03    5.166E-03   2.862E-03      LOAD FRICTION (DEG)
     1.676E-02    1.176E-02   6.768E-03      MOTOR STARTING VOLTAGE (DEG)
     9.774E-03    6.887E-03   3.999E-03      AMPLIFIER NULL (DEG)
     1.667E-02    8.333E-03   2.347E-07      FOLLOWUP ERROR (DEG)
     4.360E-03    3.215E-02   2.071E-02    TOTAL STATIC ACCURACY (DEG)
     4.621E-02    3.386E-02   2.151E-02    RESOLUTION (DEG)
                                           VELOCITY LAG DUE TO
     4.360E-02    3.215E-02   2.071E-02      STATIC ACCURACY (DEG)
     4.930E-02    3.574E-02   2.217E-02      MOTOR DAMPING (DEG)
     8.871E-02    6.789E-02   4.707E-02    TOTAL VELOCITY LAG (DEG)

         E SIGNIFIES CONVENTIONAL POWER-OF-TEN NOTATION
```

* Reprinted by courtesy of Lear Siegler, Inc., Instrument Division, Grand Rapids, Michigan.

Table 8.3*

EXAMPLE OF AN INPUT DATA FORMAT SHEET
USED FOR DIGITAL COMPUTER CALCULATIONS

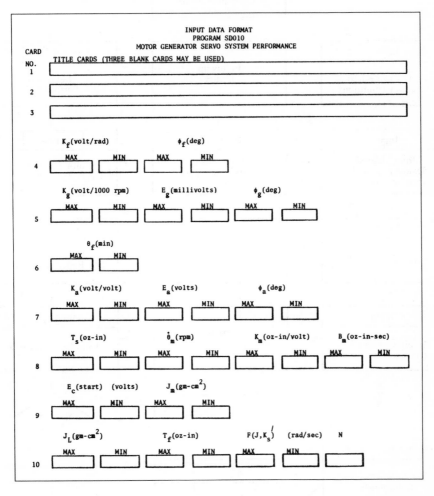

* Reprinted by courtesy of Lear Siegler, Inc., Instrument Division, Grand Rapids, Michigan.

responding input data format sheet such as Table 8.3. The data are then transferred to punched cards which are used as inputs to the digital computer.

By extending the previous concept slightly, the designer can even obtain more speed and flexibility in the design cycle. This is accomplished by taking data for standard servo components and storing them in libraries as part of the computer system. Thus, to specify data for a particular component which is in the standard library, one merely needs to apply the appropriate part number as the input. This is

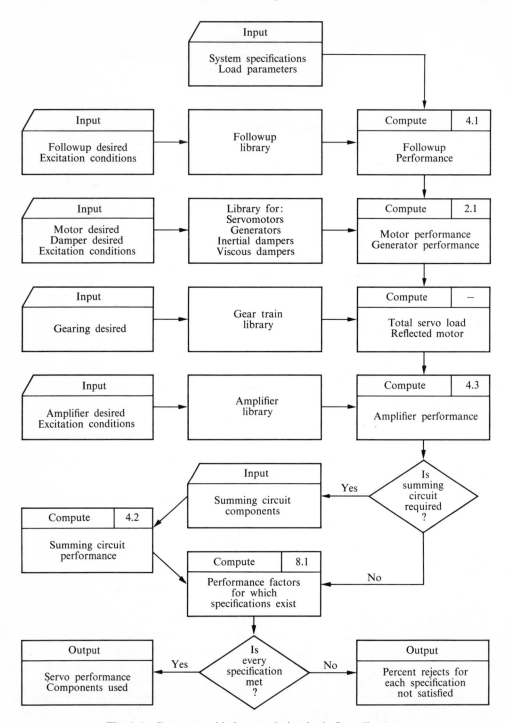

Fig. 8.4. Computer aided servo design logic flow diagram.

Table 8.4*

EXAMPLE OF COMPUTER OUTPUT SHEET
USED FOR CALCULATING PERCENT REJECTIONS

```
                                              LEAR  SIEGLER  INC.
                                              INSTRUMENT  DIVISION
                                              PROGRAM  SD006A

          SPECIFICATION  LIMIT  DEVIATION  PREDICTOR


                    ..FOLLOW  UP  RATE  (DEG/SEC)..
    SPECIFICATION  LIMITS          ACTUAL  LIMITS              PERCENT
     MAXIMUM      MINIMUM       MAXIMUM      MINIMUM          REJECTIONS
                  6.500E+01     8.069E+01    6.030E+01           5.30

                    ..TOTAL  STATIC  ACCURACY  (DEG)..
    SPECIFICATION  LIMITS          ACTUAL  LIMITS              PERCENT
     MAXIMUM      MINIMUM       MAXIMUM      MINIMUM          REJECTIONS
    4.00E-02                    4.360E-02    2.071E-02           1.98

                    ..RESOLUTION  (DEG)..
    SPECIFICATION  LIMITS          ACTUAL  LIMITS              PERCENT
     MAXIMUM      MINIMUM       MAXIMUM      MINIMUM          REJECTIONS
    4.000E-02                   4.621E-02    2.151E-02           6.80

                    ..TOTAL  VELOCITY  LAG  (DEG)..
    SPECIFICATION  LIMITS          ACTUAL  LIMITS              PERCENT
     MAXIMUM      MINIMUM       MAXIMUM      MINIMUM          REJECTIONS
    8.000E-02                   8.871E-02    4.707E-02           4.05

          E  SIGNIFIES  CONVENTIONAL  POWER-OF-TEN  NOTATION
```

* Reprinted by courtesy of Lear Siegler, Inc., Instrument Division, Grand Rapids, Michigan.

most effective when each of the performance programs, e.g., synchro summing circuit, motor, etc., are automatically linked together to form a complete analysis chain. Figure 8.4 shows a flow chart of such a computerized system of servo-mechanism design.

The primary inputs to the system are the system specifications and a definition of the load parameters. Examples of the former would be accuracy, followup rate, percent overshoot, bandwidth, etc. The definition of the load parameters consists of a simple tabulated sum of the friction and inertia values of all the load components that the servo is required to drive.

Secondary inputs are also provided, by the designer, to select the particular components and the corresponding excitation conditions that are to be used in the design. The servo component data are stored in four libraries which can be located on either magnetic disk or tape. The computer program then retrieves the data for each particular component, as directed by the designer, and proceeds with the various performance calculations for the component subassemblies as indicated. If a generator is used, a summing circuit is required and the computer program branches accordingly to read in the summing circuit components and then calculates the effective values of gain and phase shift at the amplifier input. It should be noted that the numbers in the "Compute Blocks" of the flow diagram refer, by Table number, to the computer output sheets that summarize the major calculations made in each block. The computer printout sheets that were shown in Chapter 3 are used to establish stiffness, backlash, and inertia values for updating the gear train library with new components.

Once the computer has completed the computations for the individual subassemblies, it proceeds automatically to calculate each system performance parameter that has a specification boundary. If all the system specifications are satisfied, a summary of the design is printed out in terms of servo performance and components used. If one or more of the specifications are not satisfied, the computer branches to a subroutine and calculates the percent rejects to be expected for each specification. The procedure used for this calculation was illustrated in Example 6.1 and a typical computer output sheet is shown as Table 8.4. On the basis of this output and his experience, the designer can either call the design adequate and accept the cost of the predicted rejects or he can make a new component selection and repeat the computer run.

8.5. OPTIMIZED SYSTEM DESIGN

The use of the computer-aided design procedure explained in the previous section, although many times more effective than any manual method, nevertheless represents only a passive use of the digital computer. That is, the engineer makes all the design decisions and the computer only serves as a fast calculator. The next logical step toward optimized design is to use the computer to determine how the input parameters should be varied to converge on the desired system performance. The problem is illustrated by the flow diagram in Fig. 8.5. One starts with an initial guess for the component parameters $X_1, X_2, \ldots, X_n$ and calculates the performance parameters for the system. These are then compared to the desired or specified values and if the comparison is satisfactory, the design is considered complete. If the comparison is not satisfactory, then based upon the results, new values of $X_1, X_2, \ldots, X_n$ are calculated and used to recalculate the performance parameters. This iteration process is repeated until all the calculated performance parameters satisfy the design requirements. The difficulty with this process lies in selecting the proper values of $X_1, X_2, X_3, \ldots, X_n$ for each iteration. The purpose of the remainder of this section is to illustrate how optimization techniques can be applied to aid the designer in solving this problem.

Let us start by defining a scalar function F as follows:

$$F = A_1(B_1 - Y_1)^2 + A_2(B_2 - Y_2)^2 + \cdots + A_n(B_n - Y_n)^2, \quad (8.31)$$

where

A_i = weight factor selected such that the Y specification is satisfied,

B_i = specification factor for Y_i performance parameter,

Y_i = $\mathfrak{F}(X_1, X_2, \ldots, X_n)$, a calculated performance parameter.

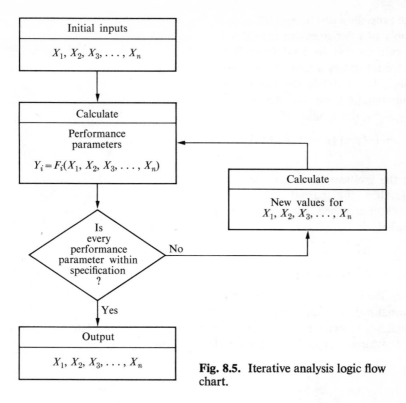

Fig. 8.5. Iterative analysis logic flow chart.

Introducing the scalar function F has reduced the multivariable optimization problem to one of simply minimizing the single function F.

Each of the weight factors A_i may be selected by considering the solution accuracy desired for each performance parameter. If we let this be defined as ϵ_i, then a satisfactory solution is guaranteed if the following inequalities are met:

$$
\begin{aligned}
(B_1 - Y_1) &\leq \epsilon_1, \\
(B_2 - Y_2) &\leq \epsilon_2, \\
&\vdots \\
(B_n - Y_n) &\leq \epsilon_i.
\end{aligned}
\tag{8.32}
$$

Arbitrarily selecting the corresponding value for the scalar function to be unity, we see that the A_i values are given by the equations

$$
\begin{aligned}
A_1 &= (1/\epsilon_1)^2, \\
A_2 &= (1/\epsilon_2)^2, \\
&\vdots \\
A_i &= (1/\epsilon_i)^2.
\end{aligned}
\tag{8.33}
$$

If these values are used in the scalar equation, then once F becomes less than unity, each Y_i is guaranteed to be within the specification limits.

The procedure can be best illustrated when only two variables are considered. This condition will be considered first. Figure 8.6 illustrates a plot of the scalar function. To minimize the number of iterations required, we wish to vary X_1 and X_2 along the gradient ∇F given by

$$\nabla F = (\partial F/\partial X_1)\hat{i} + (\partial F/\partial X_2)\hat{j}. \tag{8.34}$$

To use the gradient, it is advantageous to normalize the partial derivatives. This is accomplished by making the substitutions

$$X_1^* = X_1/\delta X_1, \tag{8.35}$$

$$X_2^* = X_2/\delta X_2, \tag{8.36}$$

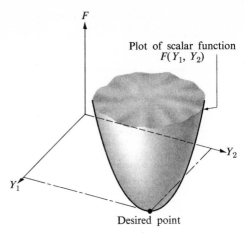

Fig. 8.6. Plot of scalar vs. Y_1 and Y_2.

and using the values X_1^* and X_2^* in place of X_1 and X_2 in the gradient calculations. The normalization factors δX_1 and δX_2 are selected as a basic increment in X_1 and X_2 directions, respectively, and will be used later also to calculate the approximate partial derivatives. A sketch of the problem is shown in Fig. 8.7.

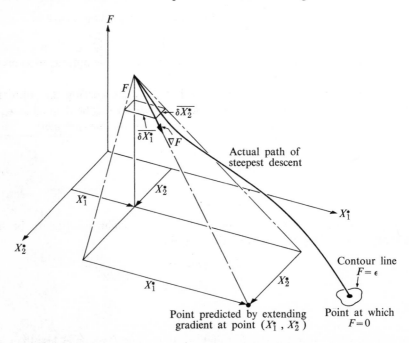

Fig. 8.7. Plot of scalar function trajectory.

The ratio of $\overline{\delta X_1^*}/\overline{\delta X_2^*}$ along the gradient is determined by constructing a circular region about the point (X_1^*, X_2^*), as shown in Fig. 8.8. The decrease in the scalar F for a change in the X_1^* direction is given by

$$\delta F_1^* = (\partial F/\partial X_1^*)\,\overline{\delta X_1^*}, \qquad (8.37)$$

and the corresponding equation for a change in the X_2^* direction is

$$\delta F_2^* = (\partial F/\partial X_2^*)\,\overline{\delta X_2^*}. \qquad (8.38)$$

The resultant decrease would be

$$\delta F = \delta F_1^* + \delta F_2^*$$
$$= (\partial F/\partial X_1^*)\,\overline{\delta F_1^*} + (\partial F/\partial X_2^*)\,\overline{\delta X_2^*}. \qquad (8.39)$$

where
$$(\delta X_1^*)^2 + (\delta X_2^*)^2 = 1$$

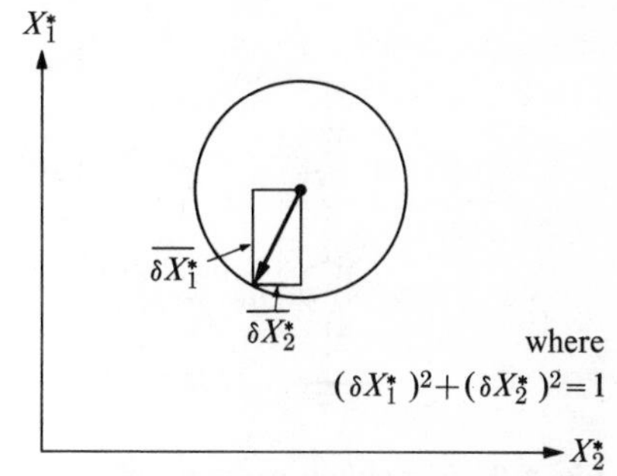

Fig. 8.8. Circular region to determine direction of steepest descent.

Substituting in for $\overline{\delta X_2^*}$ using the constraint equation, we obtain

$$\delta F = (\partial F/\partial X_1^*)\,\overline{\delta X_1^*} + (\partial F/\partial X_2^*)(1 - (\overline{\delta X_1^*})^2)^{1/2}. \qquad (8.40)$$

Taking the derivative of δF with respect to $\overline{\delta X}_1$ and setting it equal to zero to find the $\overline{\delta X_1^*}$ results in the steepest descent:

$$\frac{d(\delta F)}{d(\overline{\delta X_1^*})} = \frac{\partial F}{\partial X_1^*} + \frac{\partial F}{\partial X_2^*}[1 - (\overline{\delta X_1^*})^2]^{-1/2}(-\overline{\delta X_1^*}) = 0, \qquad (8.41)$$

$$\frac{\partial F}{\partial \overline{X}_1^*} = \frac{\partial F}{\partial \overline{X}_2^*}\left(\frac{\delta X_1^*}{\sqrt{1 - (\overline{\delta X_1^*})^2}}\right), \qquad (8.42)$$

but from the constraint equation

$$\sqrt{1 - (\overline{\delta X_1^*})^2} = \overline{\delta X_2^*}. \qquad (8.43)$$

Therefore

$$\left(\frac{\partial F}{\partial X_1^*}\right) = \left(\frac{\partial F}{\partial X_2^*}\right)\left(\frac{\overline{\delta X_1^*}}{\overline{\delta X_2^*}}\right), \qquad (8.44)$$

and the steepest descent is obtained when the ratio of $\overline{\delta X_1^*}/\overline{\delta X_2^*}$ is selected to be

$$\frac{\overline{\delta X_1^*}}{\overline{\delta X_2^*}} = \frac{\partial F/\partial X_1^*}{\partial F/\partial X_2^*}. \qquad (8.45)$$

The magnitude of the gradient is given by

$$|\nabla F| = \sqrt{\left(\frac{\partial F}{\partial X_1^*}\right)^2 + \left(\frac{\partial F}{\partial X_2^*}\right)^2}. \qquad (8.46)$$

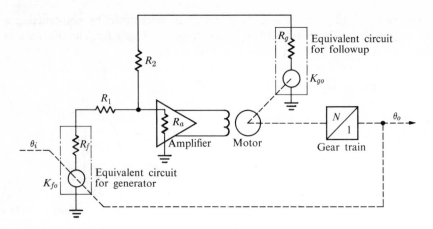

Fig. 8.9. Simplified example of motor-generator servomechanism used for optimization of summing resistors.

From Fig. 8.7 we can see that

$$F = |\nabla F| \sqrt{(\overline{\delta X_1^*})^2 + (\overline{\delta X_2^*})^2}. \tag{8.47}$$

Using the relationship that

$$\frac{\Delta X_2^*}{\Delta X_1^*} = \frac{\overline{\delta X_2^*}}{\overline{\delta X_1^*}} = \frac{(\partial F/\partial X_2^*)}{(\partial F/\partial X_1^*)}, \tag{8.48}$$

we can show that

$$\Delta X_1^* = \left\{ \frac{\partial F/\partial X_1^*}{(\partial F/\partial X_1^*)^2 + (\partial F/\partial X_2^*)^2} \right\} F, \tag{8.49}$$

$$\Delta X_2^* = \left\{ \frac{\partial F/\partial X_2^*}{(\partial F/\partial X_1^*)^2 + (\partial F/\partial X_2^*)^2} \right\} F. \tag{8.50}$$

Using the approximate slope technique for evaluating the partial derivatives, we can write the final incremental equations for ΔX_1 and ΔX_2,

$$\Delta X_1 = \delta X_1 \left(\frac{\delta F_1}{(\delta F_1)^2 + (\delta F_2)^2} \right) F, \tag{8.51}$$

$$\Delta X_2 = \delta X_2 \left(\frac{\delta F_2}{(\delta F_1)^2 + (\delta F_2)^2} \right) F. \tag{8.52}$$

Generalizing the above technique for more than two variables, one can write the equation

$$\Delta X_i = \delta X_i \left\{ \frac{\delta F_i}{\sum_{k=1}^n (\delta F_k)^2} \right\} F. \tag{8.53}$$

Table 8.5

COMPONENT PARAMETERS WITH TOLERANCES
FOR SYSTEM BEING OPTIMIZED

Parameter	Symbol	Value	Units
Open circuit followup gain	K_{fo}	21.31 ± 2.32	v/rad
Open circuit generator gain	K_{go}	0.364 ± 0.0454	v/1000 rpm
Open circuit generator null	E_{go}	10.0 ± 10.0	mv
Generator output impedance	R_g	590 ± 112	ohms
Followup output impedance	R_f	589 ± 90	ohms
Amplifier input impedance	R_a	1784 ± 442	ohms
Amplifier gain	K_a	1600 ± 210	v/v
Amplifier null voltage	E_a	4.0 ± 4.0	v
Motor torque gain	K_m	0.00304 ± 0.00101	oz-in/v
Motor damping coefficient	B_m	0.0002125 ± 0.0000705	(oz-in)/(rad/sec)
Motor starting voltage	E_s	1.95 ± 0.65	v
Followup accuracy	θ_f	7.5 ± 7.5	min
Load friction	T_{fo}	0.55 ± 0.15	oz-in
Gear ratio	N	95.92	—
Input velocity	$\dot{\theta}_i$	300	deg/sec

Equation (8.53) can be easily implemented using the following procedure on a digital computer.

1. Each X_i is set at its initial value and the scalar is calculated.

2. X_1 is varied by a small amount δX_1 (say 1% of its nominal value) and the resulting change in the scalar function δF_1 is calculated.

3. X_1 is restored to its previous value and X_2 is varied by a small amount δX_2 and the resulting changes in the scalar function δF_2 are calculated.

4. This procedure is repeated for every independent variable and the resulting increment steps ΔX_i are calculated.

5. Each X_i is replaced by $X_i + \Delta X_i$ and the new value of F is calculated.

6. The above process (steps 2 through 5) is repeated until F is minimized below the allowable value.

For an example of how this technique is applied, let us consider the system illustrated in Fig. 8.9. The problem is to select R_1 and R_2 such that the mean $+3\sigma$-values for the static accuracy and velocity lag meet some specified value given the mean and 3σ-values shown in Table 8.5 for each of the other component parameters.

Although the example is relatively simple, it still represents a significant problem to the engineer not using a formal optimization scheme. This situation can be attributed to (1) the numerous tolerances being considered and (2) the interactive

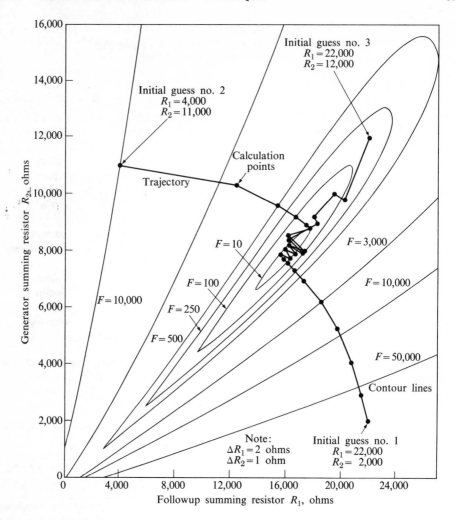

Fig. 8.10. Example of trajectories obtained for summing circuit optimization problem.

nature of the two resistors. Changing R_1 varies the followup gain that in turn varies both static accuracy and velocity lag. Changing R_2 primarily varies the effective generator gain and null, which in turn vary the velocity lag and static accuracy. A further complication exists since a change in R_1 causes a change in the load as seen by the generator and changes its effective gain; likewise, a change in R_2 causes an additional change in the effective followup gain. In short, the values of R_1 and R_2 each affect the static accuracy and velocity lag error and therefore should be selected simultaneously.

To apply the gradient method, let Y_1 and Y_2 be the calculated values for mean $+3\sigma$-static accuracy and velocity lag, respectively, and $B_1 = 0.5$ deg and

$B_2 = 12.0$ deg at 300 deg/sec be the corresponding desired values. Assume that a satisfactory solution is obtained when the following two inequalities are obtained:

$$|B_1 - Y_1| \leq 0.005, \qquad |B_2 - Y_2| \leq 0.10. \tag{8.54}$$

If the corresponding value for the scalar function is selected to be unity the A_1 and A_2 factors must be

$$A_1 = 1/(0.005)^2 = 40,000, \qquad A_2 = 1/(0.10)^2 = 100. \tag{8.55}$$

The scalar function to be minimized is then

$$F = 40,000(0.5 - Y_1)^2 + 100(12.0 - Y_2)^2. \tag{8.56}$$

The equations derived in Section 4.4 can be programmed to calculate K_f, K_g, and E_g, and those in Sections 8.1 and 8.2 can be programmed to calculate Y_1 and Y_2. The results of the iteration procedure are summarized in Fig. 8.10. Trajectories or solutions are shown starting at three initial points. Contour lines (lines of $F = $ const) are also plotted to illustrate the behavior of the scalar function over the region of interest. Each of the three trajectories terminates for $F \leq 1$ in the region near $R_1 = 15340$ ohms and $R_2 = 7553$ ohms, which is considered to be the solution.

8.6. SUMMARY

In this chapter we obtained expressions for calculating the servo accuracy and resolution, saw how the computer could be used for computer aided design, and finally developed an optimization procedure that could be used to ensure automatically that each specification is met.

We started by defining error as the instantaneous difference between the input and output displacement. From this, static accuracy was defined as the magnitude of this error that can exist under static conditions. Equations were then derived for calculating the mean and 3σ-limits of the static accuracy. This was accomplished by (1) calculating the magnitude of the errors resulting from load friction, motor starting voltage, generator null, amplifier null, and followup error, and (2) obtaining a statistical summation.

Expressions were then derived to enable the dynamic accuracy of a servo to be calculated under two sets of conditions, namely, constant velocity and step inputs. The first of these is called velocity lag and the second was expressed in terms of the integral squared error which was calculated by using Parseval's theorem. It was shown that the minimum integral squared error occurs for a damping ratio value of 0.5.

Since the resolution and sensitivity of a servo is often specified, equations were derived for calculating each. These equations were obtained by referring to the individual static error components resulting from load friction and motor starting voltage.

As a first step toward automated design, the accuracy equations as well as other servo performance calculations were computerized and two sample output sheets were given. It was then shown that by extending the performance program concept to include standard component libraries, the designer could simply specify a given configuration of component part numbers and obtain in return, after a few seconds, complete analysis of the design. If the design does not meet each of the required design specifications, the percent rejects to be expected in each area are also obtained.

The engineer using the above computer aided design process is still required to make all the design decisions. The next logical step toward automated design is to use the computer to determine how the input parameters should be varied to converge on the desired solution. To accomplish this, a scalar function was introduced to represent the system performance. A good example of such a function would be the summation of all the percent rejects. An optimization procedure was then introduced whereby this scalar function could be forced to zero by varying the component parameters along the gradient. The latter was determined by obtaining, using per-turbation techniques, the partial derivative of the scalar with respect to each of the input parameters.

PROBLEMS

*8.1. Given the same component data as in Problem 5.3, calculate the following correspond-ing mean system parameters:

a) total static accuracy (deg),
b) resolution (deg),
c) total velocity lag at 300 deg/sec (deg).

*8.2. Given the same system as above, what would be the mean value of total velocity lag at 10 deg/sec?

8.3. Modify the answers to Problem 8.1 to account for an increase in

a) amplifier gain by factor of 2,
b) generator gain by factor of 2,
c) followup gain by factor of 2.

Tabulate the results along with Problem 8.1 to show the comparison.

8.4. Neglecting the static accuracy component of the total velocity lag error, derive the following approximate equations for the velocity lag:

a) $\epsilon_{VL} = \dot{\theta}_{in}/K_V$,
b) express the above in terms of damping ratio and natural frequency,
c) to what simplified form does a) reduce when the motor damping is negligible (if carrier phase angles are also neglected)?

8.5. Make a sketch similar to Fig. 8.2 but for resolution vs. amplifier gain instead of static accuracy vs. amplifier gain. Can the resolution ever be greater than the static accuracy? Justify your answer.

*8.6. Derive the integral squared error equation for an inertially damped servo subjected to a step input.

BIBLIOGRAPHY

LEITMANN, G., *Optimization Techniques with Application to Aerospace Systems*, Academic Press, 1962.

MERRIAN, III, C., *Optimization Theory and The Design of Feedback Control Systems*, McGraw-Hill, 1964.

NEWTON, G. C., L. A. GOULD, and J. F. KAISER, *Analytical Design of Linear Feedback Controls*, Wiley, 1957.

TOMOVIC, R., *Sensitivity Analysis of Dynamic Systems*, McGraw-Hill, 1963.

APPENDIX

APPENDIX

THE LAPLACE TRANSFORM

An understanding of the Laplace transform is an important asset to the servo-mechanism designer. The purpose of this appendix is to provide the unfamiliar reader with a working knowledge of the Laplace method so that he will be better able to understand the material presented in this book. Only the rudiments are presented, and those desiring a comprehensive treatment are referred to the specialized texts listed at the end of this appendix.

The Laplace transformation converts an expression for a given quantity from a function of time $f(t)$ to a function of the Laplace operator $F(s)$, where s is the Laplace operator, which is a complex number, that is,

$$s = \sigma + j\omega. \tag{A.1}$$

A real function $f(t)$ has a Laplace transform so long as it is defined and single-valued almost everywhere for $t \geq 0$ and satisfies the relationship

$$\int_0^\infty f(t)e^{-at}\, dt < \infty \tag{A.2}$$

for some real number a. If $f(t)$ is a linear differential equation with a finite number of terms, these conditions are satisfied and $f(t)$ is said to be *Laplace transformable*. This is the case for most lumped-parameter linear systems.

For a time function that is transformable, the direct Laplace transform is denoted by the symbol $\mathcal{L}[f(t)]$ and is given by the Laplace transform integral

$$\mathcal{L}[f(t)] = F(s) = \int_0^\infty f(t)e^{-st}\, dt. \tag{A.3}$$

The idea behind using the Laplace method is to transform the differential equation $f(t)$ describing the system into the equivalent function $F(s)$. Using the equivalent function, the engineer can manipulate the system equations in an algebraic manner. The transformation is applied to the forcing function as well as to the characteristic equation for the system. Once a desirable form has been obtained by using algebraic techniques, the inverse transformation is made, resulting in the system solution in terms of time. The return to the time domain for $t > 0$ is possible because of the *uniqueness property* of the transform, which is defined by the integral

$$f(t) = \frac{1}{2\pi j} \int_{c-j\infty}^{c+j\infty} F(s)e^{ts}\, ds, \tag{A.4}$$

where the constant c must be greater than a, the value for which $f(t)$ was transformable.

In general most of the transforms required by the servomechanism designer have already been tabulated. Such a table is included as part of this appendix. A few examples follow, however, to illustrate the method by which transform pairs are derived.

1. Constant: $f(t) = A$,

$$\mathcal{L}[A] = \int_0^\infty Ae^{-st}\, dt = -\frac{A}{s} e^{-st} \Big|_0^\infty = \frac{A}{s}. \tag{A.5}$$

2. Unit step function: $f(t) = 1$ (for $t > 0$),

$$\mathcal{L}[1] = \int_0^\infty e^{-st}\, dt = \frac{1}{s}. \tag{A.6}$$

3. Exponential decay: $f(t) = e^{-\alpha t}$ (for $\alpha =$ real const),

$$\mathcal{L}[e^{-\alpha t}] = \int_0^\infty e^{-\alpha t} e^{-st}\, dt = \int_0^\infty e^{-(\alpha+s)t}\, dt$$

$$= -\frac{e^{-(s+\alpha)}}{(s+\alpha)}\Big|_0^\infty = \frac{1}{s+\alpha}. \tag{A.7}$$

4. Sinusoid: $f(t) = \sin \beta t$. Using the relationship that

$$\sin \beta t = (e^{j\beta t} - e^{-j\beta t})/2j, \tag{A.8}$$

one obtains

$$\mathcal{L}[\sin \beta t] = \frac{1}{2j} \int_0^\infty [e^{j\beta t}e^{-st} - e^{-j\beta t}e^{-st}]\, dt$$

$$= \frac{1}{2j}\left[-\frac{e^{-(s-j\beta)t}}{(s-j\beta)} + \frac{e^{-(s+j\beta)t}}{(s+j\beta)}\right]\Big|_0^\infty = \frac{\beta}{s^2 + \beta^2}. \tag{A.9}$$

It can also be shown that the Laplace transform of a derivative of $f(t)$ is

$$\mathcal{L}\left[\frac{df(t)}{dt}\right] = sF(s) - f(0+), \tag{A.10}$$

where the $f(0+)$ term is the value of the function $f(t)$ as the origin is approached from the right-hand, or positive, time side. And likewise for the second derivative,

$$\mathcal{L}\left[\frac{d^2 f(t)}{dt^2}\right] = s^2 F(s) - sf(0+) - \frac{df}{dt}(0+). \tag{A.11}$$

If the function $f(t)$ is transformable and has the transform $F(s)$, its time integral is also transformable and has the form

$$\mathcal{L}\left[\int \int f(t)\, dt\right] = \frac{F(s)}{s} + \frac{1}{s}\left[\int \int f(t)\, dt\right]\Big|_{t=0+}, \tag{A.12}$$

where $[\int \int f(t)\, dt]|_{t=0+}$ means the value of the time integral evaluated at $t = 0+$.

Table A.1

LAPLACE TRANSFORMS

	$F(s)$	$f(t)$
1	1	Unit impulse at $t = 0$
2	$\dfrac{1}{s}$	1, or unit step at $t = 0$
3	e^{-as}	Time delay of length a
4	$\dfrac{1}{s^2 + \beta^2}$	$\dfrac{1}{\beta} \sin \beta t$
5	$\dfrac{s}{s^2 + \beta^2}$	$\cos \beta t$
6	$\dfrac{1}{s + \alpha}$	$e^{-\alpha t}$
7	$\dfrac{1}{s(s + \alpha)}$	$\dfrac{1}{\alpha}[1 - e^{-\alpha t}]$
8	$\dfrac{s + a_0}{s(s + \alpha)}$	$\dfrac{1}{\alpha}[a_0 - (a_0 - \alpha)e^{-\alpha t}]$
9	$\dfrac{1}{s^2(s + \alpha)}$	$\dfrac{1}{\alpha^2}[e^{-\alpha t} + \alpha t - 1]$
10	$\dfrac{s + a_0}{s(s + \alpha)}$	$\dfrac{a_0 t}{\alpha} + \left[\dfrac{a_0}{\alpha^2} - \dfrac{1}{\alpha}\right][e^{-\alpha t} - 1]$
11	$\dfrac{s^2 + a_1 s + a_0}{s^2(s + \alpha)}$	$\dfrac{1}{\alpha^2}[(a_0 + a_1\alpha + \alpha^2)e^{-\alpha t} + a_0\alpha t + a_1\alpha - a_0]$
12	$\dfrac{1}{(s + \alpha)(s + \gamma)}$	$\dfrac{e^{-\alpha t} - e^{-\gamma t}}{\gamma - \alpha}$
13	$\dfrac{s + a_0}{(s + \alpha)(s + \gamma)}$	$\dfrac{(a_0 - \alpha)e^{-\alpha t} - (a_0 - \gamma)e^{-\gamma t}}{\gamma - \alpha}$
14	$\dfrac{1}{s(s + \alpha)(s + \beta)}$	$\dfrac{1}{\alpha\beta} - \dfrac{e^{-\alpha t}}{\alpha(\beta - \alpha)} - \dfrac{e^{-\beta t}}{\beta(\alpha - \beta)}$
15	$\dfrac{s + a_0}{s(s + \alpha)(s + \beta)}$	$\dfrac{a_0}{\alpha\beta} - \left[\dfrac{(a_0 - \alpha)}{\alpha(\beta - \alpha)}\right]e^{-\alpha t} - \left[\dfrac{a_0 - \beta}{\beta(\alpha - \beta)}\right]e^{-\beta t}$
16	$\dfrac{s^2 + a_1 s + a_0}{s(s + \alpha)(s + \beta)}$	$\dfrac{a_0}{\alpha\beta} - \left[\dfrac{\alpha^2 - a_1\alpha + a_0}{\alpha(\beta - \alpha)}\right]e^{-\alpha t} - \left[\dfrac{\beta^2 - a_1\beta + a_0}{\beta(\alpha - \beta)}\right]e^{-\beta t}$

The Laplace transforms and the corresponding time expressions for most common functions are summarized in Table A.1. The following example illustrates how this table and the Laplace transform can be used to solve a typical servomechanism problem.

Example A.1 Assuming that a servomotor at time zero has a velocity $\dot{\theta}_m(0)$, position $\theta_m(0)$, and a constant load torque T_r, derive an equation for the motor displacement $\theta_m(t)$ as a function of time for a step voltage input at $t = 0$.

The differential equation for a servomotor was derived in Chapter 2 as

$$J_m \frac{d^2\theta_m}{dt} + B_m \frac{d\theta_m}{dt} + T_r = K_m E_c(t),$$

where

$$J_m = \text{motor inertia,}$$
$$B_m = \text{motor damping coefficient,}$$
$$T_r = \text{load torque,}$$
$$K_m = \text{motor torque gain,}$$
$$E_c = \text{motor control phase voltage.}$$

Using the transforms given by Eqs. (A.5), (A.6), (A.10), and (A.11) one can write the following equation for a step input $E_c(t)$ of magnitude E_c:

$$J_m[s^2\theta_m(s) - s\theta_m(0+) - \dot{\theta}_m(0+)] + B_m[s\theta_m(s) - \theta_m(0+)] + \frac{T_r}{s} = \frac{K_m E_c}{s}.$$

Solving for the motor displacement $\theta_m(s)$ in an algebraic manner, one can obtain the following equation:

$$\theta_m(s) = \theta_m(0+)\left(\frac{s^2 + a_1 s + a_0}{s^2(s + \alpha)}\right),$$

where

$$a_1 = \frac{B_m\theta_m(0+) + J_m\dot{\theta}_m(0+)}{J_m\theta_m(0+)},$$

$$a_0 = \frac{K_m E_c - T_r}{J_m\theta_m(0+)},$$

$$\alpha = \frac{B_m}{J_m}.$$

Looking in Table A.1 for the corresponding time solution, one obtains

$$\theta_m(t) = \frac{\theta_m(0+)}{\alpha^2}[(a_0 - a_1\alpha + \alpha^2)e^{-\alpha t} + a_0\alpha t + a_1\alpha - a_0],$$

which is the desired equation for the motor displacement $\theta_m(t)$.

ADDITIONAL SUGGESTED REFERENCES

Churchill, R. V., *Operational Mathematics*, 2nd Ed., McGraw-Hill, 1958.

Gardner, M. F., and J. L. Barnes, *Transients in Linear Systems*, Wiley, 1942.

Kaplan, W., *Operational Methods for Linear Systems*, Addison-Wesley, 1962.

ANSWERS TO PROBLEMS MARKED WITH ASTERISK

Chapter 2

2.1   12,000 rpm; 8,000 rpm

2.2   (a) 0.2046 oz-in   (b) 9527 rpm   (c) 0.0108 oz-in/v   (d) 0.000205 oz-in-sec
      (e) 3.31 watts   (f) 1.78 watts   (g) 0.8 v

2.3   (a) 8209 rpm   (b) 0.0147 oz-in/v   (c) 0.000331 oz-in-sec
      (d) 6.17 watts   (e) 1.09 v

2.4 $0.565 + j\,0.288$, $40.7 + j\,7.48$ v

2.8   (a) 12.0 oz-in   (b) 100 rpm   (c) 1.146 oz-in-sec   (d) 8000 gm-cm^2
      (e) 0.1136 oz-in sec^2

Chapter 3

3.1   (a) 0.188 watts   (b) yes   (c) 9 to 132   (d) 395 deg/sec

3.2   1405 gm-cm^2, 0.02 oz-in-sec^2

3.3   4170 gm-cm^2

3.5 $t = \dfrac{J_T}{N^2 B_m} \ln\left(1 + \dfrac{N^2 B_m \dot{\theta}(0+)}{T_{fo}}\right)$; 0.129 sec; 0.372 sec

3.6   (a) 670,   (b) 76,315 gm-cm^2 (c) 0.318 oz-in   (d) 19.03 min
      (e) 34,448 oz-in/rad

3.9   (a) 42.94   (b) 2282 gm-cm^2 (c) 0.701 oz-in   (d) 14.98 min
      (e) 73,610 oz-in/rad

Chapter 4

4.1   (a) $Z_{A1} = 17.58 + j\,62.1$, $Z_{B1} = 0.45 - j\,24.9$, $Z_{C1} = 7.42 + j\,52.9$
      (b) $Z_{A2} = 30.0 - j\,443$, $Z_{B2} = 406 + j\,1075$, $Z_{C2} = 66.0 + j\,885$
      (c) 22.85 v/rad   (d) 12.86 deg   (e) $600.7 + j\,241.3$

4.2   (a) 3.669 v/rad   (b) 13.11 deg   (c) 0.1088 v/1000 rpm
      (d) −18.11 deg   (e) 2.648 mv

4.3   (a) 5.163 v/rad   (b) 9.44 deg   (c) 0.1598 v/1000 rpm
      (d) 8.453 deg   (e) 9.824 mv

Chapter 5

5.2   (a) high   (b) high   (c) low

5.3   (a) 8116 gm-cm^2 (b) 919.0 oz-in/rad   (c) 13.34 oz-in-sec
      (d) 14.21 cps   (e) 0.6479   (f) 359.0 deg/sec   (g) 15.39 cps

5.8   14.14 msec

221

Chapter 6

6.1   14.04%

6.2   mean = 15.25 oz-in-sec, tolerance = 4.16 oz-in-sec

6.5   0.6918 ± 0.123

6.8   max = 502.4, mean = 450.4, min = 398.4

Chapter 7

7.3   System is stable; nothing

7.5   It is reduced to 0.381 its original value.

Chapter 8

8.1   (a) 0.2768 deg   (b) 0.1071 deg   (c) 4.630 deg

8.2   0.4219 deg

8.6 $E = \dfrac{\tau_m \tau_d (K_V \tau_d + 1) + (\tau_m + \tau_d + \tau_{md})^2 - 2\tau_m \tau_d + (\tau_m + \tau_d + \tau_{md})/K_V}{2[(K_V \tau_d + 1)(\tau_m + \tau_d + \tau_{md}) - K_V \tau_m \tau_d]}$

INDEX

INDEX

Amplifier, purpose of, 4
  equations for, 73
  gain with quadrature, 152–155
  gain, effect on accuracy, 194
  null voltage, effect on accuracy, 193
  saturation in, 145–149
Amplifier saturation, caused by quadrature
    signal, 152–155
  and coulomb friction, 158–166
  effect on damping, 148
  effect on frequency response, 149–152
  effect on transient response, 147
Analog computer diagrams,
  for linear fourth-order system, 102
  for linear second-order system, 102
  for nonlinear system, 180
Analog computer, time scale for, 103
  nonlinear circuits for, 179
Antibacklash gearing, 44–47
Approximate slope, for calculating
    tolerance effects, 136–138

Backlash, allowable in system, 184
  definition of, 40
  describing function for, 171
  effect on system stability, 171–175
  equation for calculating, 43
  of gear train, 40–43
  negative values for, 45
  reflection of, 43
Backlash-friction curve theory, 184–185
Bandwidth of system, 107
Bearing friction, definition of, 14
  calculation of, 15–16
Block diagram, of inertially damped
    motor, 78
  of inner loop, 75–76
  of linear system, 84, 89
  of nonlinear system, 83

of servomotor, 27
Break frequencies, for inertially damped
    motor, 79
  for inertially damped system, 112

Center-tapped servomotor, complex
    coupling factor for, 24–25
  description of, 23
Central limit property, 125
Closed-loop system, description of, 3
Coefficient matrix, for state model, 101
Cogging, of servomotor, 32
Component libraries, stored in computer,
    203
Computer aided design, 199–204
Computer output sheet, for amplifier, 73
  for backlash, 44
  for inertia, 49
  for inertially damped system, 200
  for motor-generator system, 198
  for percent rejections, 203
  for servomotor, 22
  for stiffness, 40
  for summing network, 72
  for synchro followup, 49
Control phase, definition of, 9
Conversion factors, use of, 7
Coulomb friction, analysis using phase
    plane, 158–166
  effect on accuracy, 191–192
  effect on dead zone, 160
  effect on performance, 155–157
  and loaded speed, 54
  phase lag caused by, 156
  required for insufficient stiffness, 170
Coupling coefficient, for center-tapped
    motor, 24–25
  for inertial damper, 77
Cumulative distribution function, 128–129